SURVEY OF
ANALYTICAL CHEMISTRY

SURVEY OF
ANALYTICAL CHEMISTRY

Sidney Siggia
Professor of Chemistry
University of Massachusetts

McGraw-Hill Book Company
New York
St. Louis
San Francisco
Toronto
London
Sydney

Survey of Analytical Chemistry

Library of Congress Catalog Card Number 68-13526
57365

1 2 3 4 5 6 7 8 9 0 M A M M 7 5 4 3 2 1 0 6 9 8

PREFACE

The field of analytical chemistry is one of the fastest-growing in the area of chemical technology. Its growth has indeed been so fast that it has been difficult to assimilate, and it has been especially difficult for students of chemistry to keep abreast of the current composition of this segment of their profession. It is the purpose of this book to describe the field of analytical chemistry as it exists today.

In many ways this book can be compared to a map of the world, only the "world" in this case is the field of analytical chemistry. One does not use a world map to find the way from New York to Chicago; similarly, one does not use this book to find a specific method for determining iron in the presence of tin and aluminum. This is a survey book designed for the broad view of the field in order that the composition and the interrelationship of the various components of the field should become evident to the reader. This is not a detail book, since once one began with discussion of detail in any area, the book would rapidly become a comprehensive treatise and would lose the purpose it intends to achieve. If readers are interested in details in any area, they are referred to suitable references, usually at several levels of discussion.

The format of this book also takes a novel twist in order to better describe analytical chemistry. Analytical chemistry is an applied field, meaning that knowledge is applied to get answers to problems. In practice, one finds that most problems fall into distinct types. This book is segmented into chapters, each of which discusses one of the various types of problems the analytical chemist is called upon to solve—these are the areas on our "world map." In each problem area, the various analytical approaches that make up that area are listed; their physical and/or chemical basis is briefly described; their utility is discussed; the strong and weak points of each approach are mentioned and compared with the other approaches discussed. Thus the relationship of each approach to the others and to the type of analytical job being discussed is elucidated.

Tables are included at the end of each chapter to summarize the content of each chapter, to accentuate further the composition of the particular analytical area under discussion, to establish clearly the utility of each approach relative to the type of analytical problem under discussion, and also to establish clearly the relationship between analytical approaches in the solution of such problems.

It is hoped this text will be of value to both students and practicing analytical chemists. For the student, the text can form a framework around which he can build with the more detailed, factual information he gathers during his school years. For the practicing analytical chemist, the text can be used as a guide to screen available approaches with which he might handle his specific problem.

The author wishes to thank the following coworkers from Olin Mathieson who read and commented on various parts of the manuscript: Raymond Russell (Elemental Analysis); Richard Hagstrom (Automatic Analysis); Richard Finch (Tracers); Herman Hoberrecht (Mass Spectrometry); Warren Harple (Infrared Spectroscopy); and James Barrante (Molecular Spectroscopy). Thanks are also due to the following people who supplied needed statistics: L. S. Birks, United States Naval Research Labs; C. L. Pringle, Kaman Nuclear; R. A. Zickus, Jarrell-Ash Co.; George Tilley, Olin; Stanley Levine, Squibb Pharmaceutical; John Croke and Gene Martin, Philips Electronics; Alan P. Gray, Walter Slavin, and John Huley, all of Perkin-Elmer Corp.; John R. Churchill, Alcoa Research; and Jack Jenkins, Consolidated Electrodynamics Corp.

The author also wishes to thank the contributing authors who are listed on a separate page, as well as the people who contributed to the mechanics of preparing the manuscript: Dr. Robert Maizell, who did some of the reproduction; Mary Anne Kusmit, Marge Duddy, and my wife Anne Siggia, who did the typing and handled the necessary correspondence.

Special mention should be made of my students who took a course based on this text and had to use manuscript and galleys as reading material. These people who also made valuable comments to clarify certain areas include: Robert Dishman, Jane Tao, James Curley, Rod Croteau, Ann Noble, Ron Whitlock, Ken Blessel, Yao-Chi Lien, Al Blanchette, Bruce Colby, Charles Manley, Bill Zeronsa, and Eric Zink. Additional help was obtained from A. Savitsky and S. Swarin who read proofs.

Sidney Siggia

CONTENTS

Preface   *v*
Contributing Authors   *xiii*

CHAPTER ONE
INTRODUCTION

Understanding and Defining the Problem   1
History of the Sample or Problem   2
Literature Search   2
Plan of Action and Execution   3
Approaches to Unknowns   4
Types of Problems   5
    Analytical problems at the research stage   6
    Analytical problems at the development stage   6
    Analytical problems at the manufacturing stage   6
    Analytical problems at the sales stage   7
    Analytical problems connected with legal activities   8

CHAPTER TWO
ELEMENTAL ANALYSIS

Inorganic Elemental Analysis   10
    Emission spectroscopy   10
      arc-spark spectroscopy   10
      flame photometry   18
      atomic-absorption spectroscopy   20
      x-ray fluorescence   23
      electron probe   25
      neutron activation analysis   27
      mass spectrometry   31
    Chemical methods   33
    Polarography   35
    Radioactive elements   38
Organic Elemental Analysis   38
    Information to be obtained from an elemental analysis   39
    Principles involved in the determination of the various
        elements   40
      carbon and hydrogen   40
      oxygen   41
      nitrogen   42
      halogens   43
      fluorine   44
      sulfur   45

phosphorus   45
boron   46
Organic elemental analysis via mass spectrometry   46

CHAPTER THREE
FUNCTIONAL-GROUP ANALYSIS

Optical Methods   54
Infrared absorption spectroscopy   56
Near infrared absorption spectroscopy   64
Ultraviolet absorption spectroscopy   65
Vacuum ultraviolet spectroscopy   71
Visible absorption spectroscopy   72
Raman spectroscopy   74
Chemical Methods   77
Electroanalytical Methods   79
Introduction   80
Basic circuit and operations   80
Fundamental relationships   83
the Ilkovic equation   83
half-wave potentials   84
Analytical measurements and practice   85
Nuclear Magnetic Resonance (NMR)   87
Mass Spectrometry   87

CHAPTER FOUR
IDENTIFICATION AND
STRUCTURE DETERMINATION

Elemental and Functional-Group Methods   96
Chemical Tests and Reactions   97
Absorption Spectroscopic Methods   98
Mass Spectrometry   100
High-resolution Nuclear Magnetic Resonance (NMR)   102
Electron Spin (Paramagnetic) Resonance (ESR, EPR)   114
X-ray Diffraction   116
Raman Spectroscopy   121
Nuclear Quadrupole Spectroscopy   123
Microwave Spectroscopy   123
Optical Rotatory Dispersion   126
Mössbauer Spectroscopy   129
Other Structural Considerations   131

CHAPTER FIVE
MOLECULAR WEIGHT AND MOLECULAR WEIGHT DISTRIBUTION

Molecular Weight 141
Uses for Molecular Weight Determinations 142
Number-average Molecular Weight Methods 144
  Survey of the cryoscopic methods 144
    solubility of sample 145
    solid solutions 146
    interference with crystallization 146
    transitions in the solid solvent 147
    association of the sample 147
    magnitude of molecular weight 147
    heat of fusion of solvent 148
    calculations 148
  Survey of the ebullioscopic methods 148
    solubility and stability 148
    vapor pressure of solute 149
    minimum-boiling mixtures 150
    magnitude of the molecular weight of the sample 150
    association of the sample 150
    calculations 151
  Survey of the vapor-pressure lowering methods 151
    calculations 152
  Survey of the osmotic-pressure methods 152
    dynamic osmometry 153
    calculations 154
  Survey of the gas-density methods 154
    volatility of sample 154
    temperature of measurement 154
    stability of sample 155
    calculations 155
  Survey of the functional-group methods (end-group analysis) 155
    polyfunctional impurities 156
    reactivity 156
    impurities 156
Mass Spectrometry 157
X-ray Diffraction 157
Types of Molecular Weight Values for Mixtures 158

Ultracentrifugation   159
  Equilibrium sedimentation method   159
  Dynamic sedimentation method   161
Light Scattering   163
Molecular Weight Distribution   165
  Gas chromatography   165
  Fractional precipitation methods   165
  Gel permeation chromatography   169

CHAPTER SIX
PHYSICAL PROPERTIES

Density   177
  Gas-density measurement   178
  Liquid-density measurement   179
  Density measurements on solids   181
Viscosity   182
  Liquids   182
  Gases   186
Refractive Index   186
  Immersion methods   187
  Critical-angle measurements   188
  Differential refractometry   188
  Interference refractometry   188
  Image-displacement method   189
  Microscopic methods   189
  Continuous, on-stream refractometry   190
Vapor Pressure   190
Freezing (Melting) Point   194
Boiling Point   196
Surface Tension   196
Interfacial Tension   201
Miscellaneous Physical Properties   201
  Electrical properties   202
  Thermal properties   202
  Magnetic properties   203
  pH and pK 203

CHAPTER SEVEN
GROSS AND SURFACE
EXAMINATION OF MATERIALS

Microscopy   211
Particle-size Distribution   213

Examination of Surfaces   215
  Physical nature of surfaces   216
  Composition of a surface coating   217
  Thickness of surface films or coatings   220
Thickness Gauging   222

CHAPTER EIGHT
ANALYSIS FOR TRACE QUANTITIES

Noninstrumental Methods   227
  Color spot test   228
  Fluorescence spot test   228
  Low-temperature luminescence spot test   228
Instrumental Methods   229
  Ultraviolet visible absorption spectrometry   229
  Low-temperature fluorimetry   230
  Quenchofluorimetry   230
  Phosphorimetry   231
  Quenchophosphorimetry   231
  Comparison of spectral methods   231
  Infrared absorption spectrometry   234
  Gas chromatography   235
  Polarography   239
  Mass spectrometry   242

CHAPTER NINE
ASSAY IN THE RANGE OF HIGH PURITY

Freezing-point Cooling-curve Technique   246
Boiling-point Method   252
Phase-solubility Analysis   253
Electrical Techniques   255
  Conductivity   256
  Hall effect   258
  Residual resistivity measurement   259
  Thermally stimulated current   260

CHAPTER TEN
TRACERS

Nonradioactive Tracers   265
Radioactive Tracers   266

Photographic detection   267
Electrical detection   268

CHAPTER ELEVEN
ANALYTICAL SEPARATIONS

Goals of Separation   271
The Separation Problem   271
Basic Terminology   272
    Distribution   272
    Operations and goals   273
General Considerations   276
    Quantitative separations   276
    Criteria for selection of a technique   276
Individual Processes   278
    Heterogeneous equilibria   278
    Gas-liquid contact   279
    Gas-solid contact   280
    Liquid-liquid contact   280
    Liquid-solid contact   282
    Rates   284
    Miscellaneous   286
Related Factors   286
    Minimization of time   286
        gradients   287
        adjustment of the volume ratio   288
        use of second system   288
        detection   292

CHAPTER TWELVE
AUTOMATIC ANALYSIS

Index   *299*

CONTRIBUTING AUTHORS

V. P. Guinn	Gulf General Atomics San Diego, Calif.	Neutron activation analysis (pp. 27–31)
Jerry McCleary	Consolidated Electrodynamics Corp. 1500 South Shamrock Avenue Monrovia, Calif.	Mass spectrometric determination of the elements (pp. 31–33)
Alan Krivis	University of Akron Akron, Ohio	Polarographic deter- mination of elements (pp. 35–37) and of functional groups (pp. 79–87)
Robert Rittner	Olin Mathieson New Haven, Conn.	Organic elemental analysis (pp. 38–46)
G. D. Vickers	NMR Specialties New Kensington, Pa.	Nuclear magnetic res- onance (pp. 102–114)
H. Agahigian	Quinnipiac College Hamden, Conn.	Electron spin reso- nance (pp. 114–116)
G. L. Beyer	Eastman Kodak Company Rochester, N. Y.	Particle size distribu- tion (pp. 213–215)
Eugene Sawicki	Division of Air Pollution R. A. Taft Sanitary Eng. Center Cincinnati, Ohio	Trace analysis (pp. 225–235)
L. B. Rogers	Purdue University Lafayette, Ind.	Separations (pp. 271–292)

ONE
INTRODUCTION

There is a pattern in handling analytical problems. This pattern consists of general steps and thought processes that the analytical chemist employs as he initiates and pursues the steps toward the solution of the problem.

UNDERSTANDING AND DEFINING THE PROBLEM

To get the most conclusive answer in the shortest length of time is the goal of every analysis. However, to achieve this, the analyst must be clear on what information is needed for the desired purpose. For example, in qualitative analyses a complete identification is not necessary in all cases. In some, a general classification or partial identification will suffice. In the analysis of a competitive surface-active agent, for example $C_{12}H_{23}(OCH_2CH_2)_4OSO_3H$, one can go to various extents depending on the problem at hand.

1. It can be completely identified as written.
2. It may be found as simply a sulfate ester of a fatty alcohol adduct of ethylene oxide.
3. Even more simply, it may be determined to be merely an anionic detergent.

Detergent-formulation people may only be interested in an identification as in (3) because they mix nonionics, anionics, or cationics to produce certain effects. Detergent manufacturers are usually interested in a general classification as in (2), since they may only want to know if the product is in the same sphere as the products they manufacture. It is only when the specific item is of interest that a total identity need be determined. It is important to the analytical chemist to know this intensity of interest, since there is quite a difference in the amount of effort required by (1), (2), and (3).

In quantitative work the same thinking applies. In some cases, an accuracy and/or precision of $\pm 0.1\%$ is necessary; in other cases ± 5 to 10% may be perfectly adequate. Needless to say, the methods used and time consumed can vary widely in the two types of analysis.

1

This first step then defines the goal of the analysis and puts a border around the field of investigation.

HISTORY OF THE SAMPLE OR PROBLEM

This aspect also appears axiomatic, but all too often an eager analytical chemist will begin laboratory work on a job before he has looked into the background of the problem. This background can come from various sources.

The chemist, engineer, salesman, or lawyer who brought the sample for analysis should know why he needs the analysis, the circumstances under which the sample originated or the problem arose, the depth to which he would like to have the analysis pursued. For example, the chemist or engineer mixed A and B under certain conditions and did not get the expected C, but wants to know what he did get. A knowledge of A and B and the conditions used can point to possible compounds. The analyst then is no longer faced with a complete unknown but with a range of possible materials.

The salesman is troubled by a competitive product affecting the sales of one of his products, or the lawyer is interested in proving infringement. He wants this competitive product analyzed. He usually knows the general types of materials used for the particular application. He also knows the types of products made by the company in question. Again the analyst now has leads to follow up.

The utility of this background necessitates close liaison between the analyst and his clients. It can be said that the complete unknown, a sample about which nothing is known, does not exist. Every sample has a past and this is very valuable to the analyst.

LITERATURE SEARCH

There should be among analysts as among all chemists, a respect for the technical literature. The analytical chemist should concern himself not only with the analytical literature but with the general chemical literature, the patent literature, and even the commercial literature put out by the manufacturers. A study of the chemical literature can reveal the by-products of the reaction under review, thereby avoiding time-consuming identifications. The composition of industrial materials is often partially or even fully revealed in patents or in the commercial literature with no laboratory effort on the part of the analyst. Quantitative methods are well covered in existing texts and review articles; it is a relatively simple matter to find if any method exists to do the job at hand. If the literature search reveals no definite method for the particular system, it will surely provide possible approaches that can be tried in developing a new method.

PLAN OF ACTION AND EXECUTION

After the problem has been defined and the literature covered, a plan of action must be arrived at. With the goal clearly in mind, the analytical chemist selects approaches best suited to achieve the overall solution. Most often, several approaches in combination are used effectively; these might well be combinations of chemical and instrumental methods.

As data begin to be gathered, the picture of the particular situation becomes clearer and often the original plan is modified accordingly to suit the situation in its newer light. Sometimes no changes in the original plan are needed and sometimes radical changes are needed, depending on what the data bring to light.

During the data gathering, the evaluation of the data is most important. The limitations of the data must be known so that unjustifiable conclusions are not drawn. Also, all possible information must be gleaned from the data. The information will be of varying degrees of certainty, and the weight put on each piece of information will vary accordingly.

Finally, enough data are obtained for a tentative conclusion. The conclusiveness of this solution depends on the validity of the data and the soundness of the judgment of the analytical chemist. The gaps in the solution are then filled in to solidify the conclusion. The analytical chemist should try to confirm his conclusion whenever possible. For example, once the identity of an unknown has been derived from the experimental data, the identity can be firmly established by obtaining an authentic sample of the suspected material (or a derivative thereof) or by preparing it by known synthetic methods. The unknown and known are then compared by any of the "fingerprint" techniques, such as infrared absorption, x-ray diffraction, and mass spectrometry. When the "fingerprints" match, a firm identification has been made. In the case of quantitative methods of analysis, once a method or system of methods has been arrived at to analyze a certain sample or mixture, samples of known composition are made up and analyzed by the intended methods to confirm the utility of the methods. The composition of the synthetic sample must match qualitatively that of the material under study and must cover quantitatively the ranges of composition expected in the samples to be analyzed.

APPROACHES TO UNKNOWNS

The above discussion outlines a general pattern of handling a problem and describes the thought processes of *understanding, selection, evaluation,* and *correlation* that go into the solution of an analytical problem. An example of the solution of an actual analytical problem is given to illustrate what has been discussed. Note especially how the problem fits the pattern described above and note also the variety of analytical approaches, chemical and instrumental (each approach is *in italics*), used to solve the problem.

The problem was to determine qualitatively and quantitatively the identity of a competitive formulation.

Step 1. Discussions were held with the men desiring the identification. They stated that the formulation was used in a photoreproduction system and that the end use dictated that a buffer be present and also a thickening agent. The solution also had to be aqueous to be applied. The manufacturer's name was also obtained.

Step 2. With this information in hand, the literature was searched for patents held by the particular firm on processes of the type involved. No information was obtained. Literature on water-soluble thickening agents was consulted to ascertain methods of separation from aqueous media.

Step 3. A plan of attack was devised to separate the thickening agent, using the methods from the literature. The buffer would be analyzed by spectrographic emission to identify as many elements as possible. An x-ray diffraction pattern would be obtained on the dry residue from the solution, and with the emission data to screen out possibilities, the pattern of the unknown would be compared with patterns of known buffer salts.

No solid thickening agent could be isolated by using the literature methods. When the solution was *evaporated to dryness*, it did not proceed all the way to a dry salty residue, but an oily residue remained containing salt crystals. It was then surmised that the thickening material might be a water-soluble high-viscosity liquid. A separate sample of the unknown was deionized, using *ion-exchange resins* to remove the buffer. The effluent from the column was evaporated and clear, oily material remained. The number of water-soluble, high-viscosity, economical materials is limited. Glycerol or ethylene glycol was suspected.

Infrared curves proved the thickener to be glycerol by comparison of the absorption curve of the material from the unknown with the curve obtained on a known sample of glycerol.

The rest of the plan of the analysis proceeded more smoothly. The *spectral-emission analysis* of the salt obtained from the oily residue after evaporation indicated the presence of only one element, phosphorus. This was meaningful. Since phosphorus is a very unlikely cation, this pointed to ammonium ion as the possible cation (keeping in mind that the salt was a buffer salt). The *x-ray diffraction pattern* of the salt was obtained and immediately compared with the patterns for the ammonium phosphates. The salt from the unknown proved to be ammonium dihydrogen phosphate, with no indication of the presence of other ammonium phosphates. The sample could still contain phosphoric acid as a component of the buffer system, since this would also show only phosphorus on emission analysis, and being a liquid, would have no x-ray diffraction pattern. To check this point, a *Kjeldahl distillation* was run to measure the ammonium ion and an analysis for phosphate was also run. Since the salt could not be obtained in a pure form because of the presence of the glycerol, the ratio of ammonium ion to phosphate ion was obtained. This indicated that ammonium dihydrogen phosphate alone was the buffer. To confirm further the latter point, a *potentiometric titration* was run on the unknown solution and on a known sample of ammonium dihydrogen phosphate. Two potentiometric breaks were obtained in each case. In both the known and unknown, the equivalents of base consumed for the second potentiometric break in the titration curve relative to the first indicated that phosphoric acid could not be present.

To conclude the characterization, the glycerol was determined quantitatively by the *periodic acid method*. Water was determined by the *Karl Fischer method*. The total of these with the ammonium dihydrogen phosphate content as determined above came to 98.6%. The accumulated errors in the three quantitative methods could come to $\pm 2\%$ in the sum of the analyses. The analyses were then reported.

TYPES OF PROBLEMS

The section below delineates the types of problems with which the analyst is most frequently confronted.

The problems are divided into the types of chemical industrial activity with which the analyst is involved. These chemical activities can be listed as *research, development, production, sales,* and *legal.*

Analytical Problems at the Research Stage

1. Identify new compounds and/or the impurities in a new compound and/or the structure of the new materials.

2. Develop quantitative methods of analysis for the new materials and any impurities therein which might be important.

3. Determine physical parameters such as density, refractive index, viscosity, surface tension, specific heat, vapor-liquid equilibria, solubility, etc., which may be of value in the development or use of the product.

4. Determine stabilities of the new products to temperature, pressure, oxygen, contaminants, and any other conditions pertinent to the manufacture or use of the product. (The analyst is involved with this function since the basis of the study is the analysis for rate of decay of product or rate of formation of other products under the stated conditions.)

Analytical Problems at the Development Stage

1. Develop methods of analysis to follow pilot plant or prepilot plant work on processes to manufacture materials which originated in research. In general, the methods will have been already developed in the research phase, but these methods must now be adapted to the compositions and concentration ranges to be encountered in the larger-scale operations. One often encounters different qualitative and quantitative systems on scaling up from laboratory to pilot or prepilot plant. Also, often the pilot or prepilot plant operation may go toward a continuous process, whereas the laboratory research work is all batch-type synthesis. The switch to continuous processes often makes rather radical changes in the synthesis compositions, requiring major changes in analytical methods.

2. Assist in the elimination of snags in the process, such as determining the cause of yield losses by identifying the by-products and/or catalyst poisons. Determine causes of variation in quality (assay, color, odor, turbidity, etc.).

Analytical Problems at the Manufacturing Stage

1. Help keep manufacturing processes under control by analyzing checkpoints along the process to ensure that the composition of the

materials at those points is within the specified ranges. A typical process can be outlined as follows:

Raw materials → reaction step → rectification step → final purification

2. There are also snag-type analyses required at the manufacturing stage, as there were in the development phase shown above. The types of snags vary somewhat, however. In the development stage, snags occur because not too much is known about the process as yet. In the manufacturing stage, snags occur because of deliberate or unexpected variations in operating parameters, deliberate or unexpected variations in raw materials, or blunders on the part of operating personnel.

3. In plant areas, there is also the problem of environmental hygiene. Hence, the atmospheres in which the people work must be monitored for hazardous chemicals. Also, plant effluents are monitored to avoid air and stream pollution.

Analytical Problems at the Sales Stage

1. Customer complaints give rise to much analytical activity. Color, odor, assay, content of certain impurities, poor performance for the intended purpose, etc., all require analysis to get to the root of the problem.

2. Customer service is a service performed for the customer to gain his goodwill. Analytical services are among the services performed. The customer may need an analytical method to determine the product of a certain chemical company; that chemical company may develop the method for the customer to use on his formulations. Chemical companies often help customers gather data to promote the customers' product or help gather data for obtaining approvals of government agencies (e.g., Food and Drug Administration).

3. The sales activity involves keeping a close watch on the competition in the particular areas of interest to the chemical companies. Hence, analysis of competitive products is an activity in all industrial analytical departments.

4. The establishment of specifications and specification methods is another area where analysis fits into sales activities. In this same sphere is the accumulation of physical constants for publication in the sales bulletins distributed by the company to prospective customers.

5. The obtaining of approvals from governmental agencies for use of chemical materials is generally an activity carried out or coordinated by the sales group of a chemical company. These activities require much

development of analytical methods, identification of impurities, and gathering of analytical data to correlate with toxicity.

Analytical Problems Connected with Legal Activities

1. Patent infringement is always part of the chemical scene. Suspect competitive products must be analyzed to determine if their process or product infringes that of the investigating company. Product infringement involves only product identification. Process infringement requires analyses to detect telltale impurities that point to the use of a suspected process.

There is a reverse type of problem in this area of infringement. This is the exhaustive analysis of a competitive material, so that the second company can devise a process to make the same or similar material without infringing the first company's patent.

2. Chemical companies are always open to liability suits involving injury, death, property damage, or adverse performance of a purchased chemical. Analysis is usually required to prove whether the company material was really at fault.

Thus it can be seen that chemical analysis is not concerned with merely detecting or determining a specific component or the general composition of a sample. *It is the resolution or elucidation of a situation.* What caused the plant to explode? Are we liable to a lawsuit? Should we place a plant at a certain location? What caused the drop in yield or the catalyst to die? The analytical chemist must first *diagnose the situation* and decide what must be determined to resolve the situation. Then, he must devise methods to obtain the needed data, and he must present the data in the best form and degree of conclusiveness that the problem demands. The analytical chemist is by no means a secondary individual. The above breadth of activity shows his importance and degree of responsibility, as well as the capability that is required from the analytical chemist.

TWO
ELEMENTAL
ANALYSIS

The elements are the basic units of chemical materials; hence it is not surprising that analysis for the elements contained in a sample is one of the most common types of analytical problems. The elemental analysis is required for several reasons:

1. To establish the identity or elemental constitution of a certain compound. It is common practice, especially in the case of organic compounds, to determine the elements present as a first step in the identification of a compound.

2. To determine the presence and/or amount of a certain compound via the determination or detection of a characteristic element. The element is used as a convenient "handle" or "tag" to follow the compound.

3. To determine specific elements whose presence or absence produces certain desired or undesired reactions or effects.

There are two types of elemental analysis which, for the lack of any better designations, can be called analysis for the "organic" elements and analysis for the "inorganic" elements. In actuality all the elements of the periodic table can be found in both organic and inorganic compounds. However, certain elements such as carbon, hydrogen, nitrogen, sulfur, phosphorus, and halogens,when present in organic materials, are determined by one type of analysis. This consists of combustion of the organic material with conversion of the element to be measured into an easily measurable form. These same elements occur of course in inorganic compounds, i.e., carbonates, mineral acids, nitrates, sulfates, phosphates, and halides. When this happens, "inorganic" methods generally are preferable. The "organic" elements are generally not amenable to emission-spectrographic or x-ray methods, though phosphorus is certainly an exception.

The "inorganic" elements are generally all determinable by emission-spectrographic and x-ray methods even when they are present in organic compounds or mixtures. These elements consist of most of the rest of the periodic table except the rare gases and the elements already cited.

INORGANIC ELEMENTAL ANALYSIS

There are many analytical techniques for dealing with "inorganic" elements. These techniques have both qualitative and quantitative applicability, and each possesses strong and weak points from an application standpoint. Hence, the selection of the proper technique for a given task depends on the information sought. The following sections describe the strong and weak points of each approach.

Emission Spectroscopy

The basic technique consists of exciting the elements in the samples by an input of energy. The electrons are thus jolted to a higher energy state, and when they fall back to their normal energy state, radiation is emitted. The wavelengths of the emitted radiation are characteristic of the elements in the sample and can be recorded by a suitable detector. These wavelengths provide in this way an excellent qualitative test. The quantity of radiation of each wavelength, as measured photographically or electronically, can be used to measure quantitatively the amount of a given element. This is determined by comparison of the quantity of emitted light of each wavelength against the light emitted by standards of known composition. The standards are either synthesized at the known composition, or else they can be actual samples analyzed by other methods.

There are several types of emission spectroscopy. These are designated by the energy source used to excite the elements or the means used to measure the resulting radiation.

Arc-Spark Spectroscopy

This is one of the older forms of spectroscopy and of "inorganic" elemental analysis. It consists of electrical excitation of the electrons of the elements in the sample. When the electrons return to their ground state, light is emitted. The emitted light is passed through a dispersing device such as a prism or a diffraction grating to break the light into its component wavelengths. The resultant spectrum is then examined, either on a photographic plate or electronically. Each line occurring at a definite wavelength position on the spectrum designates a specific element, and the intensity of light at that wavelength can be used to measure how much of that element is present. Figure 2-1 shows an example of an (arc or spark) emission spectrographic analysis of an aluminum-base alloy and a copper-base alloy.

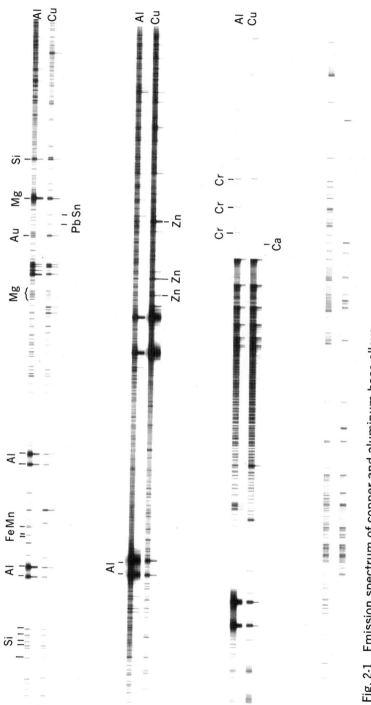

Fig. 2-1 Emission spectrum of copper and aluminum base alloys.

Arc excitation differs from spark excitation in utility. The arc source generally produces more heat than the spark source, producing more excitation and hence enabling more sensitive detection of the elements. However, the arc source is less reproducible than the spark source and thus will yield different quantities of emitted light on different runs on the same material. Therefore, arc excitation is generally better than spark excitation for qualitative purposes, since it will extend to the lower ranges of detectability. The spark source is better for quantitative purposes because of better reproducibility in the quantity of emitted light.

The range of utility of arc-spark emission spectroscopy for the inorganic elements is very broad. It will detect and determine the majority of the elements of the periodic table, and it is capable of this with any type of sample, organic, inorganic, solid, liquid, or gas. It also can operate from low concentration ranges to major concentration levels. Table 2-1 shows the elements readily detectable and determinable by arc-spark emission and also gives an idea of the limit of detectability for each element. In looking at this table, it should be kept in mind that the absolute limit of detectability can vary with the various instruments that are available but that the relative limits of detectability will remain about the same. Thus, using one analysis, this technique is able to detect and/or determine a wide range of "inorganic" elements. It is not surprising then that when one is confronted with a need to analyze qualitatively a sample, organic or inorganic, for the inorganic elements, an arc or spark emission analysis is one of the best approaches to use. Speed is one of its strong points also. A full qualitative analysis of an unknown sample rarely requires more than two hours with an experienced operator. Quantitative analysis, when accomplished photographically, requires about the same time once the calibration of the instrument has been accomplished. In arc-spark spectroscopy, direct-reading devices for quantitative analysis are available which are programmed for given elements in given samples. These automatically scan and record the emission data as percent of the various elements in a matter of a very few minutes.

The accuracy and precision obtainable by arc-spark spectroscopy will vary with the device used, the experimental technique used, and the chemical situation in which the elements occur. However, relative accuracies of better than $\pm 2\%$ for major concentrations are not difficult to obtain with moderately priced direct-reading instruments (about $20,000). Relative accuracies of $\pm 5\%$ are usually achieved with photographic instruments. The accuracy and precision for minor

Table 2-1 Lines and bands used for visual spectrochemical analysis with the d-c arc. (After Peterson and Jaffee 1953.)
Observations made with a Gaertner model L-220 spectroscope; source of excitation, d-c arc; dispersion system, two 60° flint-glass prisms, 27 by 54 mm.

Element	Wave-length, A	Approx. limit of sensi-tivity, %	Element	Wave-length, A	Approx. limit of sensi-tivity, %
Ag	5465.5⎱ 5209.1⎰	0.001	Ca	5265.6 5261.7 4454.7	
Al	3961.5⎱ 3944.0⎰	0.001		4434.9 4425.4 *4226.7*	<0.001
AlO	¹5079.3R ¹4842.1R	0.001		3968.5 3933.7	
Au	4792.6	0.3	Cd	5085.8⎱ 4799.9⎰ 4678.2	0.001
B(BO)	(2)	0.5			
Ba	6496.9 ³*5535.5* 4934.1 4554.1	<0.001	Ce	5512.1 *4628.2*	0.05
			Cl(CaCl)	¹6211.6V ¹5934.0V	1.0
Be	*4572.7*	0.01			
BeO	¹5075.2R ¹4708.7R		Co	4867.9⎱ 4840.3⎰ 4813.5 4792.9	0.05
Bi	4722.5	0.001			
Br(BaBr)	⁴5360.1 ⁴5208.2	10	Cr	5208.4⎱ 5206.0⎰ 5204.5	0.001
C₂	¹5165.2V	(5)		4289.7 4274.8	
CN	¹4216.0V	(5)		4254.3	
Ca	5349.5 5270.3		Cs	4593.2 4555.4	1.0

Table 2-1   Lines and bands used for visual spectrochemical analysis with the d-c arc. (After Peterson and Jaffe 1953.) (continued)

Observations made with a Gaertner model L-220 spectroscope; source of excitation, d-c arc; dispersion system, two 60° flint-glass prisms, 27 by 54 mm.

Element	Wave-length, A	Approx. limit of sensi-tivity, %	Element	Wave-length, A	Approx. limit of sensi-tivity, %
Cu	5218.2⎫ 5153.3⎬ 5105.6⎭	0.001	In	4511.3	0.001
			Ir	5449.5	0.5
Dy	4957.4	(6)	K	7699.0⎫ 7664.9⎭	0.1
F(CaF)	¹6064.4V ¹5291.0R	0.001		6939.0 6911.3	
Fe	5371.5 5328.5 5269.5		La	4921.8⎫ 4899.9⎭	0.05
	4957.3 4919.0		LaO	¹5599.9R	0.05
	4891.5 4878.2		Li	*6707.8* 6103.6	<0.001
	4415.1⎫ 4404.7⎬ 4383.1⎭	0.05		4603.0	
			Lu	4518.6	(7)
Ga	4172.1	0.001	Mg	5183.6⎫ 5172.7⎬ 5167.3⎭	0.001
Gd	5155.8⎫ 5103.5⎬ 5015.1⎭	(6)	Mn	4823.5⎫ 4783.4⎪ 4766.4⎬ 4762.4⎪ 4754.0⎭	0.001
Ge	4685.8	0.1			
Hf	4093.2	(7)			
Hg	5790.6⎫ 5769.6⎭	0.1	Mo	5570.5⎫ 5533.0⎬ 5506.5⎭	0.001
	5460.7				

Table 2-1   Lines and bands used for visual spectrochemical analysis with the d-c arc. (After Peterson and Jaffee 1953.) (continued)
Observations made with a Gaertner model L-220 spectroscope; source of excitation, d-c arc; dispersion system, two 60° flint-glass prisms, 27 by 54 mm.

Element	Wave-length, A	Approx. limit of sensi-tivity, %	Element	Wave-length, A	Approx. limit of sensi-tivity, %
Na	5895.9 ⎱ 5889.9 ⎰	<0.001	Rb	6298.3 6206.3 5724.5	0.1
	5688.0 5682.8		Re	5275.5 4889.2	0.1
Nb(Cb)	5350.7 ⎱ 5344.1 ⎰ 5095.3 5079.0	0.01	Rh	5599.4 4374.8	0.1
Nd	5319.8 ⎱ 5293.2 ⎰	0.1	Ru	5171.0 4554.5	0.01
Ni	5476.9 4703.8	0.01	Sb	5632.0 4033.5	5.0
Os	4420.5	0.1	Sc	5087.1 ⎱ 5085.5 ⎰ 5083.7 5081.5	0.005
Pb	6001.8 4057.8	0.001	ScO	¹6036.2R	0.005
Pd	5295.6 5163.8 4212.9	0.01	Se	4730.8	(8)
			Si	3905.5	1
Pr	5220.1 ⎱ 5110.8 ⎰ 4222.9	(6)	Sm	4883.9 ⎱ 4815.8 ⎰ 4760.3 4280.8	(6)
Pt	5301.0 5227.6 5059.5 4442.5	0.1	Sn	5631.7 4524.7	0.1

Table 2-1   Lines and bands used for visual spectrochemical analysis with the d-c arc. (After Peterson and Jaffe 1953.) (continued)
Observations made with a Gaertner model L-220 spectroscope; source of excitation, d-c arc; dispersion system, two 60° flint-glass prisms, 27 by 54 mm.

Element	Wave-length, A	Approx. limit of sensi-tivity, %	Element	Wave-length, A	Approx. limit of sensi-tivity, %
Sr	4607.3	<0.001	W	5224.7	0.1
	4215.5			5053.3	
	4077.7			4843.8	
				4680.5	
Ta	5402.5	0.5		4659.8	
	4812.7				
			Y	5087.4	0.001
Te	5130.9	8.0		4900.0	
				4883.7	
Th	6408.6	0.5		4854.9	
	5049.8			4374.9	
	5017.2				
	4919.8		YO	[1]6132.1R	0.001
	4863.2			[1]5972.2R	
Ti	5014.3		Yb	5539.1	[6]
	5007.0			5074.3	
	4999.5	0.001		4935.5	
	4991.7				
	4981.7		Zn	4810.5	
Tl	5350.5	0.001		4722.2	0.001
				4680.1	
U	5915.4	0.5	Zr	4815.6	
	5493.0			4772.3	
				4739.5	0.005
V	4881.5			4710.0	
	4875.5			4687.8	
	4864.7				
	4851.5	0.01	ZrO	[1]6473.7R	
	4832.4			[1]6344.9R	0.05
	4827.4			[1]6229.4R	

Table 2-1   Lines and bands used for visual spectrochemical analysis with the d-c arc. (After Peterson and Jaffe 1953.) (continued)
Observations made with a Gaertner model L-220 spectroscope; source of excitation, d-c arc; dispersion system, two 60° flint-glass prisms, 27 by 54 mm.

[1] Bandhead.
[2] Diffuse bands in green portion of scale.
[3] Italic numbers indicate the most sensitive line observed by this method.
[4] Headless.
[5] Always available with carbon electrodes.
[6] No standards available; perhaps 0.1.
[7] No standards available.
[8] Barely perceptible.
R and V after wavelength indicate direction of the shading of the band system toward the red or the violet.
SOURCE: Reprinted with permission from L. H. Ahrens and S. R. Taylor, "Spectrochemical Analysis," 2d ed., Addison-Wesley Publishing Company, Inc., Reading, Mass., 1961, pp. 78–79.

concentration ranges can vary widely with the particular element, its environment, and the measuring technique used; but once an optimizing technique for the specific element in its specific sample has been developed, quite satisfactory analyses are usually obtainable down to the limits of detectability for that element. To determine elements below their limits of sensitivity, concentrating techniques such as evaporation, ion exchange, adsorption chromatography, or extraction can be used. These concentrate the element into a smaller bulk and make detection possible.

The moderate accuracy, precision, high sensitivity, wide range of applicability, speed, and ability to detect and/or quantitatively determine multiple elements with one analysis on practically any type of sample make arc-spark spectroscopy one of the most useful analytical approaches for the "inorganic" elements.

One minor disadvantage of this technique is that it is destructive in that the sample is destroyed by the analysis. Another limitation of quantitative arc-spark spectroscopy is that it cannot generally be applied to elements present in excess of 10% of the total sample. Major constituents are thus best determined by other means for acceptable accuracy and precision.

Direct-reading arc-spark spectroscopy, while much more rapid than the photographic approach, can be applied only to the analysis of rather rigidly controlled systems. This approach can be applied only to elements that have been programmed into the system in matrices that are essentially the same for standards and samples.

A general limitation of all spectroscopic methods is that they are comparison techniques. Thus, for the most accurate and precise quantitative data, both sample and standards must have the same composition in regard to elemental composition, state of combination of the elements, and the matrix in which the sample is found.

Flame Photometry

This technique is also emission-spectroscopic in nature except that a flame is used as the energy source to excite the atoms of the elements. The emitted light is dispersed by a prism or grating, and the light of characteristic wavelengths is measured with a photometer.

Since the flame is not as intense an excitation source as the arc or spark, it cannot excite as wide a range of elements. It will detect only the more easily detectable elements. Table 2-2 shows the flame spectra of the elements and the general limits of detectability. However, practical analysis is limited to the alkali metals (potassium, cesium, rubidium, lithium) and the alkaline earths (calcium, barium, strontium, magnesium). The sensitivity of this approach for boron, cobalt, copper, gallium, indium, manganese, and silver permits some utility in the low ranges of concentration, but the arc-spark techniques are preferred. For the rest of the elements shown in Table 2-2 arc-spark emission or atomic absorption is definitely preferred. The use of a cyanogen-oxygen flame, which is very hot, achieves a higher level of excitation and thus a higher sensitivity. However, the toxicity of cyanogen is a drawback to its use. Acetylene-oxygen flames are the ones normally used today. Certain materials in the sample augment flame temperatures to achieve higher sensitivities; for example, lead is not readily detected (see Table 2-2) by flame photometry, but tetraethyl lead in gasoline can be monitored by this approach. The treated gasoline in this case gives a hotter flame than that obtained normally.

Though flame photometry does not enjoy as wide a range of applicability as arc-spark emission spectroscopy, it is a much simpler technique to operate and the instrumentation required is much simpler and cheaper. Where a moderately sophisticated arc-spark spectrograph costs $10,000 to $20,000, a moderately sophisticated flame photometer costs about $2,000 to $5,000. Thus, for the elements where it does apply, flame photometry is widely used. The approach is mainly used as a quantitative tool. It is a poor qualitative tool because of the limited number of elements it can detect.

Flame photometry is particularly valuable in the determination of

Table 2-2   Flame spectra of elements*

Element	Minimum detected ppm	Wavelength, mμ	Intensity
Barium	1	745†	100
		830†	50
Boron	5	548†	20
		521†	15
Cadmium	500	326.1	0.2
Calcium	0.3	624†	300
		554†	200
Cesium	0.1	852.1	1,000
Chromium	3	359.3	30
		645†	30
Cobalt	5	350.2	20
		352.7	20
Copper	1	324.8	100
		327.4	90
Gallium	1	417.2	100
Gold	50	267.6	2
Indium	1	451.1	100
Iron	10	373.6	10
Lead	300	405.8	0.3
Lithium	0.05	670.8	2,000
Magnesium	10	285.2	10
		370.8	10
Manganese	1	403.4	100
		561†	70
Mercury	50	253.6	2
Nickel	3	352.4	30
Palladium	50	340.5	2
		363.5	2
Potassium	0.05	766.5 ⎫ 769.9 ⎭	2,000
Rubidium	0.1	780.0	1,000
Ruthenium	30	372.7	3
		378.6	3
Silver	2	338.3	50
Sodium	0.01	589.0 ⎫ 589.6 ⎭	10,000

Also determinable are the rare earths, selenium and tin.

* P. T. Gilbert, Jr., R. C. Hawes, and A. O. Beckman, *Anal. Chem.*, **22**:772 (1950).

† An oxide band with its maximum value at this wavelength.

SOURCE: Reprinted with permission from J. H. Harley and S. E. Wiberley, "Instrumental Analysis," John Wiley & Sons, Inc., New York, 1954, p. 192.

the alkali metal elements, where conventional chemical methods are poor and the sensitivity of these elements to the flame is quite good. Alkaline-earth elements are also readily determinable by flame photometry.

The main limitation to the flame approach is the relatively small number of elements that are adaptable to it. It is also necessary to determine only one element at a time. As in all emission spectroscopies, the standards should be as close to the sample in qualitative and quantitative composition for the most accurate and precise analyses.

Atomic-absorption Spectroscopy

Atomic-absorption spectroscopy is really a combination of emission and absorption phenomena. It closely resembles flame photometry. In flame photometry a flame excites the elements in the sample to produce an emission spectrum. However, only a small percentage of the atoms is excited. Atomic absorption increases the sensitivity of the flame approach by utilizing the unexcited atoms in the flame. In atomic absorption as in flame photometry, the sample in solution is atomized into a flame, producing atomic vapor of the elements in question. Then a monochromatic light source (such as a hollow cathode tube containing the desired element), emitting light of the same wavelength as that of the desired element, is passed through the atomic vapor of the sample in the flame. The atoms of the desired element in the vapor in the flame are mainly in their unexcited or ground state, and they absorb the radiation from the light source. The amount of light absorbed is proportional to the amount of the element in the sample. Figure 2-2 shows a block diagram of the operation of the atomic-absorption approach.

Atomic absorption has a higher sensitivity than conventional flame photometry for some elements, and it has a wider range of application as to the number of elements it will determine. Table 2-3 shows a list of elements conveniently determinable by this technique. Atomic-absorption apparatus is about as easy to operate as flame-photometric equipment; however, it is somewhat more expensive. The basic atomic-absorption equipment costs from about $3,000 to $6,000, and separate monochromatic sources (cathode-ray tubes) are needed for each element. These tubes cost $100 to $200 apiece.

Atomic absorption, like flame photometry, is a good quantitative tool. Atomic absorption, being capable of detecting a fairly wide range of elements, could be a fair qualitative tool. However, the mechanics require that a separate source tube be inserted in the device for each

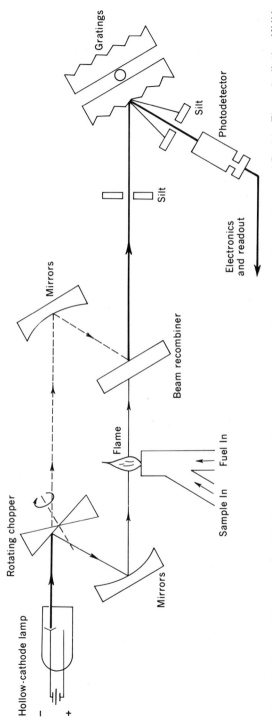

Fig. 2-2   Perkin-Elmer model 303 atomic absorption spectrometer. (*Reprinted with permission of Perkin-Elmer Bulletin, KHV 5645.*)

Table 2-3 Relative detection limits obtained in atomic-absorption spectroscopy[a]

Metal	Rel. det. limit (µg/ml)	λ (Å)	Slit (Å)	mA	Metal	Rel. det. limit (µg/ml)	λ (Å)	Slit (Å)	mA
Ag	0.01	3281	7	12	Na	0.005	5890	40	500
Al[c]	0.1	3093	0.7	40	Nb[c]	20	4059	2	40
As	0.5	1937	7	12	Nd[c,e]	2	4634	2	25
Au	0.1	2428	20	14	Ni[g]	0.01	2320	0.7	15
B[c]	15	2497	7	30	Os				
Ba[c,e]	0.1	5536	40	20	Pb[g]	0.01	2170	2	10
Be[c]	0.003	2349	2	50	Pd	0.5	2476	2	20
Bi	0.02	2231	2	10	Pr[c,e]	10	4951	2	25
Ca[c]	0.003	4227	20	10	Pt	0.5	2659	2	25
Cd	0.01	2288	7	4	Rb[b,e]	0.005	7800	40	400
Ce[c]	...	5200			Re[c]	1.5	3460	2	30
Co[b,g]	0.007	2407	2	15	Rh	0.03	3435	2	20
Cr	0.005	3579	2	10	Ru	0.3	3499		
Cs[b,e]	0.05	8521	40	400	Sb	0.2	2175	7	20
Cu	0.005	3247	7	10	Sc[c]	0.2	3912	7	40
Dy[c,e]	0.2	4212	2	30	Se	0.5	1961	2	20
Er[c,e]	0.2	4008	2	30	Si[c,g]	0.2	2516	2	30
Eu[c,e]	0.2	4594	2	20	Sm[c,e]	5	4297	2	25
Fe	0.01	2483	2	40	Sn[f,g]	0.1	2246	7	8
Ga	0.07	2874	20	4	Sr	0.01	4607	13	10
Gd[c,e]	4	3684	2	20	Ta[c]	6	2715	2	30
Ge[c]	2	2651	2	16	Tb[c,e]	2	4326	2	25
Hf[c]	15	3072	2	30	Te	0.3	2143	7	16
Hg[d]	0.2	2537	20	200	Th[e]				
Ho[c,e]	0.3	4163	2	25	Ti[c,g]	0.1	3643	2	40
In	0.05	3040	7	6	Tl	0.2	2768	20	12
Ir[c]	4	2850	7	40	Tm[c,h]	0.1	4094		
K[b]	0.005	7665	40	400	U[c]	30	3514	2	40
La[c]	80	3928	0.7	30	V[c,g]	0.1	3184	7	30
Li	0.005	6708	40	15	W[c]	3	4008	7	50
Lu[e,h]	50	3312			Y[c,e]	0.3	4077	2	25
Mg	0.0005	2852	20	6	Yb[c]	0.04	3988	2	20
Mn	0.005	2795	20	10	Zn	0.002	2138	20	10
Mo	0.1	3133	2	30	Zr[c]	5	3601	2	55

[a] Perkin-Elmer model 303 atomic absorption spectrometer.
[b] Osram spectral lamp is used.
[c] A nitrous oxide–acetylene flame is required.
[d] General Electric OZ4 mercury germicidal lamp.
[e] In presence of high concentrations of another ionizable metal.
[f] Using an air-hydrogen flame.
[g] Using Perkin-Elmer high-brightness lamps.
[h] Data from Fassel et al.[3]
SOURCE: W. Slavin, Appl. Spectr., **20**:282 (1966).

element sought. This makes it unwieldy for qualitative analysis. Arc-spark emission spectroscopy is still superior as a qualitative tool, because of its ability to detect such a wide range of elements, shown on pages 13–16, with only one determination. Also, arc-spark spectroscopy has a wide range of applicability for quantitative purposes, due to the number of elements it will determine and to the fact that it can handle solids and liquids. Atomic absorption can handle only liquids or dissolved solids. However, atomic absorption is easier to operate than arc-spark spectroscopy, because it reads results off a dial; the latter (except for direct-reading instruments) requires a photographic recording of the analysis and subsequent interpretation. Atomic absorption equipment, even in its most complete form, is somewhat cheaper to purchase and modify than is a moderate emission spectroscopy outfit (about $5,000 to $9,000 for complete atomic absorption; $10,000 to $20,000 for moderate spectrographic emission). A disadvantage of atomic absorption (like flame photometry) is that only one element at a time can be measured; arc-spark spectroscopy can measure multiple elements per analysis. As in all the emission spectroscopies, the standards should be as close as possible to the samples in qualitative and quantitative composition.

X-ray Fluorescence

X-ray fluorescence is an emission approach with a beam of high-intensity x-rays as the exciting source. These strike the sample, exciting the elements contained therein and causing them to emit their own characteristic x-rays. Figure 2-3 describes the approach. The x-rays from the source strike the sample. The emitted x-rays are collimated onto a crystal which acts as a diffraction grating, dispersing the emitted light into the characteristic wavelengths. This dispersed spectrum is then scanned by a detector. A goniometer positions the detector at each of the emitted bands. The angles of the emitted bands with the beam incident to the crystal are a function of the wavelengths of the emitted bands, and these are characteristic for the elements in the sample. The intensity of the emitted band is a function of the concentration of the specific element in the sample.

X-ray fluorescence is a fairly widely used approach, and it is growing widely in application with the advent of newer instrumentation. Crystals are now available that will handle a broad range of emitted wavelengths. Also, helium- and vacuum-path instruments have circumvented the problem of absorption of the emitted x-rays, especially those of the lighter elements. More sensitive detector systems have made possible detection of smaller quantities than was previously possible. Table 2-4 outlines the range of application of the different forms of x-ray fluorescence.

As can be seen in Table 2-4, x-ray fluorescence can be applied to roughly as many elements as arc-spark emission spectroscopy except for those below atomic number 9. In fact, the newer x-ray devices will even determine elements that emission cannot determine. Emission is insensitive to the halogens, but x-rays can detect and determine these elements. In addition, mercury and sulfur often are too volatile for arc-

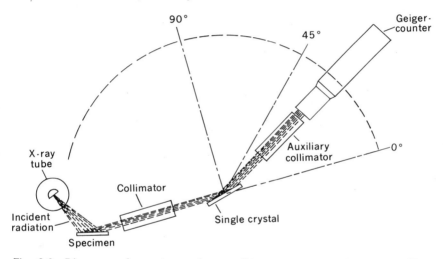

Fig. 2-3 Diagram of one type of x-ray fluorescence spectrometer. (*Reprinted with permission from G. L. Clark, "Encyclopedia of Spectroscopy," Reinhold Publishing Corp., New York, 1960, p. 750.*)

spark spectroscopy and can escape the field of excitation, unless the samples are first given special preparation to put the elements in a less volatile form. In the x-ray approach, the elements are held in the sample during analysis, and hence all that emit x-rays will do so. Also, x-ray fluorescence analysis is nondestructive and the sample is still intact after analysis. Thus analysis can be carried out on actual articles without damaging them. X-ray fluorescence approaches arc-spark emission spectroscopy in carrying out a complete analysis for many elements with a single determination. However, presently available x-ray equipment requires changing targets to cover a range comparable to emission spectroscopy. The x-ray readout is in counts per unit time, so an analytical qualitative or quantitative scan with the modern devices is com-

Table 2-4

Source	Crystal	Detector	Range of elements detectable (atomic number)	General cost range
Air path	LiF, topaz	Scintillation, flow proportional, or Geiger	22 on up	$16,000–$25,000
Helium path	LiF, topaz, NaCl, ethylene diamine ditartrate, pentaerythritol, ammonium dihydrogen phosphate	Flow proportional	12 on up	$25,000
Vacuum path	Same as He path, plus potassium acid phthalate, lead stearate	Flow proportional	9 on up	$25,000–$70,000

SOURCE: Gene Martin, North American Phillips, private communication, Apr. 18, 1966.

parable to direct-reading spectroscopy and yet is not so influenced by sample composition and history. Also, automatic x-ray devices exist which are programmed to automatically determine a fixed number of elements in specific samples. These compete in utility and speed with the direct-reading spark spectrographs mentioned on page 9. There are instruments that can be loaded with multiple samples (as many as 90, depending on the manufacturer), and these are automatically fed to the device and analyzed in sequence for a programmed number of elements. The analysis time for each sample is usually measured in minutes. The actual time per analysis depends on the number of elements being determined and the number of counts desired for the desired quality of the final result. The number of counts recorded depends on the amount of the element present and the time of exposure to the x-ray beam.

Electron Probe

The electron-probe approach is similar to the x-ray fluorescence approach except that a beam of electrons, instead of an x-ray beam, is the excitation source. The activated elements then emit characteristic x-rays which are analyzed much the same as in x-ray fluorescence (see Fig. 2-4).

The electron probe has one great advantage over x-ray fluorescence, and over all other elemental methods, in that it can irradiate (excite) a very small volume of sample (down to 1 cu μ, depending on the instru-

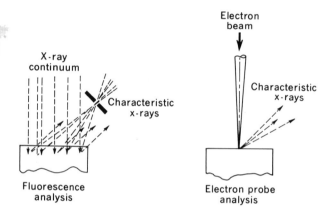

Fig. 2-4 Comparison of x-ray fluorescence analysis and electron-probe x-ray microanalysis. (*Reprinted with permission from D. B. Witty, article in "Sixty-sixth Annual Meeting Papers, Symposium on X-ray and Electron Probe Analysis," ASTM Special Technical Publication No. 349. Published by American Society for Testing Materials, 1916 Race St., Philadelphia, Pa., p. 129.*)

ment used) and still detect the elements. X-ray fluorescence requires excitation of a broader area (about 0.5 sq in.) to get detectable emitted radiation. This difference in abilities is due to the fact that the electron beam in the probe can be rather sharply focused (see Fig. 2-4), producing an intense local excitation, whereas an x-ray beam cannot be focused. Table 2-5 shows a comparison of both approaches.

The ability of the electron probe to analyze small areas is its one big advantage. It makes possible the analysis of small portions of samples as distinct from the bulk of the sample. For example, analysis of inclusions in solid samples is possible with this technique. X-ray fluorescence analysis is preferred for bulk analysis since it analyzes a rather wide area (0.5 sq in.), thus averaging any inhomogeneities in the sample. Electron-probe analysis is not satisfactory for bulk analysis but is quite good for specific determination of inhomogeneities.

The ability of the electron probe to analyze micron-sized areas is of great advantage in the science of materials. In alloys, for instance, it is not average composition alone that determines the mechanical and chemical properties, but also the distribution of elements in precipitates and inclusions. Only the electron probe can measure these precipitates or inclusions on an individual basis, to test for uniformity or completeness of aging in aircraft aluminum alloys or of heat treatment in high-temperature refractories.

Table 2-5   X-ray fluorescence and electron-probe limitations

Parameter	X-ray fluorescence	Electron probe
Lowest atomic number detectable	F(9)	B(5)
Precision for major constituents	1 per cent of amount present	3 to 5 per cent of amount present
Detectability (relative)	1 ppm	100 ppm
Detectability (absolute)	10^{-8} g	10^{-14} g

SOURCE: Reprinted with permission from L. S. Birks, Symposium on X-ray and Electron Probe Analysis, *op. cit,* p. 152, with changes as per telephone conversation with Birks on Apr. 27, 1966.

In other areas of applications, the electron probe is used to identify bits of harmful foreign matter in semiconductor assemblies. In biology, it measures concentrations of metals in particular membranes or cells and thus elucidates the life processes responsible for certain diseases or defects.

Quantitative analysis via the electron probe is possible, though it is quite complex. Much of its complexity is due to the inability to obtain standards that duplicate sample conditions. Also, it is an expensive approach, the devices ranging from $40,000 to $100,000.

Neutron Activation Analysis*

This is a method of elemental analysis based upon quantitative measurement of the amount of radioactivity induced in the sample by bombardment with neutrons. The different elements present form different radioisotopes, the amount of each depending upon the neutron

* Written by V. P. Guinn, Technical Director, Activation Analysis, Gulf General Atomic, San Diego, Calif.

flux to which the sample is exposed, the amount of the element in the sample, the "cross section" for the nuclear reaction, the duration of the neutron irradiation, and the half-life of the induced radioisotope. The basic neutron activation equation is simply:

$$A_0 = Nf\sigma S$$

where A_0 = disintegration rate of a particular induced activity, in disintegrations per sec, just at the end of the irradiation

N = number of target nuclei of the proper type in the sample, and is equal to waN_A/AW, where w is the weight of the element present (in g), a is the fractional isotopic abundance of the particular stable isotope of the element that forms the measured radioisotope among the various stable isotopes of that element, N_A is Avogadro's number (6.023×10^{23}), and AW is the chemical atomic weight of the element

f = average neutron flux (in n/sq cm-sec) of neutrons of specified energy to which the sample is exposed

σ = nuclear reaction cross section (effective nuclear cross-sectional area), in sq cm/nucleus, for that stable isotope and neutrons of the energy specified

S = "saturation" factor, and is a dimensionless number, equal to $1 - e^{-0.693t_i/t_{0.5}}$, where t_i is the duration of the neutron irradiation, and $t_{0.5}$ (in the same units of time as t_i) is the radioactive decay half-life of the induced radioactive species. S has values of $\frac{1}{2}$, $\frac{3}{4}$, $\frac{7}{8}$, $\frac{15}{16}$, . . . , at $t_i/t_{0.5}$ values of 1, 2, 3, 4, ...

The method is completely independent of the chemical form or forms of the elements present.

After activation, the sample can often be analyzed instrumentally (nondestructively) by multichannel gamma-ray spectrometry, since most of the elements form radioisotopes which decay with the emission of one or a few gamma rays of characteristic energies. The different gamma rays emitted by the activated sample show up in the gamma-ray spectrum as "photopeaks." These serve to identify the various induced radioisotopes, and hence the elements. Quantitative measurement of the photopeak areas, compared with that of a standard sample of the element similarly activated and counted, provides a quantitative value for the amount of element present.

If other gamma-ray emitters provide too large an interference in the detection of the desired activity, or if the activity of interest does not emit gamma radiation, the activated sample can be dissolved with the addition of an accurately known amount (typically 10 mg) of the same element as a "carrier." After chemical equilibration with the carrier, the element can be separated, purified, and counted (now without interferences) and the element recovery measured.

Rather than relying on literature values (often only approximate) for reaction cross sections, and experimental values for the neutron flux and the counting efficiency, one normally employs a comparator method, which eliminates these quantities. Thus, by dividing the basic activation equation for the unknown by that for a standard sample of the element of interest (irradiated and counted identically), one obtains the simple equation

$$\frac{A_0(\text{sample})}{A_0(\text{standard})} = \frac{w(\text{sample})}{w(\text{standard})}$$

In practice, the ratio of the counting rates (net photopeak counts per minute), or for pure activities, the total net count per minute at any fixed decay time, is used in place of the ratio of disintegration rates, since the ratios are numerically the same. Sample and standard are usually counted at somewhat different decay times, but can be corrected to the same decay time by means of the radioactive-decay equation

$$A_t' = A_t e^{-0693(t'-t)/t_{0.5}}$$

Most neutron-activation analysis work employs slow ("thermal") neutrons which are readily captured by most elements, usually to form a radioactive product which can be detected. For example, Cl^{37} (24.47 % of ordinary Cl) has a thermal-neutron capture σ of 0.56 b (1 barn = 10^{-24} sq cm/nucleus), and forms Cl^{38}. Cl^{38} is radioactive, decaying with a half-life ($t_{0.5}$) of 37.3 min, emitting beta particles (β^-) and gamma rays of energies of 1.59 and 2.16 Mev (Mev = million electron volts). With the very high thermal-neutron flux of a modern research-type nuclear reactor ($f \sim 10^{13}$ n/sq cm-sec, cost $\sim$ \$200,000), most elements can be determined down to very low levels, as shown in Table 2-6 for 75 elements, the limits ranging from as low as 10^{-7} μg to as high as 10 μg, with a median of 0.001 μg. Small neutron generators (of the Cockcroft-Walton or Van de Graaff types) can provide thermal-neutron fluxes of about 10^8 n/sq cm-sec; less sensitive but nonetheless often quite useful analysis is possible with them. For a 10^8 flux, the limits of detection shown in Table 2-6 must all be multiplied by 10^5 (thus, a median element is detectable down to 100 μg).

Table 2-6 Interference-free limits of detection for 75 elements by neutron activation analysis at a thermal-neutron flux of 10^{13} n/sq cm-sec (for 1 hr maximum) (median sensitivity = 0.001 μg)

Limit of detection, μg	Elements
$1\text{--}3 \times 10^{-7}$	Dy
$4\text{--}9 \times 10^{-7}$	Eu
$1\text{--}3 \times 10^{-6}$	
$4\text{--}9 \times 10^{-6}$	Mn, In, Lu
$1\text{--}3 \times 10^{-5}$	Co, Rh, Ir
$4\text{--}9 \times 10^{-5}$	Br, Sm, Ho, Re, Au
$1\text{--}3 \times 10^{-4}$	Ar, V, Cu, Ga, As, Pd, Ag, I, Pr, W
$4\text{--}9 \times 10^{-4}$	Na, Ge, Sr, Nb, Sb, Cs, La, Er, Yb, U
$1\text{--}3 \times 10^{-3}$	Al, Cl, K, Sc, Se, Kr, Y, Ru, Gd, Tm, Hg
$4\text{--}9 \times 10^{-3}$	Si, Ni, Rb, Cd, Te, Ba, Tb, Hf, Ta, Os, Pt, Th
$1\text{--}3 \times 10^{-2}$	P, Ti, Zn, Mo, Sn, Xe, Ce, Nd
$4\text{--}9 \times 10^{-2}$	Mg, Ca, Tl, Bi
$1\text{--}3 \times 10^{-1}$	F, Cr, Zr
$4\text{--}9 \times 10^{-1}$	Ne
$1\text{--}3$	S, Pb
$4\text{--}9$	Fe

For some elements (for example, B, N, O, F, Si, P, Cr, Fe), activation with fast (high-energy) neutrons can be more sensitive and/or more convenient than with thermal neutrons. Table 2-7 lists the lower limit of detection for these eight elements when employing a 10^9 n/sq cm-sec flux of 14-Mev neutrons and a maximum irradiation time of 5 min. Such 14-Mev neutron fluxes can be produced with a 2×10^{11} n/sec-

Table 2-7 Fast-neutron limits of detection (10^9 n/sq cm-sec, 14 Mev, $t_i \leq 5$ min)

Element	Reaction	Product half-life	Limit, μg
B	$B^{11}(n,\alpha)Li^8$	0.84 sec	100
N	$N^{14}(n,2n)N^{13}$	10.0 min	90
O	$O^{16}(n,p)N^{16}$	7.14 sec	30
F	$F^{19}(n,p)O^{19}$	29.4 sec	25
Si	$Si^{28}(n,p)Al^{28}$	2.27 min	1
P	$P^{31}(n,\alpha)Al^{28}$	2.27 min	10
Cr	$Cr^{52}(n,p)V^{52}$	3.76 min	10
Fe	$Fe^{56}(n,p)Mn^{56}$	2.58 hr	30

output small Cockcroft-Walton deuteron accelerator (costing about $20,000).

In neutron-activation analysis work, sample sizes can range from microscopic samples on up to some weighing even 100 g. Thus, an element detectable down to as low as 0.001 μg can be determined down to as low as 0.0001 ppm in a 10-g sample, to 0.01 ppm in a 0.1-g sample, and to 1 ppm in a 1-mg sample. In almost all matrices, neutrons (fast or slow) are highly penetrating; thus the entire sample is exposed to activation. The gamma rays emitted by the gamma-emitting radioisotope products are also highly penetrating; thus they can escape from the activated sample and be detected. Even at the high neutron fluxes of reactors, the sample composition is, for all practical purposes, unchanged—e.g., a 1-hr activation at 10^{13} thermal-neutron flux only converts about four millionths of 1% of the amount of a typical element present in the sample. The purely instrumental form of the method is nondestructive and very rapid (total analysis time is typically 5 to 15 min per sample; some, even 1 min). Induced activities that are regularly utilized in analyses can be those with half-lives even in the range of seconds to minutes. In such cases, a fast pneumatic transfer tube is used and samples are processed one at a time. With activities with half-lives of hours or longer, longer irradiations give improved sensitivity, but then many samples can be activated simultaneously and leisurely counted one at a time. The multichannel gamma-ray spectrometry counting equipment used in both reactor and neutron-generator work costs about $15,000, complete. For routine work, a technician can carry out the analyses simply, accurately, and with complete safety (with the reactor or generator properly shielded). At levels well above the limits of detection, precisions and absolute accuracies of about ± 1 to 3% of the values are usually attainable.

Mass Spectrometry*

Materials to be analyzed by mass spectrometry are first vaporized, then ionized, in the source of the instrument. The resultant charged particles, which may be elemental, molecular, and/or fragmental, are then passed through a dispersing medium (the analyzer) which separates them into discrete beams as a function of their mass-to-charge ratios (m/e). The analyzer is normally a magnetic field (single focusing) or a combination of electrostatic and magnetic fields (double focusing),

* Written by Jerry McCleary, Production Manager for Mass Spectrometers, Consolidated Electrodynamics Corporation, 1500 South Shamrock Ave., Monrovia, Calif.

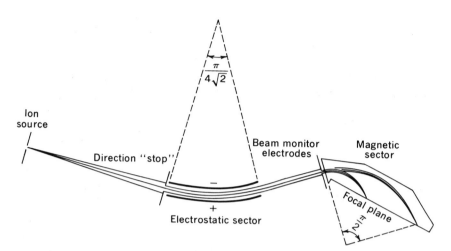

Fig. 2-5 Double-focusing principle of the 21-110B mass spectrometer showing basic Mattauch-Herzog geometry. (*Consolidated Electrodynamic Bulletin No.* 21110, *April*, 1964.)

depending on the energy spread of the ion beam and the resolution required. The separated or resolved ion beams are individually collected and measured.   (See Fig. 2-5.)

For elemental analysis of high-boiling-point inorganic materials, vaporization and ionization are normally achieved with an electrical discharge or surface ionization source. Those compounds that can be vaporized at temperatures up to 350°C can be ionized with a conventional electron-bombardment ion source utilizing a heated-inlet system.

With few exceptions, any element in any matrix can be detected, including most of the isotopes of each species. The resolution of commercial instrumentation is such that isotopic peaks generally can be separated from interfering hydrocarbon peaks (background) and multiply charged peaks can be separated, as can other peaks at the same nominal mass. Sensitivity is usually sufficient to detect concentrations in the low parts-per-billion range.

The intensity of each recorded ion beam or mass peak is the basis for quantitative analysis. The position of the elemental peak in the spectrum is a function of its mass-to-charge ratio, and this is the basis for qualitative analyses. Precise measurement of peak position with reference to a peak of known mass is being used to determine the atomic weights of the elements with a precision of 1 part in 10^6 or better.

Mass-spectrometric analyses are generally more time-consuming and can be somewhat more complicated than those obtained with an emission spectrograph. However, the extreme sensitivity of the method and the ability to distinguish isotopes make the mass spectrometer a complementary rather than a competitive instrument. Actual analysis time can vary from a few minutes to a few hours per sample. This time depends on the degree of contamination from the previous sample (which would require a rigorous cleaning of the source region if trace quantities of the contaminant are to be detected in the next sample), the sample preparation required, the sensitivity desired, and the complexity of the spectrum. The accuracy and precision are generally comparable with those of the emission method. Cost of the equipment varies from about \$50,000 for a single-focusing, electron-bombardment instrument to \$100,000 for a double-focusing, spark-source instrument. To obtain maximum utilization of a mass-spectrometric installation, experienced personnel are required to operate and maintain the instrument.

Mass-spectrometric analysis of inorganic materials is used in a variety of industries. Two of the largest users to date are the metallurgical and semiconductor industries. The demand for ultrahigh-purity metals and semiconductor materials requires that impurities be checked to the low parts-per-billion range. Techniques have been developed so that not only solid mixtures but powders and single crystals can be analyzed.

Facilities engaged in nuclear research and production use the mass spectrometer's ability to distinguish isotopic species to control and evaluate the materials used in nuclear reactors. Similar instrumentation is used in geochemistry for geologic age dating.

Other applications include the analysis of thin-film materials before and after deposition and the general category of analysis of "unknown" substances.

Chemical Methods

The chemical properties of the elements are very characteristic and have provided a very usable means to qualitatively detect and quantitatively determine the elements. The use of chemical methods for qualitative elemental analysis has decreased sharply with the advent and upsurge of the emission methods discussed above. It need only be pointed out that a rather complete multielemental qualitative analysis can be carried out by arc-spark or x-ray emission spectroscopy in a few minutes to a few hours. A rather complete qualitative elemental analysis by chemical means could run into days. Also, the degree of certainty in the results from an emission method is much higher than that in the chemical methods, especially as the complexity of the sample increases. The emission qualitative analysis is based on specific wavelengths or energy positions of emitted radiation. For many elements more than one emitted wavelength of radiation exist; this multiplicity of parameters concretely cements the validity of an identification. With the chemical qualitative methods, the test is based on a characteristic color or precipitate; these are single parameters subject to the interpretation of the observer, and are often very dependent on the other elements contained in the sample. Reliable qualitative analysis by chemical means usually requires two or more tests for certainty. Also, time-consuming separations are often required to remove elements from the interferences before a test can be run.

However, qualitative analysis by chemical means is the cheapest possible as far as equipment is concerned. It requires only standard laboratory glassware and common reagents. However, it is so time-consuming that manpower costs are generally much higher than for the instrumental methods. Much clever analysis was done with these chemical methods when only they were available; and some clever work is still done by older analysts not yet converted to newer methods, or in laboratories too small to afford the more expensive instrumental methods.

The picture is different where quantitative analysis is involved. The chemical methods here are still widely used. Practically all the emission methods discussed above require calibration. This is most often accomplished with samples already analyzed by chemical methods. In addition, for many elements, the chemical methods are often the most accurate and precise available. Where routine analyses are involved, as in chemical or metallurgical plants, mines, etc., most analyses are usually accomplished instrumentally, since the materials being examined remain rather constant in composition and content. Hence, instruments can be calibrated and otherwise automated to handle the particular materials.

In nonroutine areas such as research laboratories and analytical consulting laboratories, where samples of all types are received with few types ever reappearing, it is generally impractical to prepare standards and calibrate for instrumental analysis; it is too time-consuming for the few samples in question. In these cases, the use of standard quantitative chemical methods is usually preferred, since the samples can generally be run without calibration.

The quantitative methods are based on acid-base, oxidation-reduction, precipitation, or color-forming properties of the various elements. The acid-base, oxidation-reduction methods and a few of the precipitation methods are volumetric in character. The bulk of the precipitation methods are gravimetric in nature.

The advantages of the chemical methods are the high accuracy and precision, wide range of application, and no requirement of standardization. Another strong advantage of the chemical methods is that they can differentiate between the different oxidation states of the same element, e.g., stannous and stannic, ferrous and ferric, etc. Polarography is the only other approach discussed in this chapter that can achieve this discrimination.

These methods are still used widely to analyze samples, to prepare standards for the instrumental methods, and also to "umpire" discrepancies among other methods. The main disadvantages are long times for analyses and high manpower requirements, with attendant costs.

Polarography*

The electrical potentials at which the various inorganic elements are oxidized or reduced can be used to qualitatively identify many of the inorganic elements. The magnitude of the potential is an indication of the element present (half-wave potential), and the magnitude of the diffusion current for this particular electrolysis is a measure of the specific element present. Tables 2-8 and 2-9 present polarographic characteristics of some metal ions.

The basic equation for the use of polarography in the determination of the elements is the same as that shown for functional groups on pages 83–84.

As a qualitative tool, polarography is not good. The half-wave potential is not as characteristic of the elements as one would require for a high degree of certainty. The half-wave potential is not a constant for each element; it varies quite widely with the conditions under which the element is found. Ionic strength, pH, even organic impurities can greatly affect the half-wave potential for a given element.

As a quantitative tool, polarography enjoys greater utility. It can be used quite well at low concentrations of elements, detecting in some cases a few parts per million. The sensitivity increases with the number of electrons involved in the reaction. Thus, reduction of a six-valent

* Written by A. Krivis, Associate Professor of Chemistry, The University of Akron, Akron, Ohio.

Table 2-8. Polarographic characteristics of metal ions in acetate media, pH 4.8

Element	$E_{1/2}$ 1 M NaOAc + 1 M HOAc	Characteristics	$E_{1/2}$ 2 M NH$_4$OAc + 2 M HOAc	Characteristics	Electrode process
Ag(I)	...	...	>+0.2	W	$+1 \rightarrow 0$
As(III)	...	...	−0.92	P	$+3 \rightarrow 0(?)$
As(V)	...	...	N.W.		
Au(III)	...	...	>0.0	W	$+3 \rightarrow ?$
Bi(III)	−0.200	WN	−0.250	W	$+3 \rightarrow 0(?)$
Cd(II)	...	...	−0.653	WR	$+2 \rightarrow 0$
Co(II)	−1.2	PB	N.W.	B	$+2 \rightarrow 0$
Cr(III)	−0.9	P	−1.2	P	$+3 \rightarrow +2(?)$
Cu(II)	−0.051	WN	−0.072	W	$+2 \rightarrow 0$
Fe(III)	−0.004	PN	>0.0	P[a]	$+3 \rightarrow +2$
Fe(II)	−1.4	PN	N.W.	B	$+2 \rightarrow 0$
Ga(III)	...	...	N.W.		
Hg(II)	+0.136	WN[a,b]	>0.0	W	$+2 \rightarrow 0$
In(III)	...	...	−0.708	WR	$+3 \rightarrow 0$
Mn(II)	N.W.	...	N.W.		
Mo(VI)	...	...	−0.6; −1.1; −1.2	P[c]	?
Ni(II)	−1.0	PN	−1.1	PB	$+2 \rightarrow 0$
Pb(II)	−0.476	WR	−0.499	WR	$+2 \rightarrow 0$
Pd(II)	...	...	−0.6	P	$+2 \rightarrow 0$
Sb(III)	−0.4	P	−0.400 −0.593	N[d]	?
Sn(II)	−0.599 −0.2	WR[a] WN[a,e]	−0.624 −0.156	WR W[e]	$+2 \rightarrow 0$ $+2 \rightarrow +4$
Sn(IV)	...	...	−1.1	P	$+4 \rightarrow +2$
Tl(I)	−0.458	WR	−0.467	WR	$+1 \rightarrow 0$
U(VI)	...	...	−0.448	WR	$+6 \rightarrow +5$
V(V)	...	...	>0.0	P	$+5 \rightarrow +4$
V(IV)	...	...	−1.2	PB	$+4 \rightarrow +3(?)$
W(VI)	...	...	(−0.70)	f	
Zn(II)	−1.039	WN	−1.1	WNB	$+2 \rightarrow 0$
Zr(IV)	N.W.				

W = well defined wave and diffusion current, P = poorly defined wave and diffusion current, R = reversible, N = not reversible, B = breakdown of supporting electrolyte interferes with the wave, and N.W. = no wave.

[a] Hydrolysis, resulting in precipitate formation, gives difficulty.

[b] Half-wave potential pH dependent. Potential given is zero current potential for a solution 1.0×10^{-3} M in mercuric ion and 1.0 M in ammonium acetate (pH = 7.0).

[c] Three ill-defined waves.

[d] Two well-defined waves of about equal height.

[e] Anodic wave.

[f] Very small wave, even after standing 24 hours. Does not correspond to a normal polarographic reduction.

SOURCE: M. A. DeSesa and D. N. Hume, *Anal. Chem.*, **25**:983 (1953).

**Table 2-9 Diffusion current constants
in acetate supporting electrolytes
at 25°C**

Element	I^a	I^b
Bi(III)	4.1	3.5
Cd(II)	3.1^c	3.5
Cu(II)	2.9	3.1
In(III)	...	3.7
Pb(II)	2.9	2.7
Sb(III)	...	4.2^d
Sn(II)	...	2.6^e
Tl(I)	2.4	2.3
U(VI)	1.5^c	1.7^f
Zn(II)	1.8	1.5

[a] $i_d/(Cm^{2/3}t^{1/6})$ in 1 M NaOAc, 1 M HOAc with 0.001 % gelatin.
[b] $i_d/(Cm^{2/3}t^{1/6})$ in 2 M NH$_4$OAc, 2 M HOAc with 0.01 % gelatin.
[c] $i_d/(Cm^{2/3}t^{1/6})$ in 1 M NH$_4$OAc.
[d] For the sum of both waves.
[e] Sn(II) → Sn.
[f] U(VI) → U(V).
SOURCE: M. A. DeSesa and D. N. Hume, *Anal. Chem.*, **25**:983 (1953).

element is inherently more sensitive than reduction of a one-valent element. However, at the major-component level, polarography is not as desirable as other approaches, owing to a rather low precision and accuracy.

All in all, polarography is not a widely used approach for elemental analysis. However, there is one area where it can be used to advantage. In samples where an element and an organic moiety both have to be determined, polarography can sometimes measure both on the same sample. None of the approaches discussed above, except possibly the chemical approaches, can do the same thing. One example of such a case in the author's experience is the measurement of zinc in mercaptan samples. The zinc existed as the ion, as the zinc mercaptide, and the sample could also contain free mercaptan. The polarograph could measure all three.

Another strong point in favor of polarography is that it can differentiate between the different oxidation states of the elements. Hence, ferrous ion can be determined apart from ferric, cobaltous from cobaltic, etc. Except for the chemical methods, none of the other elemental approaches discussed above could accomplish this differentiation.

Radioactive Elements

These elements are very easily and specifically determined by analysis of their emitted radiation. The nature of their emitted radiation and the half-life of their activity serve as very specific and very sensitive qualitative measures of the elements. The intensity of the radiation serves as the quantitative measure of these elements. Devices are available which are so sensitive that atmospheric contamination by atomic blasts readily determines the radioactive elements involved in the fallout and the quality of each present even though the quantities are infinitesimal.

ORGANIC ELEMENTAL ANALYSIS*

The elements considered to be "organic" are those commonly associated with organic compounds, and they are determined by combustion of the sample, whereby the element in question is converted to a measurable form. The commonly determined elements in organic compounds are carbon, hydrogen, oxygen, nitrogen, halogens, sulfur, phosphorus, and boron. Metallic elements in organic materials are generally determined by the methods shown above for "inorganic" elements.

Organic elemental analysis got its start approximately 50 years ago at the University of Graz, Austria, in the laboratory of F. Pregl. Pregl succeeded in converting most of the existing macromethods for the determination of the elements into micromethods which were of equivalent accuracy [20]. The great advantage of microanalysis is its ability to analyze organic materials quickly, at low cost, by utilizing small samples (less than 10 mg), and without sacrificing any accuracy. Hardly any organic elemental analysis is run by macromethods.

Since Pregl's time, elemental analysis has undergone many radical changes. All of Pregl's methods have been modified and many alternative procedures have been developed which offer greater speed, accuracy, and manipulative simplicity. Within the past few years, many automatic instruments have become available for the determination of the elements. The Coleman Instrument Company has come out with three automatic instruments: automatic nitrogen, carbon-hydrogen, and oxygen analyzers. The American Instrument Company also has an automatic carbon and hydrogen analyzer. Several instrument companies have automatic instruments which utilize gas-

* Written by Robert C. Rittner, Olin Mathieson Chemical Company, New Haven, Conn.

chromatographic and other techniques for the final determination of carbon, hydrogen, and nitrogen simultaneously. Among these are the F & M, Fisher, Perkin-Elmer, and Technicon companies. Some of the automatic instruments are still in their early developmental stages, and only time will tell how useful they will be.

Information to Be Obtained from an Elemental Analysis

The empirical formula of an unknown sample may be determined from the results of a quantitative elemental analysis. For example, let us suppose that a research chemist runs a reaction, isolates a product, and wishes to identify it. He submits a small amount of the material for analysis. Before the sample is analyzed quantitatively, it is advisable that the analyst first qualitatively determine what elements are present. This is done simply by fusing the sample with metallic sodium to convert the elements present (except for carbon, hydrogen, and oxygen) to ionic forms which can be readily identified [25]. Halogen is converted to halide ions, nitrogen is converted to cyanide ion, and sulfur to sulfide ion, etc. The elements which are found to be present are then analyzed quantitatively. The sum of all elements analyzed should total approximately 100%. This serves as a check on the reliability of the various analyses. For the interpretation of the results of an analysis in terms of an empirical formula, the first step is to divide the percentage composition of each element by its atomic weight, and then to divide the resulting numbers by the smallest one of the group, and so ascertain the atomic ratios. Let us take a typical analysis as an example.

An unknown organic sample is fused with sodium and found to contain nitrogen and sulfur in addition to carbon and hydrogen. These elements are then determined quantitatively. Since the results of these analyses do not total 100%, an oxygen analysis is also run, and the sum now of all the elements analyzed is 100%. The calculation of the empirical formula from the percentage composition is then as follows:

Element	% (found)	Atomic wt		
C	30.11 ÷	12.011	= 2.51	3.06
H	5.00 ÷	1.008	= 4.96	6.05
O	26.41 ÷	16.00	$= 1.65 \times \dfrac{1}{0.82} = 2.01$	
N	11.49 ÷	14.008	= 0.82	1.00
S	26.89 ÷	32.066	= 0.84	1.02

The empirical formula of the sample is therefore $C_3H_6O_2NS$. If a molecular weight determination were run on this sample, we could then calculate the molecular formula. If, for example, the molecular weight of this material is found to be $\sim$240, then the molecular formula is $C_6H_{12}O_4N_2S_2$, since the molecular weight of the empirical formula is $\sim$120.

The approximate purity of a known sample may also be determined by microquantitative analysis within the limits of accuracy of the various analyses. The average error involved in all microanalysis is ±0.2 to 0.3% absolute.

Principles Involved in the Determination of the Various Elements

Carbon and Hydrogen

The microdetermination of carbon and hydrogen first developed by F. Pregl [20] is one of the most exacting procedures in organic microanalysis. The operator is usually highly skilled and must be keenly observant of the behavior of the sample during combustion. In principle, the procedure is quite simple. The organic sample is combusted in an atmosphere of pure oxygen either in the presence of an oxidizing catalyst such as CuO [20], Co_3O_4 [29], or the decomposition product of $AgMnO_4$ [13], or in an empty tube [3, 4, 8, 10] at a temperature of 900°C. The carbon in the sample is converted to CO_2 and the hydrogen to H_2O.

$$\text{Sample (CH)} + O_2 \xrightarrow{\Delta} CO_2 + H_2O$$

Appropriately filled absorption tubes, one for the H_2O $[Mg(ClO_4)_2]$ and one for the CO_2 (Ascarite*), are weighed before the combustion and at the completion of the run. The gain in weight of each is proportional to the amount of carbon and hydrogen in the sample. The calculation is as follows:

$$\% \text{ C} = \frac{\text{wt } CO_2 \times 0.2729 \times 100}{\text{wt sample}}$$

$$\% \text{ H} = \frac{\text{wt } H_2O \times 0.1119 \times 100}{\text{wt sample}}$$

* Sodium hydroxide impregnated on asbestos.

Oxygen

It has only been within the past two decades that oxygen has been determined directly to any great extent. Previous to this period, oxygen was determined indirectly by simply subtracting the total of all other elements present from 100%. This procedure is, of course, subject to the accumulation of possible errors from the other determinations. The first direct procedure for oxygen was developed by Schutze [24] and later modified by Zimmermann [34] and Unterzaucher [28]. The method involves the combustion of the sample in an inert atmosphere (nitrogen or helium). The decomposition vapors then pass over carbon at a temperature of 1120°C, whereby all the oxygen is converted to CO. The reactions are represented by the following:

$$H_2O + C \xrightarrow{\Delta} CO + H_2$$
$$CO_2 + C \xrightarrow{\Delta} 2CO$$

The CO is then either oxidized over CuO to CO_2 and absorbed on Ascarite (gravimetric finish), or oxidized to CO_2 by I_2O_5 and the equivalent amount of I_2 liberated (after oxidation to iodate) is determined titrimetrically with $Na_2S_2O_3$. The chemical sequence shown employs coefficients which reflect the stoichiometry in a series of reactions.

$$5CO + I_2O_5 \rightarrow 5CO_2 + I_2$$
$$I_2 \rightarrow 2IO_3^- \underset{I^-}{\overset{H^+}{\rightleftharpoons}} 6I_2$$

Calculation:
  (Gravimetric)

$$\% \ O = \frac{wt \ CO_2 \times 0.363 \times 100}{wt \ sample}$$

  (Titrimetric)

$$\% \ O = \frac{(ml \ 0.01N \ Na_2S_2O_3) \times 0.06667 \times 100}{wt \ sample \ mg}$$

Kirsten [12] has found that by absorbing both the I_2 and CO_2 formed by reaction of CO with anhydroiodic acid on Ascarite, there is an increase of sensitivity and simplicity in the method.

It should also be mentioned that there is a catalytic-hydrogenation method for the direct determination of oxygen which was developed by TerMeulen [27]. This method is not used too frequently, however, because the platinum catalyst used in the hydrogenation is poisoned readily by halogens and sulfur and, therefore, only simple compounds can be determined. In addition, the unfavorable conversion factor for H_2O to O renders the method less accurate.

Calculation:

$$\% \; O = \frac{\text{wt } H_2O \times 0.8881 \times 100}{\text{wt sample}}$$

Nitrogen

There are essentially two micromethods for determining nitrogen in organic compounds: the Dumas combustion procedure which was adapted to the microscale by Pregl [21] and the Kjeldahl titrimetric method, which is a microadaptation devised by Pilch [19] and later modified by Pregl [20].

Dumas Combustion   The micro-Dumas method is amenable to the determination of many more classes of organic nitrogen compounds than is the micro-Kjeldahl. Basically, it involves the decomposition of a sample mixed with CuO in an atmosphere of CO_2 at temperatures of approximately 700°C. The decomposition products, among which are nitrogen and oxides of nitrogen, are then led over hot copper where the nitrogen oxides are reduced to nitrogen. The total nitrogen is then swept by the CO_2 stream into a nitrometer which is filled with 50% KOH. The CO_2 sweep-gas dissolves in the KOH, and the volume of nitrogen collected is then ascertained from the nitrometer reading and converted to its equivalent weight through measurement of the pressure and temperature of the system. The reactions involved are as follows:

$$\text{Sample} \xrightarrow[\text{CuO}]{\Delta} N_2 + N \text{ oxides} + CO_2 + H_2O + Cu$$

$$N \text{ oxides} \xrightarrow[\text{Cu}]{\Delta} N + CuO$$

Kirsten [11] has found that running the combustion at 1000°C in the presence of nickel oxide instead of CuO ensures the complete oxidation of the sample.

Kjeldahl   The micro-Kjeldahl procedure, although not as versatile as the Dumas method, can still successfully handle a large variety of compounds. Materials which are particularly suited to the Kjeldahl method are amines, amides, nitriles, cyanates, and isocyanates. By incorporating a prereduction step with reagents such as red phosphorus and HI [6], or Zn, Fe, and HCl [26] followed by the normal Kjeldahl procedure, the range of compounds successfully handled can be extended to nitro, nitroso, azo, oximino, hydrazine, etc., types of materials.

The method is based on the assumption that a nitrogen-containing sample, when digested with concentrated H_2SO_4 in the presence of suitable catalysts such as Hg, Se, Cu^{++}, is converted to ammonium acid sulfate and the organic material is destroyed. The NH_3 is then liberated with strong alkali (a mixture of NaOH + $Na_2S_2O_3$ is used if Hg is present) and steam-distilled into 2% boric acid where it can be titrated effectively with standard $0.01N$ HCl in the presence of a methyl red–bromocresol green mixed indicator [15].

The equations involved are as follows.

(1)   Sample $\xrightarrow[\text{catalysts}]{H_2SO_4}$ CO_2 + H_2O + NH_4HSO_4

(2) NH_4HSO_4 + 2NaOH $\xrightarrow{\Delta}$ NH_3 + Na_2SO_4 + $2H_2O$

(3) NH_3 + HCl → NH_4Cl

Calculation:

$$\% \ N = \frac{V_{HCl} \times N_{HCl} \times 14.008 \times 100}{\text{wt sample mg}}$$

where V_{HCl} = volume of HCl

N_{HCl} = normality of HCl

Halogens

The determination of chlorine, bromine, iodine in organic compounds can be accomplished quite readily by first combusting the sample to convert the organically (covalently) bound halogen to halide ion and then determining the free halide ion by any of the conventional procedures, such as gravimetrically by precipitation and weighing of the Ag halide; titrimetrically by a Mohr [18] or Volhard [30] titration; or potentiometrically by use of Ag indicating and reference electrodes [9]. The combustion can be accomplished by fusion in a nickel bomb with a mixture composed of sodium peroxide, potassium nitrate, and sugar, or by the Pregl [20] catalytic-combustion method where the sample is heated in a slow stream of oxygen over hot platinum. A very simple, accurate, and fast procedure for determining halogen is the Schoniger oxygen-flask combustion method [23]. In this method, the sample is combusted in a closed flask which has been saturated with O_2. The flask also contains an absorbing solution which is appropriate for the halogen being determined. For chlorine, the flask may just contain H_2O or aqueous NaOH and H_2O_2; for bromine and iodine, a 2% hydrazine sulfate solution is recommended [5]. The reactions involved are as follows:

$$RCl \xrightarrow[O_2]{\Delta} HCl + CO_2 + H_2O$$

$$RBr \xrightarrow[O_2]{\Delta} Br_2 + CO_2 + H_2O$$

$$RI \xrightarrow[O_2]{\Delta} I_2 + CO_2 + H_2O$$

In bromine and iodine determinations, the hydrazine sulfate serves as an effective reducing agent.

$$N_2H_4 \cdot H_2SO_4 + 2Br_2 \rightarrow 4HBr + N_2 + H_2SO_4$$
$$N_2H_4 \cdot H_2SO_4 + 2I_2 \rightarrow 4HI + N_2 + H_2SO_4$$

The free halide ions are then determined as mentioned above. It should be stated that one definite advantage of a potentiometric measurement is the ease with which mixtures of halogens, such as bromine in presence of chlorine, or iodine in presence of bromine, may be determined.

Fluorine

The determination of F is discussed separately from the other halogens, since AgF is very soluble in water and therefore not amenable to an argentimetric procedure. It is one of the most difficult analyses to perform on a micro scale. The basic procedure is to first convert the fluorine-containing material to ionic fluoride by fusion in a nickel bomb with either metallic Na or K, or Na_2O_2, or by Schoniger flask combustion, as above for halogens. An appropriately sized aliquot (containing not more than 0.1 mg F) is steam distilled in the presence of silica and $HClO_4$ to separate the fluoride as fluosilicic acid from any interfering phosphates or sulfates which may be present [32]. The distillate is then titrated with $Th(NO_3)_4$ in the presence of Chrome Azurol S [17] or Alizarin Red S [33] by a suitable color-matching procedure. A color-matching procedure is preferred over a direct titration, since it has been found that the titration is nonstoichiometric. The volume of $Th(NO_3)_4$ used is referred to a previously prepared calibration curve and the percent F calculated. The distillation may be eliminated if no interfering elements such as P, S, or As are present in the sample.

Sulfur

The organic sample containing sulfur is combusted in a fashion similar to that described for the halogens. The sulfur in the material is converted to sulfate, and then determined either titrimetrically with barium perchlorate [2, 7, 31] or gravimetrically as barium sulfate.

As in the case of the halogens, a convenient method for the determination of sulfur is again the Schoniger oxygen-flask method [23]. The sample is combusted in an atmosphere of oxygen and the products of combustion are absorbed in dilute NH_4OH containing a few drops of 30% H_2O_2. The contents of the flask are then boiled to expel NH_3 and excess H_2O_2. The solution is transferred to a beaker, made acidic with HCl, and $BaCl_2$ is added to precipitate the sulfate as $BaSO_4$. The $BaSO_4$ is then filtered, dried, and weighed.

If phosphorus is also present in the sample, magnesium carbonate should be added before the addition of $BaCl_2$ to precipitate out the phosphate as magnesium phosphate, and this is filtered off. If the phosphate is not removed in this manner, high results may be obtained.

Calculation:

$$\% \, S = \frac{\text{wt } BaSO_4 \times 0.1374 \times 100}{\text{wt sample}}$$

Phosphorus

Phosphorus in an organic sample is determined by conversion to phosphate either by combustion in a nickel bomb or by wet oxidation. The resultant phosphate may then be converted to ammonium phosphovanadomolybdate [16] which can be measured spectrophotometrically, or it may be determined gravimetrically by conversion to ammonium phosphomolybdate [14].

The sample is digested in a Kjeldahl flask in the presence of sulfuric acid and a few drops of concentrated nitric acid. The resultant solution containing phosphoric acid is then transferred quantitatively to a volumetric flask. Appropriate solutions of ammonium vanadate and ammonium molybdate are then added, the solution is made up to volume, and measured spectrophotometrically at 410 mμ. The absorbance is compared with a previously prepared calibration curve and the percent P calculated. Arsenic interferes in the determination.

Boron

The increased importance of boron in organic chemistry in the past few years requires that specific attention be given to the methods for its determination. The organic sample containing boron is decomposed either by wet digestion with strong acid (H_2SO_4 [22]; H_2SO_4—HNO_3— and $HClO_4$ [1]) or by combustion in a nickel bomb, and the resultant boric acid titrated with standard alkali in the presence of mannitol.

The sample can be decomposed in a micro-Parr bomb with a mixture of Na_2O_2, KNO_3, and glucose to give boric acid. The bomb is opened and its contents dissolved in water. After acidification, the solution is boiled to expel CO_2 and then cooled and titrated with standard $0.01N$ NaOH in the presence of mannitol. The addition of mannitol forms a strong acid which can be titrated with aqueous NaOH. Without mannitol the boric acid is too weak an acid to be titrated.

Calculation:

$$\% \text{ B} = \frac{N_{\text{NaOH}} \times V_{\text{NaOH}} \times 10.82 \times 100}{\text{wt sample mg}}$$

where N_{NaOH} = normality of NaOH
V_{NaOH} = volume of NaOH

Organic Elemental Analysis via Mass Spectrometry

For the sake of completeness, it should be mentioned here that high-resolution mass spectrometry can be used to determine elemental composition of an organic material. Computer treatment of the mass spectrometer data is usually required. Of course, the organic sample must be volatile enough for the mass-spectrometric approach to apply. Because of the great expense of high-resolution mass spectrometry and attendant computer, one would not normally use this approach merely for obtaining an elemental analysis; one would get the elemental analysis in the normal process of a mass-spectrometric structure study.

Table 2-10 Elemental analysis—summary evaluation of available methods of analysis

Approach	General qualitative applicability (range)	General quantitative applicability (range)	General sensitivity (qual.)*	General accuracy and precision (quant.)†	Ease of operation and maintenance‡	General cost§	Standardization	Analysis¶	Prevalence in industry
Arc-spark emission	Wide	Wide	Moderate to high	Moderate	Moderate	Moderate to high	Necesssary	D	Wide
Flame photometry	Rather narrow	Rather narrow	Moderate to high	Moderate	Easy	Low	Necessary	D	Wide
Atomic absorption	Moderate	Moderate	Moderate to high	Moderate	Easy	Moderate	Necessary	D	Fast growing
X-ray fluorescence	Wide	Wide	Moderate to high	Moderate	Moderate	Moderate to high	Necessary	ND	Moderate now but growing
Electron probe	Limited to work on small cross-sectional areas	Limited to work on small cross-sectional areas	Low to moderate	Moderate to low	Moderate to difficult	High	Necessary	ND	Low compared with other analytical approaches
Neutron activation analysis	Moderate to narrow	Narrow	High	Moderate to low	Difficult	High		ND	Low due to high cost and difficulty to operate

Table 2-10 Elemental analysis—summary evaluation of available methods of analysis (continued)

Approach	General qualitative applicability (range)	General quantitative applicability (range)	General sensitivity (qual.)*	General accuracy and precision (quant.)†	Ease of operation and maintenance‡	General cost§	Standardization	Analysis¶	Prevalence in industry
Mass spectrometry	Wide	Wide	Moderate to high	Moderate	Difficult	High	Necessary	D	Low
Chemical methods	Wide	Wide	Low to high; depends on test	Moderate to high	Moderate	Low	Not necessary	D	Qualitative is low; quantitation is holding its own at rather high level
Polarography	Narrow	Moderate to narrow	Moderate to high	Moderate	Moderate	Low	Necessary	D	Moderate

* Low denotes > 1%; moderate denotes 50 ppm to 1%; high denotes 1 ppm to 50 ppm.
† Low denotes > ±5% relative; moderate denotes ±1% to ±5% relative; high denotes < ±1% relative.
‡ Easy denotes need of technician of little training; moderate denotes need for skilled technician or B.S.-level technical man; difficult denotes need for skilled professional.
§ Low denotes < $5,000; moderate denotes $5,000 to $15,000; high denotes > $15,000.
¶ D = destructive; ND = nondestructive.

Literature Cited

1   E. Abramson and E. Kahane, *Bull. Soc. Chim.*, France **15**:1146 (1948).
2   J. F. Alicino, *Microchem. J.*, **2**:83 (1958).
3   R. Belcher and C. E. Spooner, *J. Chem. Soc.*, **1943**:313.
4   R. Belcher and G. Ingram, *Anal. Chim. Acta*, **4**:118 (1950).
5   C. E. Childs, E. E. Meyers, J. Cheng, E. Laframboise, and R. B. Balodis, *Microchem. J.*, **7**:266–271 (1963).
6   A. Friedrich, *Z. Physiol. Chem.*, **216**:68 (1933).
7   J. S. Fritz and S. S. Yamamura, *Anal. Chem.*, **27**:1461 (1955).
8   G. Ingram, *Analyst*, **73**:548 (1948).
9   G. Ingram, *Mikrochim. Acta*, **1956**:877.
10 G. Ingram, "Methods of Organic Elemental Microanalysis," Reinhold Publishing Corporation, New York, 1962, pp. 20–51.
11 W. J. Kirsten, *Mikrochemie*, **39**:245 (1952); **40**:121 (1953).
12 W. J. Kirsten, *Microchem. J.*, **4**:501 (1960).
13 J. Korbl, *Coll. Czecho. Chem. Comm.*, **20**:948 (1955).
14 N. Lorenz, *Z. Anal. Chem.*, **51**:161 (1912).
15 T. S. Ma and G. Zuazaga, *Ind. Eng. Chem. Anal. Ed.*, **14**:280 (1942).
16 T. S. Ma and J. D. McKinley, *Mikrochim. Acta*, **1953**:4.
17 R. F. Milton, H. Liddell, and J. Chivers, *Analyst*, **72**:43 (1947).
18 F. Mohr, *Ann. of Chem.*, **97**:335 (1856).
19 F. Pilch, *Monatsh. Chem.*, **32**:21 (1911).
20 F. Pregl, "Quantitative Organic Microanalysis" (E. Fylerman, trans., 2d German ed.), Churchill, London, 924.
21 F. Pregl, "Quantitative Organic Microanalysis," 4th English ed., p. 78, Churchill, London, 1945.
22 R. C. Rittner and R. Culmo, *Anal. Chem.*, **35**:1268 (1963).
23 W. Schoniger, *Mikrochim. Acta*, **1956**:869.
24 M. Schutze, *Z. Anal. Chem.*, **118**:241 (1939).
25 R. L. Shriner and R. C. Fuson, "Identification of Organic Compounds," 3d ed., John Wiley & Sons, Inc., New York, 1948.
26 A. Steyermark, B. E. McGee, E. A. Bass, and R. R. Kaup, *Anal. Chem.*, **30**:1561 (1958).
27 H. TerMeulen, *Rec. Trav. Chim.*, **41**:509 (1922).
28 J. Unterzaucher, *Ber.*, **73**:391 (1940).
29 M. Vecera, D. Snobl, and L. Synek, *Mikrochim. Acta*, **1958**:9.
30 J. Volhard, *Prakt. Chem.*, **117**:217 (1874).
31 H. Wagner, *Mikrochim. Acta*, **1**:19 (1957).
32 H. H. Willard and O. B. Winter, *Ind. Eng. Chem. Anal. Ed.*, **5**:7 (1933).
33 H. H. Willard and C. A. Horton, *Anal. Chem.*, **22**:1190 (1950).
34 W. Zimmermann, *Z. Anal. Chem.*, **118**:258 (1939).

Suggested Readings

Arc-Spark Emission Spectroscopy

Brode, W. R.: "Chemical Spectroscopy," 2d ed., John Wiley & Sons, Inc., New York, 1943. (Detailed text.)

Clark, George, L.: "The Encyclopedia of Spectroscopy," Reinhold Publishing Corporation, New York, 1960, pp. 99–328. (Encyclopedia series of articles, each covering an aspect of emission spectroscopy.)

Kniseley, R. N.: "Standard Methods of Chemical Analysis," 6th ed., vol. 3, pt. A, F. Welcher (ed.), D. Van Nostrand Company, Inc., Princeton, N.J., 1966. (Brief introduction to the subject.)

Nachtrieb, N. H.: "Principles and Practice of Spectrochemical Analysis," McGraw-Hill Book Company, New York, 1950. (Detailed text.)

Sherman, J.: "Physical Methods in Chemical Analysis," 2d ed., vol. 2, Walter G. Berl (ed.), Academic Press Inc., New York, 1960, pp. 249–325. (Detailed summary.)

Flame Photometry

Clark, G. L.: "The Encyclopedia of Spectroscopy," Reinhold Publishing Corporation, New York, 1960, pp. 330–371. (Encyclopedia series of articles on subject, especially dealing with applications.)

Dean, J. A.: "Flame Photometry," McGraw-Hill Book Company, New York, 1960. (Detailed text.)

Mavrodineanu, R., and H. Boiteaux: "Flame Spectroscopy," John Wiley & Sons, Inc., New York, 1965. (Detailed text.)

Willard, H. H., L. L. Merritt, and J. A. Dean: "Instrumental Methods of Analysis," 4th ed., D. Van Nostrand Company, Inc., Princeton, N.J., 1965, pp. 309–356. (Detailed summary.)

Atomic Absorption

Elwell, W. T., and J. A. F. Gidley: "Atomic Absorption Spectrophotometry," The Macmillan Company, New York, 1962. (Detailed text.)

X-ray Fluorescence

Birks, L. S.: "X-ray Spectrochemical Analysis," Interscience Publishers (Division of John Wiley & Sons, Inc.), New York, 1959. (Detailed, general text.)

Pfeiffer, H. G., E. H. Winslow, P. D. Zemany, and H. A. Liebhafsky: "X-ray Absorption and Emission in Analytical Chemistry," John Wiley & Sons, Inc., New York, 1961. (Detailed, general text.)

Electron Probe

ASTM Special Technical Publication 349, "Sixty-sixth Annual Meeting Papers, Symposium on X-ray and Electron Probe Analysis," American Society for Testing Materials, 1916 Race St., Philadelphia, Pa., 1964. (Collection of papers on various aspects of subject.)

Birks, L. S.: "Electron Probe Microanalysis," Interscience Publishers (Division of John Wiley & Sons, Inc.), New York, 1963. (Detailed text.)

Brooks, E. J.: "Standard Methods of Chemical Analysis," vol. 3, pt. A, 6th ed., F. Welcher (ed.), D. Van Nostrand Company, Inc., Princeton, N.J., 1966, pp. 186–197. (Brief introduction to the subject.)

Neutron Activation Analysis

Taylor, D.: "Neutron Irradiation and Activation Analysis," D. Van Nostrand Company, Inc. Princeton, N.J., 1964. (General text.)

Mass Spectrometry

Brown, R., R. D. Craig, and R. M. Elliott: "Advances in Mass Spectrometry," vol. II, R. M. Elliott (ed.), Pergamon Press, New York, 1963, p. 141 ff.

Chemical Methods

Qualitative

Clifford, A.: "Inorganic Chemistry of Qualitative Analysis," Prentice-Hall, Inc., Englewood Cliffs, N.J., 1961. (General text.)

Feigl, F.: "Spot Tests," vol. I (Inorganic Applications), American Elsevier Publishing Company of New York, 1954. (Specific spot tests for inorganic elements.)

Quantitative

Furman, N. H.: "Standard Methods of Chemical Analysis," 6th ed., vol. I, D. Van Nostrand Company, Inc., Princeton, N.J., 1962. (General handbook of practical methods of analysis.)

Hillebrand, W. F., G. E. F. Lundell, H. A. Bright, and J. I. Hoffman: "Applied Inorganic Analysis," 2d ed., John Wiley & Sons, Inc., New York, 1953. (Handbook of general methods.)

Polarography

Kolthoff, I. M., and J. J. Lingane: "Polarography," vols. I and II, Interscience
Publishers (Division of John Wiley & Sons, Inc.), New York, 1952.

Organic Elemental Analysis

Ingram, G.: "Methods of Organic Elemental Analysis," Reinhold Publishing
Corporation, New York, 1962.
Steyermark; A.: "Quantitative Organic Microanalysis," 2d ed., Academic
Press Inc., New York, 1961.

THREE
FUNCTIONAL-GROUP ANALYSIS

A functional group in a molecule is a combination of atoms with characteristic properties. It is the properties of the functional groups that generally govern the properties of the total molecule.

The term *functional group* is commonly considered a term for organic combinations of atoms such as hydroxyl, carbonyl, ester, amide, etc., groups. However, carbonate, sulfate, nitrate, nitrite, etc., though inorganic, also fit the definition of functional groups. The techniques used to detect and measure the functional groups are the same whether organic or inorganic molecules are involved. It might be added that functional groups need not necessarily be considered groups of a small number of atoms, such as those stated above. The aromatic ring can be considered a functional group, as can the polyaromatics, and also the steroid "backbone." These configurations contribute specific properties.

Since the functional group is a characteristic portion of the molecule, it makes one of the best "handles" for qualitative detection of chemical materials or the quantitative determination of them. Hence in this chapter we are really discussing qualitative and quantitative analyses as obtained via detection and determination of specific characteristic groupings on the molecule.

Our term *qualitative* in this chapter refers to the detection of a molecule through the functional groups but not to complete qualitative identification of a molecule. The latter is discussed in Chap. 4, where multiple approaches must be used to not only detect the functional groups present but also to position them in the molecule.

In the quantitative sense functional group analysis is employed with the functional group acting as the "tag" by which the system in question can be monitored.

A list of general applications of functional-group analysis can be as follows:

Qualitative

1. Detection of a suspected compound: as a by-product or product in a reaction system; in a competitor's product; as a catalyst poison; as a

reaction inhibitor; as cause of some undesirable property in product; as cause of yield loss; as cause of fire, explosion, toxicity; as cause of corrosion; for patent infringement or legal liability proceedings.

2. Determination of reaction mechanisms.

Quantitative

1. Determination of composition of chemical materials.

2. Following the course of reactions in research, development, and production by monitoring consumption of starting materials and/or formation of product and by-products.

3. Establishing reaction kinetics.

4. Obtaining engineering data for plant design.

5. Determination of equivalent or molecular weights of pure materials.

6. One can include here the quantitative measure of all materials discussed above in (1) under qualitative.

It can be readily seen that the role of the analysis of functional groups is a large and useful one.

OPTICAL METHODS

Optical absorption methods, as the name implies, utilize the absorption of portions of the electromagnetic spectrum. Figure 3-1 shows the various portions of the electromagnetic spectrum. The boundaries between the various zones are somewhat arbitrary but the figure serves to indicate the general areas.

The energy in an atom is solely electronic and exists in discrete quantized energy levels. Hence, atomic emission or absorption spectra consist of sharp lines of specific spectral wavelengths. The energy of polyatomic molecules consists of *electronic energy,* involved with the electrons in the atoms; *rotational energy,* involved with the rotation of a molecule about its center of gravity; *vibrational energy,* consisting of the elastic vibrations of the atoms relative to each other along their internuclear axes. These energies are also quantized, and absorption or emission occurs at specific wavelengths. However, these three energies are interdependent, so when one type of energy is affected, the other two are also affected. This results in spectra with broad bands at the specific wavelengths instead of discrete lines.

The absorptions in the ultraviolet (UV) and visible regions are mainly electronic in nature and are associated with resonating structures in the molecule. The absorptions in the infrared (IR) region are due to the vibrational energies of the groupings in the molecule and the rotational energies of the molecule itself. By observing the absorption

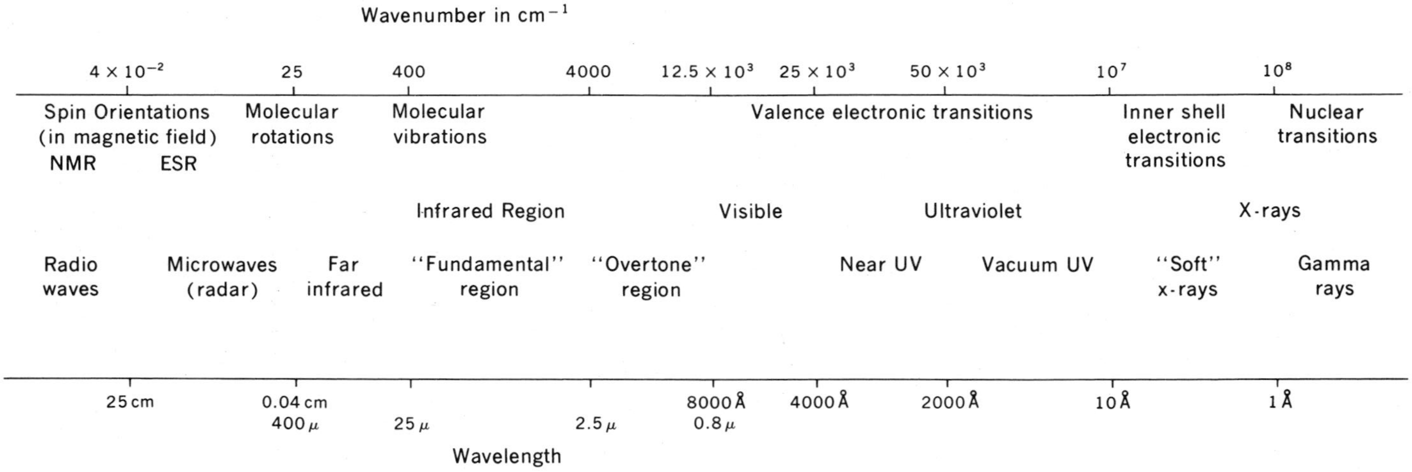

Wavenumber in cm^{-1}

4×10^{-2}	25	400	4000	12.5×10^3	25×10^3	50×10^3	10^7	10^8

Spin Orientations (in magnetic field) NMR ESR

Molecular rotations

Molecular vibrations

Valence electronic transitions

Inner shell electronic transitions

Nuclear transitions

Infrared Region

Visible Ultraviolet X-rays

"Fundamental" region "Overtone" region

Near UV Vacuum UV "Soft" x-rays Gamma rays

Microwaves (radar) Far infrared

Radio waves

25 cm	0.04 cm 400 μ	25 μ	2.5 μ	8000 Å 0.8 μ	4000 Å	2000 Å	10 Å	1 Å

Wavelength

Fig. 3-1 Schematic diagram of electromagnetic spectrum. Note that scale is nonlinear. Boundaries between adjacent regions are generally quite arbitrary. (Reprinted with permission from R. P. Bauman, "Absorption Spectroscopy," John Wiley & Sons, Inc., New York, 1962, p. 11.)

characteristics of a chemical material, it is possible to gain information concerning the qualitative nature and quantitative composition of that material.

Infrared Absorption Spectroscopy

This approach involves the dispersing of a polychromatic infrared beam of light using a suitable prism or diffraction grating. Narrow wavelength bands of infrared light are isolated by a slit and allowed to pass through the sample. The analysis is run by passing the polychromatic light through the sample, which absorbs portions of the light. The remaining light then passes through a prism or grating where it is dispersed into its component wavelengths. The resultant spectrum is scanned over a detector which records the intensity at each wavelength. Figure 3-2 shows a schematic disgram of an infrared analyzer. The sample will preferentially absorb specific wavelengths of the radiation depending on the vibrational and rotational energies of the bonds in the molecule. The various functional groups are composed of definite atomic configurations with definite vibrational and rotational energies, and hence absorb quite characteristic wavelengths. Infrared absorption analysis thus provides a very useful approach to analysis via these functional groups. For the sake of definition, the infrared portion of the spectrum discussed in this section extends from 2.5 to 40 μ. It is this area that is most useful for the analysis of organic and inorganic functional groups.

Figure 3-3 shows a chart by N. B. Colthup of the wavelength regions where various common organic and inorganic functional groups absorb. The abbreviations s, m, and w under the region markers indicate that the bands are strong, medium, or weak. The position of the bands indicates the usual region of the spectrum where absorption is likely to occur for each grouping. Figure 3-4 shows a typical infrared spectrum. It should be emphasized that the infrared discussions in this chapter are related to functional group analysis and detection only. The application of IR to identification and structure of materials is covered in Chap. 4.

Whereas the wavelength of infrared radiation absorbed permits qualitative detection of the functional group, the intensity of the radiation is a quantitative measure of the functional group present. Since practically all functional groups absorb, it is obvious that infrared absorption is a very useful analytical tool. However, the fact that so many chemical bondings appear in the spectrum is also a disadvantage, since interfering absorptions are common. For example, only few sol-

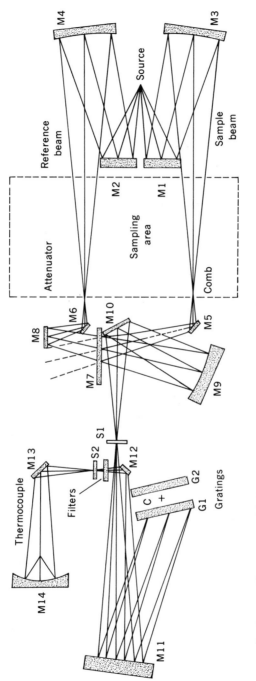

Fig. 3-2 Perkin-Elmer model 621 infrared spectrometer. (*Perkin-Elmer Corporation.*)

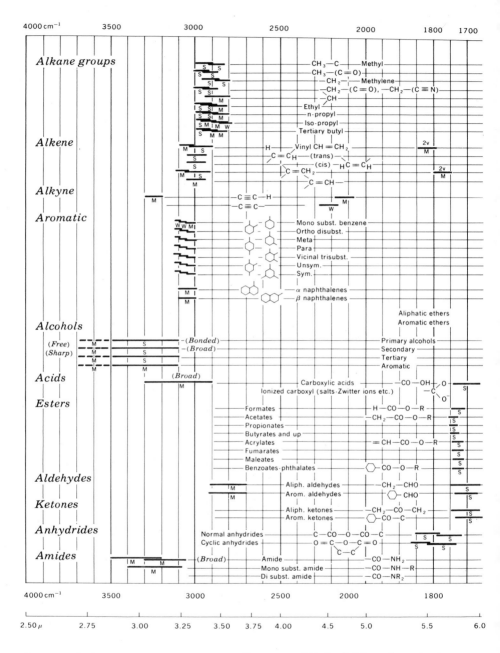

Fig. 3-3 Infrared absorption chart. *(Courtesy of N. B. Colthup, Stamford Research Laboratories, American Cyanamid Company. Reprinted with permission from J. H. Harley and S. W. Wiberley, "Instrumental Analysis," John Wiley & Sons, Inc., New York, 1954, pp. 86–87.)*

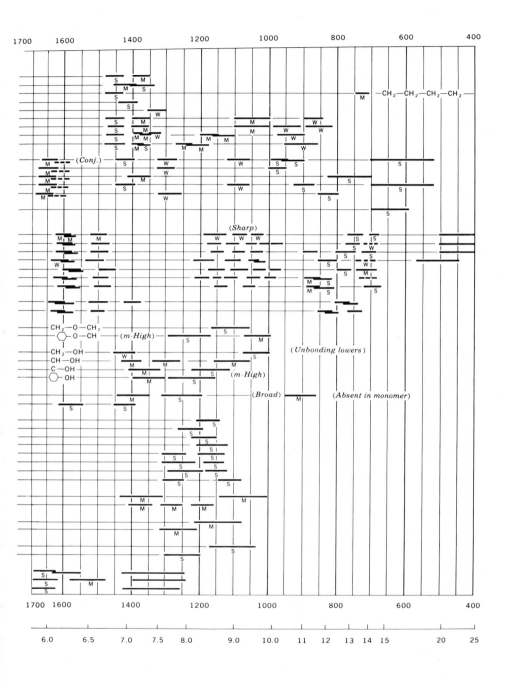

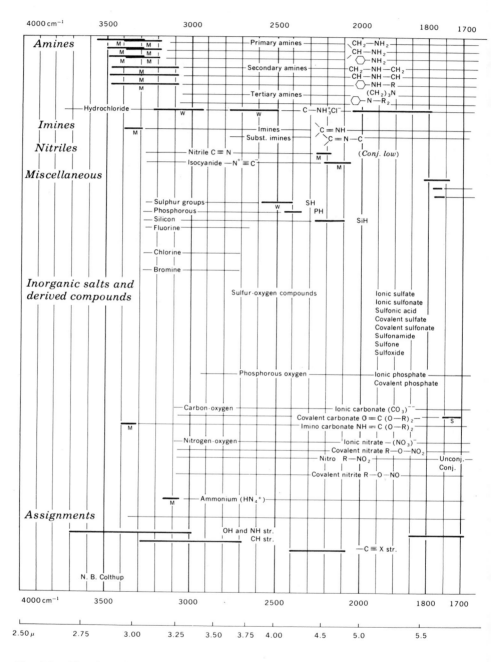

Fig. 3-3 (Continued)

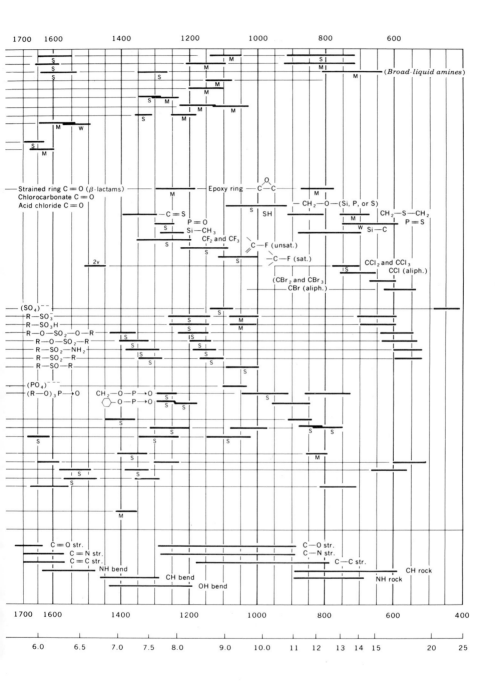

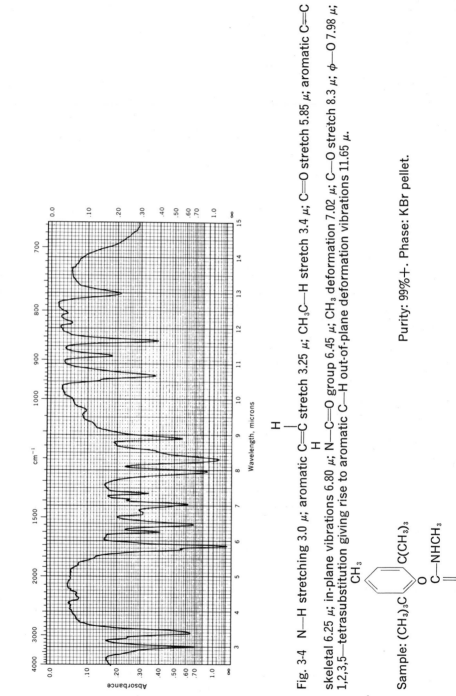

Fig. 3-4 N—H stretching 3.0 μ; aromatic C=C stretch 3.25 μ; CH₃C—H stretch 3.4 μ; C=O stretch 5.85 μ; aromatic C=C skeletal 6.25 μ; in-plane vibrations 6.80 μ; N—C=O group 6.45 μ; CH₃ deformation 7.02 μ; C—O stretch 8.3 μ; ϕ—O 7.98 μ; 1,2,3,5—tetrasubstitution giving rise to aromatic C—H out-of-plane deformation vibrations 11.65 μ.

Sample: (CH₃)₃C

Purity: 99%+. Phase: KBr pellet.

62

vents can be used in IR analysis since most solvents absorb IR so strongly. Though many solvents have "clear" regions with relatively low absorption, these can be used if the solute absorbs strongly in these regions. From the Colthup chart shown in Fig. 3-3, it appears rather simple to interpret spectra. However, there are several factors which can influence the spectra and which must be taken into account in interpreting the spectra for detection and determination of functional groups. Substituents and molecular symmetry will shift functional-group absorption locations and will affect the intensity of the absorption bands. For example, the absorption for the triple bond in acetylenic molecules is intense for unsymmetrical molecules ($RC \equiv CH$), but is weak for symmetrical molecules ($RC \equiv CR$). In addition, sample crystallinity, solute-solvent, solute-solute interactions, and pressure (for gases) all affect the appearance of the spectrum. Also, if the sample is prepared in solution, as a mineral oil (Nujol) mull or as a potassium bromide pellet, or if the pure sample is presented to the instrument, different spectra for the same material can result.

IR absorption is somewhat weak in cases where small quantities must be detected. Absorption bands of components below 1% are not often detectable. Instruments are available with so-called scale expanders which magnify weak bands, and at best one order of magnitude is obtainable. Thus both qualitative and quantitative analysis in the range below 1% is generally poor with infrared, unless one is dealing with strong absorbing groups such as isocyanate, hydroxyl, and some C–Cl groups. Quantitative analyses improve as concentration of the component being measured rises; however, a limiting accuracy and precision in the general range of ± 0.5 to $\pm 2\%$ is reached beyond which the approach cannot generally go.

IR methods can be applied to solids, liquids, and gases. Solid samples can be run neat, though this is not recommended since the sample must be very thin to transmit enough light to record a spectrum. Solids can also be run by reflectance techniques, however. Nujol (mineral oil) or fluorocarbon mulls are widely used as are pressed pellets of the samples in potassium bromide. The potassium bromide is optically transparent to the infrared radiation and acts as binder and/or solvent for solids. It is well to keep in mind that KBr sometimes reacts with the sample under the tableting pressure and causes an erroneous spectrum to be obtained. The pellets of sample in KBr are really wafers comparable to round microscope cover slips. Solids can also be run in solution.

Liquids can be run as received or they can be run in solution.

Gases are usually run as is in special gas cells designed to fit the spectrophotometer. These cells vary in path length (length of sample through which light must pass) from 2.5 cm up to 40 m in path length. The latter cells themselves are not 40 m long but contain mirrors, so that the beam of light is reflected many times through the sample to achieve a total path of 40 m of sample. Gases can also be run in solution though this is not often done.

Interference in samples can be circumvented by (1) physically separating the desired components in the sample from the interference, (2) chemically reacting either the desired component or the interference so both no longer absorb at the same wavelength, (3) handling the analysis of the data mathematically to compensate for interfering absorptions. (See Bellamy, suggested readings, for complete details of this mathematical treatment.)

A strong aspect of IR analysis is that it will differentiate isomeric groups. For example, cis-trans double-bonded compounds can be resolved (e.g., oleic and elaidic acids). Also, functional groups in different positions on aromatic rings can be resolved (for instance, 2,4-toluene diisocyanate can be distinguished from 2,6-toluene diisocyanate). Homologs, however, cannot generally be distinguished unless they vary widely in molecular weight.

The time required to complete an infrared analysis varies widely from minutes to hours. The time of the actual IR scan is a matter of a few minutes, but the sample preparation can vary widely with the particular circumstances. The longest time for analysis occurs when components in the sample must be reacted chemically or separated physically before the actual IR scan is made.

Infrared spectrophotometers vary widely in cost from $3,000 to about $20,000, depending on the resolution, range of wavelengths covered, and reproducibility desired.

Near Infrared Absorption Spectroscopy

This area of the infrared spectrum can be considered to be from 0.7 to 2.5 μ, though some consider the range to extend to 3.0 μ as shown in Table 3-1. This region is primarily concerned with overtone vibrations, and thus the absorption bands are generally weaker than those in the conventional infrared region. A difference between near and conventional IR in instrumentation is that with near IR an ordinary incandescent-light source can be used; in addition quartz optics (or diffraction gratings) and also quartz cells for handling liquids can be used along with lead-sulfide detectors. Conventional IR covers the range 2 to 40 μ and requires a source of infrared radiation, crystal optics (sodium, potassium, cesium, calcium, barium or silver halides, or sapphire), and bolometer or thermocouple detectors.

The utility of near IR is limited, but the approach performs some functions worthy of note. Because of few absorption peaks, it is a poor qualitative tool. However, within its wavelength range, it can readily quantitatively determine hydroxy compounds such as alcohols, phenols, and carboxylic acids, as well as hydrazides, imines, and the like, though it cannot generally distinguish between them (see Table 3-1). The C-H bands occur in this region but are generally not characteristic enough for analytical use.

The accuracy, precision, and time-of-analysis aspects of near IR closely resemble those of UV and visible absorption. The UV and visible instrumentation containing prisms and gratings as dispersing devices usually also covers the near IR range.

Ultraviolet Absorption Spectroscopy

The principle of operation of ultraviolet absorption spectrophotometers is similar to that of infrared spectrophotometers as described on page 56 except that a polychromatic ultraviolet light source is used. Also, in the case of ultraviolet spectrophotometers, the prism or diffraction grating is placed before the sample so that only narrow wavelength bands pass through the sample at any given time. If the undispersed light were passed through the sample, as is done with infrared, the large UV input of energy could cause fluorescence to occur which would confuse the spectrum. Futhermore, large amounts of UV energy could cause photochemical reactions to occur with some materials. Figure 3-5 shows a UV spectrophotometer.

The utility of UV absorption, however, varies markedly from that of infrared. In the case of UV, few atomic configurations in molecules absorb. Those that do absorb do not have to be functional groups as we normally conceive of them, but are generally highly resonating molecular configurations. The energy involved is due to electron transitions from one energy state to another. For example, conjugated unsaturation such as —C=C—C=C— absorbs; aromatic systems with their conjugated cyclic structures absorb. Table 3-2 shows functional groups and structures that absorb UV radiation.

UV absorption spectra are generally much simpler than IR spectra, meaning that there are fewer absorption peaks in the spectrum. In fact, few UV spectra have more than one or two broad peaks. Figure 3-6 shows a UV spectrum of p-ethoxybenzoic acid. Because of this lack of multiple absorption peaks, UV analysis is not very applicable for

Table 3-1 Spectra-structure correlations and average molar absorptivity data for near-infrared region[a]

Microns

	1.0	1.1	1.2	1.3	1.4	1.5	1.6	1.7	1.8	1.9	2.0	2.1	2.2	2.3	2.4	2.5	2.6	2.7	2.8	2.9	3.0	3.1
Terminal =CH₂ Vinyloxy(—OCH=CH₂) Ether	I	I		I / 0.02			0.3 / 0.3					0.2 / 0.2–0.5										
Terminal —CH—CH₂ \O		I		I				0.2					1.2									
Terminal —CH—CH₂ \CH₂				I	I		I						I									
Terminal ≡CH	I					1.0															50	
cis CH=CH—	I			I			I					0.15										
CH₂ \C/ \O (oxetane) CH₂		I		I			I					I	I			I						
—CH₃		0.02		I					0.1				I	0.3								
—CH₂			0.02	I					0.1						0.25							
—C—H			I		I				I													
—CH aromatic				0.1			0.1					I										
—CH aldehydic													0.5									
—CH (formate)													1.0									
—NH₂ amine Aromatic Aliphatic	0.04 / I			0.2 / I	1.4 / 0.5						1.5 / 0.7								30 / 1–5	30 / 2		
NH amine Aromatic Aliphatic	I / I					0.5 / 0.5													20		1	

66

Group					
—NH₂ amide	100 100	3⊢⊣ 0.5 0.5	⊢0.7		100
NH amide	⊢100	⊢0.5	⊢1.3		100
N–H anilide (φ)	⊢100	0.9 0.4⊢⊣0.3	⊢0.7		100
NH imide	I		I	I	I
—NH₂ hydrazine	I	50	0.5⊢⊣0.5	I	I
—OH alcohol			⊢2	I I I	
—OH hydroperoxide Aromatic / Aliphatic	30⊢⊣30 80	⊢1.3 ⊢0.8	1⊢⊣1 ⊢2		
—OH phenol Free / Intramolecularly bonded	Variable ⊢200	⊢3 I	⊢3 I		⊢10–100
—OH carboxylic acid					
—OH glycol 1,2 / 1,3 / 1,4	50⊢⊣50 20–50⊢⊣20–100 50–80⊢⊣5–40	I I I			
OH water	30⊢⊣7	⊢1.2	⊢0.7		
=NOH oxime	⊢200		I		
HCHO (possibly hydrate)	I				
—SH		⊢0.05			
PH		⊢0.2			
C=O		I			3
—C≡N		⊢0.1			

[a] Published data, mostly obtained in CCl₄ solution. Units are liter/mole-cm.

SOURCE: Reprinted with permission from R. F. Goddu and D. A. Delker, *Anal. Chem.*, **32**:140 (1960).

Table 3-2 Ultraviolet absorption of chromophoric groups

Group	Absorption, $m\mu$	Conjugation	Absorption, $m\mu$
C—C	<153		
C=C	175–185	![C triangle C——C—C=C]	>175
		![O triangle C——C—C=C]	<210
		C=C—C=C	220
C≡N	180	![C triangle C——C—C=N]	210
		C=C—C=N	214–217
C=S	208		
O ‖ C—OH	208	O O ‖ ‖ HO—C—C—OH	250
S—H	228		
C=O	270–280	![C triangle O C——C—C=]	290
		O O ‖ ‖ C—C	286
		O ‖ C=C—C	310–330
		O O ‖ ‖ C—C—OH	331
		O ‖ C=C—C—C=C	340
N=O	302	O ‖ O=N—	366

68

Table 3-2   Ultraviolet absorption of chromophoric groups (continued)

Group	Absorption, mμ	Conjugation	Absorption, mμ
N=N	350	N⟋N—N (triazole ring)	288
benzene—R	259	benzene—C⟋O⟍C (epoxide)	260
		benzene—C⟋C⟍C (cyclopropane)	274
		benzene—C=C	290
naphthalene	311		
anthracene	475		

SOURCE: Reprinted with permission from J. H. Harley and S. E. Wiberley, "Instrumental Analysis," John Wiley & Sons, Inc., New York, 1954, p. 58.

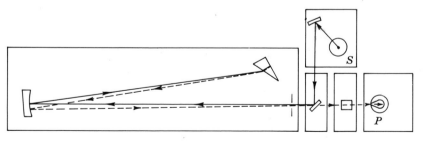

Fig. 3-5   Beckman DU spectrometer for ultraviolet and visible regions. *(Beckman Instruments, Inc.)*

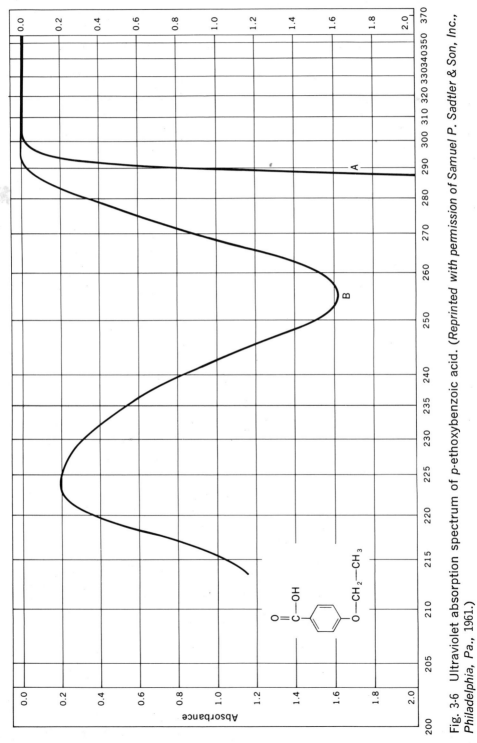

Fig. 3-6 Ultraviolet absorption spectrum of *p*-ethoxybenzoic acid. *(Reprinted with permission of Samuel P. Sadtler & Son, Inc., Philadelphia, Pa., 1961.)*

qualitative analysis. Some idea of class of compound can be obtained but it is not conclusive. Only in the cases of highly conjugated systems such as the aromatics, where several absorption peaks exist, does UV absorption have any qualitative application, and even these analyses are not as concrete as those obtained by IR.

The fact that not many structures or groups absorb ultraviolet radiation limits this technique for qualitative purposes, but it is a boon for quantitative purposes. Those few structures and groups that do absorb are less likely to be affected by interferences. Another quantitative advantage of ultraviolet analysis is that those configurations that do absorb often absorb very strongly, making analysis of trace quantities easy. Analysis at the parts-per-million level is common. On the other hand, this strong absorption makes analysis of large concentrations of absorbing component difficult, since these require great dilutions for the readings to be on scale. These large dilution factors curtail the accuracy and precision of major-component analyses.

UV absorption analysis is generally only applicable to solutions or liquid samples. Since the UV absorptivity of most materials is low, there is little difficulty in finding a suitable solvent. Figure 3-7 shows the clear UV areas of common solvents. Solids that cannot be run in solution can be analyzed with UV by reflectance. Gases can be analyzed in solution. Also, gas cells can be used.

The accuracy and precision of quantitative UV analyses can generally be obtained in the range of ± 0.5 to 2.0% at the maximum sensitivity of the approach. This is in the lower ranges of concentration. This precision and accuracy will get poorer as you go below the maximum sensitivity region (which varies with each material being measured) to the disappearance of all absorption. They also get poorer as you go above the maximum sensitivity region since dilution is then required. The time required for analysis by UV absorption is very much the same as for IR absorption.

The equipment is fairly low-cost, ranging from $2,000 to $15,000.

Vacuum Ultraviolet Spectroscopy

Almost all compounds absorb in this portion of the ultraviolet spectrum which extends from 2000 to 1 Å. This fact, which would seem to make this approach so valuable, is one of its drawbacks. Cell, prism, and lens materials are a problem, with the only usable materials being LiF, CaF_2, and synthetic sapphire; natural quartz or fused silica components can be used, but only down to about 1500 Å. Usable solvents are also very few, and most samples are run neat. As the name of the method implies, even oxygen and nitrogen must be excluded.

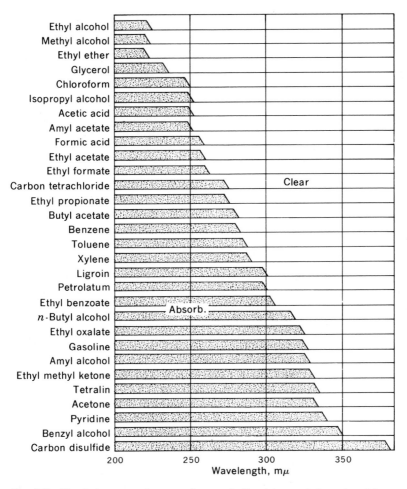

Fig. 3-7   Useful range of several organic liquids as determined by Brode. [*Reprinted with permission of W. R. Brode, J. Phys. Chem.,* **30:**56 (1926).]

This approach is used mainly by physicists to study ionization potentials, electronic structures, and substitution effects.

Visible Absorption Spectroscopy

Here again the principle of operation of the instruments is the same as that described on page 65 for ultraviolet analysis; Fig. 3-5 could depict a visible spectrophotometer, except that a source of visible light is used. In fact most ultraviolet spectrophotometers cover the visible region also, although the reverse is not always true. A visible spectrophotometer is nothing more than a sophisticated colorimeter since visible light is being measured. There are visible spectrophotometers that use light filters and there are spectrophotometers that use prisms or diffraction gratings to isolate specific wavelength bands. The filters permit only a wavelength section of the light from the source to pass through the samples. Since these filters permit fairly broad bands of radiation to pass, the resolution obtained is poor. Only few filters are usable and thus one cannot get a meaningful spectrum scan with these filter spectrophotometers. These devices, however, make excellent, inexpensive, quantitative colorimeters and are used widely for colorimetric analysis. The prisms and grating devices provide much higher resolution.

Visible spectra are generally simple, with one or two broad peaks. Of course, spectra can only be obtained with colored materials. Table 3-2 shows common colored and color-augmenting groups. These are listed in the section on ultraviolet absorption, since the absorption in the visible is closely allied with that of the ultraviolet. Many absorbing groups in the visible region also absorb in the UV region; absorbers in the UV region enhance absorption in the visible region. The analytical capabilities of visible absorption are, therefore, very similar to those of UV absorption. Qualitative application is poor. Quantitative application is good where absorption is available. Chances of interference are slim since so few structures absorb. (In the yellow-orange range of the spectrum, 400 to 500 mμ, interference can be common for organic materials, since yellow substances are common. Even decomposition products of organic materials contribute yellow color.) Since colors are generally intense when they are encountered, analysis for trace quantities is often feasible. The utility of visible absorption analysis with concentration range is similar to that for UV (see page 71). It should be mentioned that all colorimetric analysis fits into this realm of visible absorption. The approach is used for measuring not only colored components of the sample as is but also the colors formed by the reaction of the sample with given reagents. In UV and IR absorption analysis, it is rare that reactions are carried out with measurement of an absorbing reagent or an absorbing product. In the latter cases, the desired component is generally measured directly.

For visible analysis, generally only solutions or liquids can be handled. Insoluble solids can be run by reflectance. Reflectance techniques are difficult in both the UV and visible areas, with much care necessary.

The time required for analysis by visible spectrophotometry is the same as for UV and IR with the same discussion.

The cost of equipment ranges from a few hundred dollars for filter photometers to as high as $30,000.

Raman Spectroscopy

In this approach the sample is irradiated with monochromatic radiation generally either from a mercury lamp at 4358 Å or from a suitable laser. Some radiation is absorbed but some is also scattered. Some of the scattered radiation is due to normal scattering of the sample and is of the same wavelength as the incident light. However, some of the bonds of the molecule can absorb the energy from the incident radiation to make a transition to a higher permitted energy level, causing scattering of light of wavelength different from the incident light. The Raman spectrum is composed of the new wavelengths created in the process. The wavelengths in this spectrum are qualitatively characteristic of the chemical bonds, and thus, of course, of the functional groups. The intensity of these radiations can be used to quantitatively measure the groupings.

It should be pointed out that there is a close alliance between infrared absorption spectroscopy and Raman spectroscopy. Both depend on the vibrational and rotational energies in the bonds of the molecule. Raman spectroscopy will detect bonding characteristics not found by IR absorption and vice versa (see Fig. 3-8). Table 3-3 shows a listing of some of the functional groups determinable by Raman analysis.

Raman spectroscopy has not enjoyed a wide application in functional-group analysis. This is due mainly to the high cost of the equipment and the complications involved in getting good spectra. The Raman spectra are generally very weak and contain a few bands, so that their qualitative use is limited. Also, samples which fluoresce cannot be used, since the fluorescence blots out the weak Raman spectrum. High-energy incident radiation (even from lasers) has been used to intensify the spectrum, but the intensity also increases side problems such as fluorescence or photolytic reaction or decomposition. Problems are also found with the wavelength of the incident light; the intensity of the Raman effect is related to the fourth power of the wavelength. It is more advantageous to use the more energetic shorter wavelengths. However, as one does so, the undesired fluorescence and photolytic reactions also are magnified.

Examples of Spectra

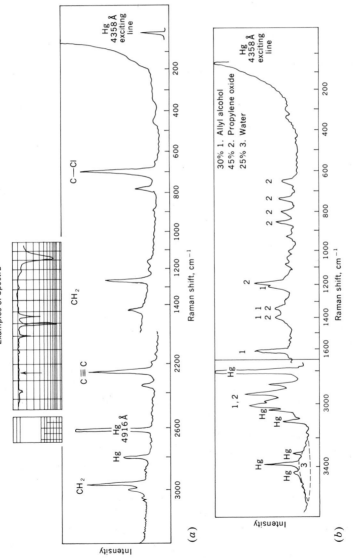

(a)

(b)

Fig. 3-8 (a) Comparison of the Raman and infrared spectra of ClH₂C.C=CCH₂Cl liquid. Illustrates how groups difficult to detect by infrared absorption may often be detected by Raman spectroscopy. The group in this example is the C≡C group. (b) The Raman spectrum of an aqueous solution. (*Reprinted with permission from "Modern Methods of Research and Analysis," Dow Chemical Co, 5th rev., Chemical Physics Research Laboratory, Midland, Mich., January, 1966.*)

The low intensity of the spectrum causes instrumental problems, because complex electronics are required to augment the signal-to-noise ratio and maintenance becomes a difficulty. Also, spectrometers of high gathering power are needed; this increases the complexity of the instruments.

The low intensity of the spectrum also affects quantitative functional group work, making only major component analysis feasible. Fluorescence of course is not reproducible from sample to sample, and can cause serious errors.

Table 3-3   Typical linkages and characteristic Raman shifts

Type of linkage	Wave numbers per cm	Type of linkage	Wave numbers per cm
H—H	4158	C=C	1620
O—H	3650	C=O	1700
N—H	3370	O=O	1600
Cl—H	2880	C=N	1650
Br—H	2558		
S—H	2572		
C—C	993	C≡C	2120
C—O	1030	C≡N	2150
C—N	1033	C≡O	2146
C—S	650	N≡O	2224

SOURCE: Reprinted with permission from J. H. Hibben, "Physical Methods in Chemical Analysis," vol. 1, 2d ed., W. G. Berl (ed.), Academic Press Inc., New York, 1960, p. 400.

Another complication stems from the fact that the sample must be essentially colorless to obtain a good spectrum. If the sample is colored, it will tend to absorb too much of the incident radiation, leaving little energy to produce the Raman effect.

Raman spectroscopy does have some advantages, however. The main advantage is that aqueous systems can be handled. Sample cells in Raman spectroscopy are made of glass, and water has a weak and diffuse Raman spectrum (see Fig. 3-8). Aqueous systems are not readily handled in infrared absorption spectroscopy, because water is a strong absorber and also attacks many of the cell materials (usually alkali metal halides). Also, the fact that Raman spectroscopy will respond to chemical bonds not readily detectable by IR absorption is a distinct advantage. For example, whereas highly symmetrical molecules generally absorb IR poorly (e.g., the triple bond in symmetrical acetylenic compounds is weakly detected), molecular symmetry is not so important in Raman spectroscopy, though it does exert an influence. Raman spectroscopy is thus a good adjunct to IR absorption. However, one has to weigh the high cost of the instruments ($22,000 to $61,000) against the interference problems of fluorescence, color, and photolytic reactions. The ever possible presence of the latter problems also lengthens analysis time, since it must be established if they are playing a role.

CHEMICAL METHODS

This is the oldest approach to functional-group analysis and utilizes the chemical reactions characteristic of the various functional groups. It can be said that the chemical type of functional-group analysis is the most selective of all the approaches in this chapter. After all, each functional group is so categorized because it *functions chemically* in a certain way. An aldehyde is an aldehyde because it undergoes certain characteristic reactions. These reactions then become one of the best ways of detecting and measuring that particular group.

The reactions of each functional group are well catalogued (see references). The qualitative reactions are based on characteristic color reactions, precipitation reactions, and gas liberation. These reactions are, in many but not all cases, fast and quite specific. However, for qualitative detection of functional groups, infrared absorption is preferred, keeping in mind that IR can sometimes miss an existing group or appear to show one that is not really there. IR requires a little care in interpreting results, and so does the observation of the chemical tests. The IR detection of functional groups is generally faster, with various groups on the molecule being detected at the same time, and with other molecular characteristics (crystallinity, chain lengths, isomerism) also being detectable. Chemical qualitative tests and IR scans make good adjuncts to one another in detecting functional groups, because they are entirely different from one another and are not affected by the same interferences. For example, OH and NH groups absorb in the same place in the IR spectrum, but they give quite different chemical tests. The carbonate-group absorptions are often diffuse and indecisive. However, the evolution of CO_2 with acid helps prove its presence. In addition, IR examination of products of chemical reactions on samples already examined by IR can help prove points. For example nitro groups presumed to be present by IR can be verified by simple hydrogenation to amino groups which are then detected. Unsaturation can also be verified by a hydrogenation test, with the IR absorption for the ethylenic or acetylenic groups disappearing on hydrogenation.

In summary, chemical and IR absorption methods for qualitative analysis are both useful, with the IR approach the stronger. Together, they can make for firm detection of functional groups.

In the area of quantitative analysis, chemical methods enjoy the widest utility of all methods for functional-group analysis. These methods are based on the volumetric measurement of acid, base, oxidant, reductant, gas, metal ion, or colored material liberated or consumed by a characteristic reaction of the functional group. There are also gravimetric methods based on the formation of a characteristic, quantitative precipitate. The wide range of utility is based on the following facts.

All functional groups have characteristic reactions amenable to chemical measurement. Many functional groups undergo several different reactions usable for determining the same group. For example, aldehyde groups can be determined by oxime formation, bisulfite addition, imine formation, and oxidation to acids. With this wide range of available systems, suitable reactions can be found to handle specific cases. For example, if interferences are present with one method, another method is generally available where the interferences are no problem. If the functional group is present in trace quantities, a sensitive, probably colorimetric, analysis can generally be found. If high precision and accuracy are required, a suitable reaction is likely to be available. Also, most chemical methods are absolute, meaning that no calibration is needed.

By comparison, infrared absorption quantitative methods require calibration. They are "static" in that the optical situation is as obtained. If it is not satisfactory for any reason, something must then be done to the sample to make IR applicable: either a separation or chemical reaction must be run (for removing interferences); a concentration of the desired component must be achieved (for increased sensitivity); or a more intense absorption must be created (for higher accuracy and/or precision).

When one considers the aspect of time of analysis, instrumental methods are generally preferred in *routine situations*. In these cases, it is worth preparing pure standards and calibrating the appropriate instrumental approach. This is a time-consuming step, but once it is accomplished, large numbers of routine analyses can be run. Routine analyses are here defined as analyses for the same group on the same compound and within a specified range of concentration. In nonroutine situations, such as in a research laboratory, the same functional group is found in different compounds and in widely ranging concentrations. It is not economical to calibrate instruments in these cases, because too few samples of each case are handled, and preparing pure standards and calibration is too time-consuming for the few samples. In these instances, chemical methods are best. Even in some routine situations, chemical methods can easily compete with instrumental methods. Chemical analyses can be "mass produced"; that is to say, they can be run assembly-line style, many at the same time. The author has seen 60 glycerol analyses run by one operator and 85 phosphate analyses by another operator in an 8-hr day, both using chemical methods.

From a cost standpoint, the chemical methods are very inexpensive since the equipment required is generally only common glassware and reagents. However, it must be kept in mind that the cost of an operation is gauged, not just by the cost of equipment, but by the total cost required to operate the laboratory. Chemical methods require little equipment but could involve many operators. Instrumental methods for functional-group analysis can help lower personnel costs, depending on the particular situation. Automated chemical analytical equipment now available has speeded up routine chemical functional-group analyses to such an extent that several hundred analyses can be run in one day.

ELECTROANALYTICAL METHODS*

Electroanalysis consists of the various analytical methods which utilize some measured electrical parameter of a system undergoing electrolysis, i.e., where two electrodes are dipped into a solution and an electrical current is passed between them. The parameters measured may be current, potential, resistance (or conductance), capacitance, and electric charge, or combinations of these. Of the many techniques in use, only two offer qualitative or structural information: *voltammetry*, which involves the current-voltage relationship during an electrolysis, and *dielectric constant measurement*, which is based on capacitance data. The dielectric constant can be related to dipole moment and, therefore, may give true structural information, since it is the electronic-charge distribution of the molecule that is observed. Voltammetry primarily is useful for functional-group characterization in addition to serving as a quantitative tool. For purposes of the present text, we shall limit the discussion to this technique. Because of space limitations, only the basic outlines can be covered, and the reader is referred to more complete texts or monographs for additional details. For overall electro-

* Written by A. F. Krivis, Associate Professor of Chemistry, The University of Akron, Akron, Ohio.

analytical coverage, Refs. 1 to 4 are recommended. A listing of individual monographs on specialized topics can be found in Refs. 1 and 2.

Introduction

In voltammetry, a voltage is applied to the electrodes which are dipped into the solution under study, and the resulting current flow is measured. This process is repeated with different applied voltages, until a complete voltage sweep (usually about 2 volts) has been carried out. The measured currents are then plotted as a function of applied voltage to produce a curve similar to that shown in Fig. 3-9 if an electroactive species is present. If no electroactive material is present,

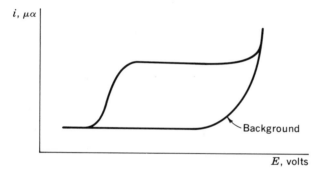

Fig. 3-9   Typical ideal polarogram.

then a curve similar to that marked "background" in Fig. 3-9 will be obtained. The sharply rising portion of the curve is called a *wave* and is due to the reduction (or oxidation) of the electroactive species.

Voltammetry, or specifically, *polarography*, was invented by J. Heyrovsky in 1922 [5]. Heyrovsky used a slowly dropping mercury electrode (DME) and the term polarography is reserved for voltammetric work where a DME is used as an electrode. The DME has some very distinct advantages over other types of electrodes, and polarography, therefore, is an extremely important part of the overall technique of voltammetry; we shall limit our discussion in this section to polarography.

Basic Circuit and Operations

Figure 3-10 shows the basic voltammetric circuit and demonstrates the simplicity of the equipment. All that is needed is a source of known variable voltage and a means of measuring current, such as a galvanometer, in addition to the electrolysis cell. The voltage source should be capable of delivering a range of approximately 0 to 3 volts to the cell, with the applied voltage being known to at least ± 0.01 volt and, preferably, to ± 0.001 volt. The necessary sensitivity for the current measurement is of the order of at least ± 0.01 μa.

The steps necessary to obtain a polarogram are simple and rapid. The test solution, containing the electroactive species, a background electrolyte, and, perhaps, a maximum suppressor, is transferred to the cell; and a gas, such as hydrogen or nitrogen, is bubbled through the solution to remove dissolved oxygen. The latter is reducible and must

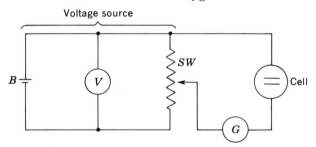

Fig. 3-10 Basic voltametric circuit. The components are battery *B*, voltmeter *V*, linear slidewire *SW*, and galvanometer *G* or other current-measuring device.

be removed before making a run. After the purging is completed, the gas is diverted to blanket the solution surface so that atmospheric oxygen cannot contact the solution. The "indicating" electrode is then inserted into the cell. If a DME is used, it is adjusted to a vertical position and the mercury head set to give a drop time of 2 to 5 sec. The "reference" electrode may be a pool of mercury at the bottom of the cell or an external calomel electrode. Electrical contact with both electrodes is made, and the system is ready for the data to be obtained.

The voltage applied to the indicating electrode is varied in small increments over the range of 0.0 to -2 or -3 volts, and the current flow at each increment of voltage is measured. A plot of current versus voltage produces a curve such as shown in Fig. 3-11.

At voltages which are less than the decomposition potential of the electroactive species, no reduction takes place, and very low currents, called residual currents, flow. When the decomposition potential is reached, reduction starts and a sharp rise in current can be noticed. As reduction takes place, the concentration of active species at the surface of the electrode is depleted, and a concentration gradient from the electrode surface to the bulk of the solution is produced. This gradient causes the active material to diffuse to the surface of the electrode at a rate proportional to the concentration difference. Upon increasing the voltage, further reduction occurs, with an increase in current flow and a still greater depletion of the concentration of active species at the electrode surface. If the solution were thoroughly stirred, the current would increase continuously with increasing voltage according to Ohm's law. However, the solution is maintained in a quiet state, and a point is reached at which the concentration of active species is zero at the electrode surface. After this voltage is attained,

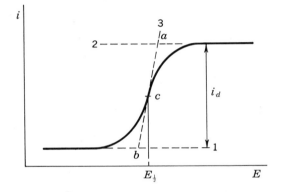

Fig. 3-11 Graphical estimation of $E_{1/2}$ and i_d.

the *rate* of diffusion to the electrode surface becomes constant and is controlled by the concentration present in the remainder of the solution. When this voltage has been reached, the current levels off and a constant value is maintained which is called the *limiting current*. Subtraction of the value of the residual current from that of the limiting current produces the current due to the actual electrolytic process (Faradaic current), and the final value is called the *diffusion current*. The S-shaped curve which is produced is called a *polarographic wave*.

The total current flowing during the electrolysis really is composed of three separate parts: the diffusion current, the residual current, and the migration current. As we have seen, the residual current is eliminated by a simple subtraction. The migration current, which is the current carried by species which are electrically attracted to the electrode, is eliminated in a different way. If an excess of an indifferent electrolyte (one which is not reduced or oxidized over the range under study), such as KCl, is present, it will carry all of the migration current. Therefore, this indifferent electrolyte, or *background electrolyte*, is used in all voltammetric work.

Fundamental Relationships

The Ilkovic Equation

Because the rate of diffusion of the active material to the electrode is concentration-dependent, one would expect the diffusion current to be related to the concentration of the species undergoing electrolysis. D. Ilkovic [6], in conjunction with Heyrovsky, derived the mathematical relationship between diffusion current and concentration for a dropping mercury electrode. The equation, which is known as the Ilkovic equation, is

$$i_d = 607 n D^{1/2} C m^{2/3} t^{1/6} \tag{1}$$

where i_d = average diffusion current during lifetime of drop, μa
$\quad n$ = number of electrons in electrode reaction
$\quad D$ = diffusion coefficient of electroactive species
$\quad C$ = concentration, millimoles/liter
$\quad m$ = flow rate of mercury from the capillary
$\quad t$ = drop time

The Ilkovic equation can be considered to contain three sections: one dealing with the electroactive species, one concerning the electrode characteristics, and one containing some fundamental constants. The portion $n D^{1/2} C$ involves the electrolyzed material and gives information concerning concentration and the type of reaction actually being produced. It is this part of the equation which is of the greatest interest to the chemist; the remainder of the equation permits the interchangeability of data between laboratories and equipment.

Since there is a direct proportionality between diffusion current and concentration, it is possible to prepare calibration curves of i_d versus C which can be used for quantitative analysis. The usual range of concentration over which a linear plot may be obtained is from about 0.1 to $10 \times 10^{-3} M$.

One may utilize Eq. (1), directly, for quantitative purposes. Let us rewrite the equation in the form

$$I = 607 n D^{1/2} = \frac{i_d}{C m^{2/3} t^{1/6}} \tag{2}$$

where I is the diffusion current constant [7]. We can see that I should be a constant for any particular electrode reaction, and the experimental value, i_d, for an individual solution may be converted to concentration by simply dividing i_d by I.

Half-wave Potentials

The fact that redox reactions occur at characteristic potentials is well known. In fact, tables of oxidation and reduction potentials are available from a variety of sources. The polarographic method, because it is a redox technique, should give some function of potential which can be correlated with the particular moiety involved. Heyrovsky and Ilkovic [8], from an examination of the complete polarographic wave, that is, the potentials and corresponding currents obtained, were able to show this relationship.

If the electrode reaction is a thermodynamically reversible one, the Nernst equation will hold for the system and the potential of the electrode at any point on the polarographic wave will be given by

$$E = E^0 - \frac{RT}{nF} \ln \frac{C'_{red}}{C'_{oxid}} \tag{3}$$

where E^0 is the standard potential of the reaction and E is the average potential during the drop life. C'_{red} and C'_{oxid} are the concentrations of the reduced and oxidized species at the electrode surface. By substituting current terms from the Ilkovic equation for the concentration terms in Eq. (3), we can arrive at an overall equation for the wave such that

$$E = E^0 - \left(\frac{RT}{nF} \ln \frac{k_{oxid}}{k_{red}}\right) - \left(\frac{RT}{nF} \ln \frac{i}{i_d - i}\right) \tag{4}$$

where k is the proportionality factor relating current and concentration. At a point where the current is equal to one-half the diffusion current, the log-current portion of Eq. (4) will become zero and drop out. The potential at this midpoint of the wave is the *half-wave potential*, $E_{1/2}$, and is given by

$$E_{1/2} = E^0 - \frac{RT}{nF} \ln \frac{k_{oxid}}{k_{red}} \tag{5}$$

From the Ilkovic equation, it is obvious that the k values are equal to $607 n D^{1/2} m^{2/3} t^{1/6}$, and that for any particular reaction, the ratio of k_{oxid}/k_{red} will reduce to the ratio of the two diffusion coefficients, D_{oxid}/D_{red}. This latter ratio is essentially one, and we can neglect the log portion of Eq. (5) to write

$$E_{1/2} = E^0 \tag{6}$$

Thus, the half-wave potential is the same as the standard potential of the reaction. In practice, $E_{1/2}$ is close to the so-called formal potential rather than the standard potential.

Equation (6) demonstrates that a polarographic potential function can be directly related to a standard potential for the oxidation or reduction of a particular species. This property forms the basis for any qualitative information which can be obtained from polarographic analysis.

Analytical Measurements and Practice

The polarogram shown in Fig. 3-9 is typical of a reversible reaction and the curve may be treated graphically to obtain the necessary numerical values. The first steps would be to draw straight lines through the horizontal portions of the wave and then a straight line through the rising portion of the wave; the latter intersects both top and bottom horizontal lines (Fig. 3-11) at a and b. The center of the rising line between points a and b can be located by use of a ruler and then marked (point c). Dropping a vertical line to the potential axis locates the half-wave potential, $E_{1/2}$. The difference in current between lines 1 and 2 is the diffusion current, i_d, for the wave.

In actual practice, many polarographic waves are not reversible and curves of the sort shown in Fig. 3-12a, b, c are obtained. These curves

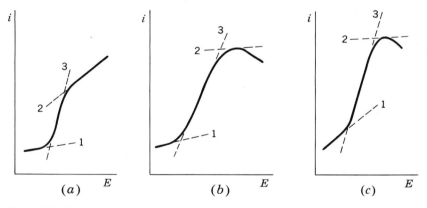

Fig. 3-12 Graphical estimate of $E_{1/2}$ and i_d for irreversible waves.

are treated in the same general way that reversible waves are analyzed. That is, the best approximations to lines 1, 2, and 3 of Fig. 3-11 are drawn and the half-wave potential located. The diffusion current is usually measured as the current between lines 1 and 2, *at the half-wave potential*. In all of these cases, the values actually obtained are empirical and it is especially important that the graphical analysis be consistent. All of the curves for a particular compound must be handled in exactly the same manner.

As described previously, the half-wave potential for a particular reaction is reproducible and fairly specific for that reaction. However, one other item should be discussed which is very important in organic polarography, the effect of the test solution on the polarographic wave.

The components of the solution which is used for polarographic analysis of a sample have a profound effect on the data obtained; all of the polarographic values may be altered markedly by changes in the solution. Each of the components, i.e., solvent, background electrolyte

Table 3-4 Approximate $E_{\frac{1}{2}}$ values for various functional groups in neutral or basic media

Functional group	Approximate $E_{\frac{1}{2}}$
$-\overset{\overset{\displaystyle O}{\|\|}}{C}H$	> -1.6
$-\overset{\overset{\displaystyle O}{\diagup\!\diagup}}{C}OH$	-1.8
$-\overset{\overset{\displaystyle O}{\|\|}}{\underset{\displaystyle \|}{C}}-$	$-2.5*$
$-\overset{\displaystyle \|}{\underset{\displaystyle \|}{C}}-X$	$> -1.7\dagger$
$-NO_2$	-0.9
$-N{=}O$	-0.2
$-NH_2$	$-0.5\ddagger$
$-OOH$	-0.5
$-SH$	$-0.5\ddagger$
$-S-S-$	-1.8

* In R_4NX salt medium.
† In aqueous media.
‡ Anodic waves.

and/or buffer, and maximum suppressor, can be selected to obtain the optimum data.

The solvent used, besides dissolving the sample, also must dissolve sufficient electrolyte to minimize any potential drop between the electrodes, allow good buffering capacity, and eliminate any migration current. A polar solvent is almost a necessity in order to satisfy these requirements.

Water is the most popular solvent because it meets all the requirements except, perhaps, that for solubility of the sample itself. As a means of obtaining more solubility for specific compounds, organic solvents are added to the water. Polar solvents which are miscible with water, e.g., alcohols or dioxane, are among the more commonly used additives.

In inorganic polarography, the background electrolyte serves to carry the current which is not of analytical use. For organic systems, the simple electrolyte is replaced by a pH buffer with a high capacity. The reason for the use of a buffer is based on two factors. Polarographic reactions of organic compounds almost always involve addition or removal of protons and, with acids or bases, the pH controls the species present in solution. In order to maintain constant conditions, a high-capacity, rapidly acting buffer system should be used in the solution.

Half-wave potentials of organic compounds obtained under optimum conditions can then be used to qualitatively characterize the compound. A tabulation of the ranges of potentials for a selected group of functionalities is shown in Table 3-4. If materials suspected to be similar (or, preferably, the same) are available, they should be run under exactly the same conditions as the unknown, and the half-wave potentials compared.

NUCLEAR MAGNETIC RESONANCE (NMR)

This approach is discussed in Chap. 4 on identification and structure determination. The application of NMR to functional-group analysis is incorporated into the total discussion.

MASS SPECTROMETRY

Even though this tool is basically a structure-identification tool like NMR, it has some value in the detection and determination of functional groups. A more detailed discussion of the basics of mass spectrometry is given in Chap. 4, pp. 100–102. However, by its nature, mass spectrometry is not as selective for functional groups as are NMR and infrared absorption. The latter two yield peaks at rather specific points in their spectra for diverse groups. However, mass spectrometry reports mass-to-charge ratios for fragments (see page 100) obtained on bombarding a molecule with electrons. While in some cases the functional groups are chopped off as single fragments to some degree, this is not always the case. Sometimes the fragment containing the functional group also contains the portions of the parent molecule; at other times the functional group itself is fragmented. Hence, mass spectrometry is rather nonselective for functional groups. This limits its usefulness in this type of analysis.

Table 3-5 Functional-group analysis—summary evaluation of available methods

Approach	General qualitative applicability	General quantitative applicability	General quantitative accuracy and precision			General time of analysis[a]	Cost of equipment[b]	Destructive or nondestructive analysis	General sample limitations	Problems with interferences
			Trace concentration range	Moderate concentration range	High concentration range					
Infrared absorption	Excellent	Wide	Poor	Good to excellent	Good	Short to long[c]	Low to high	ND	Must not attack the optics	Common but circumventable
Near infrared absorption	Limited	Very narrow	Poor	Good	Fair to good	Short to long[c]	Low to moderate	ND	Must be liquid or soluble in solvent; solids done by reflectance	Common
Ultraviolet absorption	Limited	Narrow to moderate	Poor to excellent[d]	Good	Fair to good	Short to long[c]	Low to moderate	ND	Must be liquid or soluble in solvent; solids done by reflectance	Seldom
Visible absorption	Limited	Narrow to moderate	Poor to excellent[d]	Good	Fair to good	Short to long[c]	Low to moderate	ND	Must be liquid or soluble in solvent; solids done by reflectance	Seldom

Method									
Chemical methods	Good	Wide	Fair to good	Excellent	Fair to good	Short to long	Low	D	Must be soluble	Common but circumventable
Nuclear magnetic resonance	Moderate[e]	Narrow to moderate[f]	Poor	Good	Fair	Moderate to long[c]	High	ND	Must be liquid or soluble in solvent	Seldom
Mass spectrometry	Limited[f]	Narrow to moderate[f]	Poor	Good	Fair	Long	High	D	Must be vaporizable	Seldom
Polarography	Limited	Narrow to moderate	Poor to excellent[d]	Fair	Poor	Moderate to long	Low	D	Must be soluble, and there is a limited range of solvents usable	Common but circumventable
Raman spectroscopy	Limited	Poor	Poor	Fair	Fair	Long	High	ND	Sample must be colorless and liquid or soluble in suitable solvent	Common
Vacuum ultraviolet absorption	Poor	Poor	Poor	Poor	Poor	Moderate to long	High	ND	Must not attack optics	Very common

[a] Short denotes <0.5 hr; moderate denotes 0.5–1.5 hr; long denotes >1.5 hr.
[b] Low denotes <$5,000; moderate denotes $5,000–$15,000; high denotes >$15,000.
[c] The actual measurement is short, but sample preparation can be long.
[d] Not many functional groups can be detected; hence approach is not generally applicable, but those that are detectable can generally be sensitively detected in low concentration range.
[e] This approach is limited by the number of atoms with magnetic nuclei.
[f] Keep in mind that here we are discussing the qualitative and quantitative application of these approaches for functional groups. The structure aspects of these approaches are discussed in Chap. 4. There the application is wide.

Literature Cited

1   J. J. Lingane, "Electroanalytical Chemistry," 2d ed., Interscience Publishers (Division of John Wiley & Sons, Inc.), New York, 1958.
2   A. F. Krivis, "Electroanalysis of Organic Compounds," Marcel Dekker, Inc., New York, in press.
3   I. M. Kolthoff and P. J. Elving (eds.), "Treatise on Analytical Chemistry," pt. I, vol. 4, Interscience Publishers (Division of John Wiley & Sons, Inc.), New York, 1963.
4   A. Weissberger, "Technique of Organic Chemistry," Interscience Publishers (Division of John Wiley & Sons, Inc.), New York, 1961.
5   J. Heyrovsky, *Chem. Listy,* **16**:256 (1922).
6   D. Ilkovic, *Collection Czech. Chem. Commun.,* **6**:498 (1934).
7   J. J. Lingane, *Ind. Eng. Chem., Anal. Ed.,* **15**:588 (1943).
8   J. Heyrovsky and D. Ilkovic, *Collection Czech. Chem. Commun.,* **7**:198 (1935).

Suggested Readings

General Spectroscopy

Freeman, S. K.: "Interpretive Spectroscopy," Reinhold Publishing Corporation, New York, 1965. (Text covering most spectroscopic techniques as used for structure and functional-group determination.)
Silverstein, R. M., and G. C. Bassler: "Spectometric Identification of Organic Compounds," 2d ed., John Wiley & Sons, Inc., New York, 1967. (Good introductory text.)

General Absorption Spectroscopy

Bauman, R. P.: "Absorption Spectroscopy," John Wiley & Sons, Inc., New York, 1962. (Text.)
Siggia, S., and H. J. Stolten: "An Introduction to Modern Organic Analysis," Interscience Publishers (Division of John Wiley & Sons, Inc.), New York, 1956, pp. 77–129. (Survey chapter.)

Infrared

Anderson, D. H., N. B. Woodall, and W. West: Physical Methods, in A. Weissberger, ed., "Technique of Organic Chemistry," 3d ed., vol. I, pt. III, Interscience Publishers (Division of John Wiley & Sons, Inc.), New York, 1960, pp. 1959–2020. (Comprehensive survey.)
Bellamy, L. J.: "The Infrared Spectra of Complex Molecules," John Wiley & Sons, Inc., New York, 1958. (Text.)

Gore, R. C.: "Determination of Organic Structures by Physical Methods," E. A. Braude and F. C. Nachod (eds.), Academic Press Inc., New York, 1955, pp. 195–228. (Survey chapter.)

Near Infrared

Goddu, R. F., and D. A. Delker: *Anal. Chem.*, **32**:140–141 (1960). (Brief article on utility.)

Ultraviolet and Visible

Boltz, D. F., and M. G. Mellon: "Standard Methods of Chemical Analysis," 6th ed., vol. 3, pt. A, F. Welcher (ed.), D. Van Nostrand Company, Inc., Princeton, N.J., 1966, pp. 3–22. (Good, brief introduction to the subject of spectroscopy in the visible region only.)

Braude, E. A.: "Determination of Organic Structures by Physical Methods," E. A. Braude and F. C. Nachod (eds.), Academic Press Inc., New York, 1955, pp. 131–186. (Survey chapter.)

Rao, C. N. R.: "Ultraviolet and Visible Spectroscopy," Butterworth & Co. (Publishers), Ltd., London, 1961. (Text.)

West, W.: Physical Methods, in A. Weissberger (ed.), "Technique of Organic Chemistry," 3d ed., vol. I, pt. III, Interscience Publishers (Division of John Wiley & Sons, Inc.), New York, 1960, pp. 2021–2061. (Comprehensive survey.)

Vacuum Ultraviolet

Clark, G. L.: "The Encyclopedia of Spectroscopy," Reinhold Publishing Corporation, New York, 1960, pp. 77–79. (Brief survey.)

Turner, D. W.: "Determination of Organic Structures by Physical Methods," vol. 2, F. C. Nachod and W. D. Phillips (eds.), Academic Press Inc., New York, 1960, pp. 339–399. (Detailed article.)

Raman Spectroscopy

Cleveland, F. F.: "Determination of Organic Structures by Physical Methods," vol. 1, E. A. Braude and F. C. Nachod (eds.), Academic Press Inc., New York, 1955. (Survey article.)

Hibben, J. H.: "Physical Methods in Chemical Analysis," 2d ed., vol. 1, W. G. Berl (ed.), Academic Press, New York, 1960. (Survey article.)

Jones, R. N., and J. B. DiGiorgio: "Standard Methods of Chemical Analysis," 6th ed., vol. 3, pt. A, F. Welcher (ed.), D. Van Nostrand Company, Inc., Princeton, N.J., 1966, pp. 59–77. (Good brief introduction to the subject.)

Chemical Functional-group Analysis

Quantitative

Critchfield, F. E.: "Organic Functional Group Analysis," Pergamon Press, New York, 1963. (Text of selected methods for the various groups.)

Mitchell, J., Jr., I. M. Kolthoff, E. S. Proskauer, and A. Weissberger: "Organic Analysis," vols. 1–4, Interscience Publishers (Division of John Wiley & Sons, Inc.), New York, 1953–1960. (Series of texts with predominantly wet chemical methods.)

Siggia, S.: "Quantitative Organic Analysis via Functional Groups," 3d ed., John Wiley & Sons, Inc., New York, 1963. (General comprehensive text predominantly of wet methods.)

Qualitative

Cheronis, N. D., J. B. Entrikin, and E. M. Hodnett: "Semimicro Qualitative Organic Analysis," 3d ed., Interscience Publishers (Division of John Wiley & Sons, Inc.), New York, 1965.

Schneider, F. L.: "Qualitative Organic Microanalysis," Academic Press Inc., New York, 1964.

Shriner, R. L., R. C. Fuson, and D. Y. Curtin: "Systematic Identification of Organic Compounds," 5th ed., John Wiley & Sons, Inc. New York, 1964.

Electroanalytical

Kolthoff, I. M., and J. J. Lingane: "Polarography," vol. 2, Interscience Publishers (Division of John Wiley & Sons, Inc.), New York, 1952.

Krivis, A. F.: "Electroanalysis of Organic Compounds," vol. 1, Marcel Dekker, New York, in press.

Nuclear Magnetic Resonance

Bible, R. H.: "Interpretation of NMR Spectra," Plenum Press, New York, 1965.

Flett: "Physical Aids to the Organic Chemist," American Elsevier Publishing Company of New York, 1962.

Foster, H.: "Standard Methods of Chemical Analysis," 6th ed., vol. 3 pt. A, F. Welcher (ed.), D. Van Nostrand Company, Inc., Princeton, N.J., 1966, pp. 598–615. (Good brief introduction to subject.)

Jackman, L. M.: "Applications of Nuclear Magnetic Resonance Spectroscopy in Organic Chemistry," Pergamon Press, New York, 1959.

Pople, J. A., W. G. Schneider, and H. J. Bernstein: "High Resolution Nuclear Magnetic Resonance," McGraw-Hill Book Company, New York, 1959.

Silverstein, R. M., and G. C. Bassler: "Spectrometric Identification of Organic Compounds," 2d ed., John Wiley & Sons, Inc., New York, 1967. (Good introductory material.)

Varian Associates Staff: "NMR and EPR Spectroscopy," Pergamon Press, New York, 1960. (Descriptive material.)

Mass Spectrometry

Beynon, J. H.: "Mass Spectrometry and Its Applications to Organic Chemistry," American Elsevier Publishing Company of New York, 1960.

Biemann, K.: "Mass Spectrometry: Organic Chemical Applications," McGraw-Hill Book Company, New York, 1962.

McLafferty, F. W.: "Mass Spectrometry of Organic Ions," Academic Press Inc., New York, 1963.

FOUR
IDENTIFICATION AND STRUCTURE DETERMINATION

Identification and structure proof are discussed together because they are interrelated and the same analytical tools are used for both types of problems. The relationship is as follows: once a structure has been proven, an identity has automatically been established; however, identification can be made without necessarily proving structure. For example, establishing a structure as

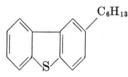

is also providing an absolute identity. However, establishing a detergent as a fatty alcohol–ethylene oxide reaction product, $R(OCH_2CH_2)_xOH$, is an identification, but no structure has been proven.

Identification of materials as discussed here is concerned with identification of molecular entities (compounds) alone and in mixtures. The qualitative detection of elements and of functional groups has already been discussed in Chaps. 2 and 3. This section is concerned with the whole molecule. In many instances, one only needs to identify an element or a group; for example, one may already know that a certain compound may be present, and detection of a characteristic element or group is enough to prove its presence or absence in the sample. Also, very often it is a certain element or group that causes a desirable or undesirable effect. The nature of the total molecule is immaterial in many of these cases, and identification of the total molecule is unnecessary. In such cases, the qualitative tests as shown in Chaps. 2 and 3 suffice.

The identification of total molecules can be divided into three types, depending on the depth of information required: (1) *Characterization.* This type of identification delineates the type of compound but goes no further. For example, it often suffices to know that the detergent being examined is a nonionic detergent. This is a superficial identification, but it suffices for certain needs. Another such characterization could be that the unknown is simply a hydrocarbon type of material. (2) *General identification.* This type of identification goes beyond the characterization, narrowing the identification further, but still not completely pinning down the identity of the material. For example, in the detergent analysis above, the nonionic could be further delineated as an ethylene-oxide adduct of a fatty alcohol, $R(OCH_2CH_2)_xOH$, and the hydrocarbon material could be further specified as hydrocarbon of the C_6 range. (3) *Complete identification.* This type of identification pins down exactly the identity of the material. The above detergent then would be $C_{11}H_{23}(OCH_2CH_2)_{12}OH$, and the hydrocarbon would be $(CH_3)_2CHCH(CH_3)_2$. It is obvious that complete identification may require structure proof, but that characterization and general identification do not. Structure proof, in turn, obviously requires complete identification.

Since the analytical approaches to all the types of identification and to structure determination are the same, the discussion that follows takes up each analytical approach and specifies how it can be applied to the various identity and structure problems.

It must be remembered that most concrete identifications or structure proofs rely on more than one of the approaches to be described subsequently. No one technique is generally decisive enough to do a complete job, leaving no areas open to question. Many specialists in specific techniques, such as nuclear magnetic resonance or mass spectrometry, can claim that their tool is all that is needed for complete identification and structure proof. Although this is often true, a single technique is not generally efficient because, in order to circumvent the areas of uncertainty, one may have to look at families of analogous compounds and may have to prepare suitable derivatives.

ELEMENTAL AND FUNCTIONAL-GROUP METHODS

These types of analysis, be they chemical or instrumental, are usually necessary for *complete identification* or *structure proof*. It is essential to first establish which elements are present and their ratios to each other. Then it is necessary to establish which functional groups are present. *Characterizations* usually do not require elemental analyses, except to exclude certain possibilities, but they often require functional-group analyses. *General identifications* may or may not require elemental analyses but usually require functional-group analyses.

CHEMICAL TESTS AND REACTIONS

The use of chemistry fits into identification and structure work in several ways. There are so-called classification tests to detect general classes of compounds. In the case of detergents as an example, there are chemical tests to indicate each type: cationic, anionic, and nonionic. There are tests for azo dyes, acid dyes, and basic dyes. There are tests for alkaloids, sugars, and proteins. These tests serve well only for the *characterization* type of identification. They can serve as only a first step in *general identifications* or *complete identifications*.

There is another use of chemistry in identification work which still has value. This value is mainly as an adjunct to the instrumental techniques described below. Before the instrumental approaches originated, all identifications, whether of the general or complete type, were accomplished by chemical techniques. This work was very time-consuming and exacting, but even difficult identifications were done, and done well. For example, the literature is full of identifications of sugars, proteins, dyes, biologicals, and many other complex materials accomplished solely by chemical means. Instrumental techniques given below have made the same types of jobs possible in very much shorter time, so one sees the decline of the chemical techniques. However, the use of chemistry still has value when used as support for the instrumental methods. For example, using the instrumental techniques, one often arrives at several possible identifications or structures, but a specific one cannot be selected. Or, one can derive most of a particular structure, but one fragment may be elusive. In such cases, chemical reactions can be used to prepare suitable derivatives of the total molecule or fragments thereof to resolve the final answer. For example, in an actual identification, two configurations were possible from the instrumental data:

(A)

or

(B)

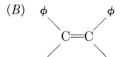

Chemical oxidation of the material led to

$$\begin{array}{c} \phi \\ \diagdown \\ \diagup \\ \phi \end{array} C{=}0$$

therefore configuration (A) was the correct one. It cannot be stated too strongly that, though chemistry is no longer used for complete identification, it still has a very firm role as an adjunct to instrumental methods.

ABSORPTION SPECTROSCOPIC METHODS

Ultraviolet and visible absorptions are of limited help in identification work. The absorptions are relatively nonspecific for functional groups and structures, and hence of little value (see Chap. 3 on functional-group analysis, pages 65 and 68). But they are of some help in narrowing fields of investigation. For example, UV absorption cannot say that a compound is aromatic in character, because aromatic groups do not always absorb the same wavelengths of UV; however, UV can say that aromatic rings are absent, because they usually absorb somewhere in the UV range. The same can be said for linear conjugated unsaturated systems, such as $-C{=}C-C{=}C-$ and $-C{=}C-C{=}O$, which usually absorb UV; the absence of absorption is indicative of their absence, but presence of UV absorption is not always indicative of their presence. Hence, UV and visible absorption techniques can usually supply only secondary, or adjunct, information toward any of the different types of identification or structure proof (pages 65 and 68 discuss this further).

Infrared absorption is very useful in all types of identification and structure proof. This is due to the fact that IR absorption bands are characteristic of not only the functional groups on a molecule but also, to a lesser degree, somewhat characteristic of the structural configuration of the molecule. For example, in the detergent example used earlier, the *characterization*-type analyses are easily obtained. The quaternary nitrogen configurations of the cationic detergents are usually discernible, as are the sulfonate, sulfate, or carboxylate configurations of the anionic detergents, and the hydroxyl and ether linkages of the nonionics. Since infrared absorptions can also point out aromatic groups, or small-chain alkyl, long-chain alkyl or branched-chain alkyl groups, the identification easily goes beyond the general characterization and becomes a *general identification,* and the skeleton of the molecule becomes fairly well outlined. Thus, it is noted that infrared absorption spectra can readily yield information for *general identifications* without prior data. For example, elemental analyses or the classification tests are generally not needed for IR to proceed directly to a *general identification*. Pages 56–64 on infrared analysis show the broad utility of the approach, particularly Fig. 3-3. This shows the characteristic absorptions available for the various common organic and inorganic functional groups and also for other common structural entities. In the case of inorganic salts, the infrared spectra are not always as conclusive as one would like, and supportive evidence of some kind or other is needed to confirm the presence or absence of certain groups.

Though infrared can usually detect the presence of certain functional groups, infrared analysis alone cannot usually lead to a *complete identification* or *structure determination* of an unknown, but requires the help of other analytical tools, such as mass spectrometry and nuclear magnetic resonance. This is because infrared can detect the groups, but is a generally weak tool for positioning the groups and for giving details of the skeletal structure of the molecule. Mass spectrometry and nuclear magnetic resonance give position and structural information, but operate more effectively and/or efficiently with IR data to lean on. Hence, it is common to see all three approaches used for *complete identification* or *structure determination*. It is possible to obtain complete identifications or structure proofs by any one of the three approaches alone, with the application of chemistry to prepare suitable derivatives to bolster the weak points of the approach; this is not generally necessary if the three tools are used together, however.

There is a type of *complete identification* where IR absorption can stand relatively alone. This is the "fingerprint" type of identification, where a specific material is suspected and the IR spectrum of the unknown is compared with the IR spectrum of a sample whose identity is known. Very extensive files exist of infrared spectra of known materials; it is a common and useful practice to compare the spectrum of an unknown material with the literature spectra. The chances are very good that the *complete identification* can be made without other data.

Compounds investigated by IR absorption must be pure for identification work since the procedure records all data. There is no way to differentiate a suspected impurity by this approach alone (knowledge of the sample along with the IR can sometimes suggest the impurity). Thus, with mixtures, separation of the desired material is usually necessary for identification and structure work.

MASS SPECTROMETRY

This identification and structure approach consists of bombarding a molecule with a beam of electrons. The molecule is fragmented into charged ions, each with a specific mass. These charged fragments are electrostatically accelerated and fed into a magnetic field (single-focusing instrument). As the stream of charged fragments proceeds through the magnetic field, the particles are deflected according to mass and charge, with particles of the same mass-to-charge ratio being focused into single bands on the detecting portion of the instrument. Thus different deflections are produced for each mass-to-charge ratio, resulting in bands representing all the fragments produced in the particular experiment. From the masses of all the particles produced, one can reconstruct the parent molecule. So-called double-focusing instruments are also available for identification and structure work (see Fig. 2-5, page 32). These use an electric field as well as the magnetic field to focus the charged fragments. Double focusing yields higher resolution than the single-focusing device and permits discrimination of fragments which could not be done by the single-focusing instrument. For example, in carbon monoxide, nitrogen, and ethylene which have masses of 28.0038, 28.0151 and 28.0403, respectively, discrimination is possible by double-focusing but not by single-focusing approaches.

Mass spectrometry yields certain data pertinent to identification and structure. First, mass spectrometry usually gives the molecular weight of the material in question. This is very valuable. Also, the intensity of the electron bombardment can be controlled and the energies required to rupture certain bonds are known.

Though mass spectrometry may achieve a *complete identification* or *structure* on its own, it oftens needs the assistance of data obtained by other means. Infrared and/or nuclear magnetic resonance data are sometimes required to obtain or certify the complete identification or structure. Analysis for the element and/or functional groups often can help. The preparation of chemical derivatives is also often used in order to verify certain aspects of a study. For example, deuterium is often substituted for hydrogen in a suspected configuration; as a result, if a peak in the spectrum is then seen at a mass number one unit higher than that previously obtained, the position of the hydrogen-containing configuration is verified. Any number of chemical reactions can be used.

The chief application of mass spectrometry to identification work is toward *complete identification* and *structure determination*. Mass spectrometry has almost no value for a *characterization* type of identification since its data are detailed and cannot be viewed on a broad basis. Mass spectrometry does have some value for *general identification*, since here the rather specific data of mass spectrometry are more amenable. However, the data are usually so specific that the analyst can go right through to the *complete identification*. For instance, in the detergent example cited on page 96, the mass-spectrometry approach cannot stop at the general identification of a fatty alcohol condensed with ethylene oxide. It will "see" the exact fatty alcohol; it will not only "see" the oxyethylene groups, but it also gives the molecular weight, so that the complete structure is automatically obtained.

Complete identification by mass spectrometry is also possible by the "fingerprint" approach. That is to say, if the unknown is a suspected known compound, a mass spectrum of that known compound can either be obtained experimentally or from the literature, and compared with the mass spectrum of the unknown. If they coincide exactly, the identity has been proven. However, problems do arise with certain cis-trans isomers where both give identical spectra.

Computerized mass spectrometry is now possible whereby the mass-spectrometric data from a double-focusing mass spectrometer are fed directly into a computer. The data are then computed to yield directly the various fragments possible from that information. The chemist can then assemble the molecule, but with much less effort than by noncomputerized means. The computerized mass-spectrometric approach can determine the elemental composition of the compound in question. This computerized approach promises to be one of the most effective and efficient *structure* and *complete identification* approaches. The only deterrent at present is the high cost (about $130,000 for the mass spectrometer, and $50,000 to $100,000 on up for the computers, depending on the degree of sophistication).

Mass spectrometry, like infrared absorption, requires pure samples for most effective work. Where infrared could not generally detect a mixture, mass spectrometry can often, though not always. In mass spectrometry a mixture yields for each component fragments which are generally not related; this inconsistency can often be detected, and a mixture is suspected. Separation techniques are often employed to isolate the desired material. The most popular separation technique used with mass spectrometry is gas chromatography. While fractions from a gas chromatograph can be isolated and then fed into the mass spectrometer, it has been found much more effective and efficient to connect the exit port of a gas chromatograph directly to the mass spectrometer. In this way the fractions are fed directly to the mass spectrometer. With the modern "fast scan" mass spectrometers, the mass scans are very rapid (1 sec for the conventional instruments to several μ sec for the "time of flight" mass spectrometers), so that the total effluent of the gas chromatograph can be monitored, with multiple mass spectra obtained on each fraction. In this way, many components, if not all, can be identified on a single sample of a mixture. If the mixture is not amenable to separation by gas chromatography, other separation techniques must be used (see pages 271–294).

HIGH-RESOLUTION NUCLEAR MAGNETIC RESONANCE (NMR)*

This is a powerful structure tool. Like the other spectroscopic techniques, it is based on irradiation of a sample with electromagnetic radiation and absorption of characteristic portions of that radiation. In the case of NMR, the radiation is in the radiofrequency range and is characteristic of the position of certain nuclei in the molecule. (See Fig. 3-1, page 55.)

The nuclei with which NMR is concerned have magnetic properties. All nuclei are charged. In some nuclei, this charge spins about an axis. This spinning charge causes a magnetic field to develop along the spinning axis of the nucleus. However, each proton and neutron has its own spin, and the resulting spin of the nucleus is the resultant of all the spins of its components. Let I = spin number of the nucleus. If the sum of protons and neutrons in the nucleus is an even number, then I is zero or an integer (1, 2, 3, etc.). If the sum is an odd number, then I is a half-integer ($\frac{1}{2}$, $\frac{3}{2}$, $\frac{5}{2}$, . . .). If both the protons and neutrons are present in even numbers, then $I = 0$. When $I = 0$, then there is no resultant spin, hence no magnetic dipole. When $I = \frac{1}{2}$, there is a spin with resultant magnetic dipole. When $I = 1$ or more, the charge distribution of the nucleus is generally not spherical. This electrical asymmetry produces quadrupolar electrical moments instead of dipolar moments. This yields magnetic properties to the nucleus, but of a rather complex nature when compared with $I = \frac{1}{2}$.

The spin number I determines the number of orientations a nucleus may assume in an external magnetic field as governed by the quantity $2I + 1$. When $I = \frac{1}{2}$, there can be only two orientations. Hence with $I = \frac{1}{2}$, the nuclei can only resonate between the two orientations. If $I = 1$ or more, there are three or more possible orientations and the resonance phenomena become more complicated, since the nuclei can

* Written in collaboration with G. D. Vickers, NMR Specialties, New Kensington, Pa.

resonate between any permutations and combinations of energy levels.

Carbon 12 and oxygen 16 have even numbers of protons and neutrons, hence have $I = 0$ and no magnetic properties at all. Hydrogen 1, fluorine 19, carbon 13, phosphorus 31 have $I = \frac{1}{2}$. Nitrogen 14 and hydrogen 2 have a spin number $I = 1$. Boron 11, chlorine 35, chlorine 37, bromine 79 and bromine 81 have $I = \frac{3}{2}$. Table 4-1 shows elements that exhibit NMR spectra.

Table 4-1   Relative sensitivities for different nuclei

Isotope	Resonant frequency, MH$_z$ per kilogauss of field strength	Natural abundance	Relative sensitivity at constant field
H^1	4.2577	99.984	1.000
B^{11}	1.3660	81.17	0.165
C^{13}	1.0705	1.108	1.59×10^{-2}
N^{14}	0.3076	99.635	1.01×10^{-3}
O^{17}	0.5772	3.7×10^{-2}	2.91×10^{-2}
F^{19}	4.0055	100	0.834
Si^{29}	0.8460	4.70	7.85×10^{-2}
P^{31}	1.7235	100	6.64×10^{-2}
S^{33}	0.3266	0.74	2.26×10^{-3}

SOURCE: Reprinted with permission from NMR Table, Varian Associates, 611 Hansen Way, Palo Alto, Calif.

Nuclei with magnetic moments will align in an external magnetic field. Those nuclei with spin number $\frac{1}{2}$ will orient themselves in only two possible orientations, a low-energy state where the "north pole" of the nucleus is toward the "south pole" of the external field, and a high-energy state where the "north pole" of the nucleus is toward the "north pole" of the external field. By irradiating the sample with the proper radiofrequency electromagnetic radiation, the oriented nuclei can be made to flip from the low-energy N-S orientation to the higher-energy N-N orientation.

The frequency ν of the introduced radiation is related to the strength of the external magnetic field, Ho, by the fundamental NMR equation

(A) $$\nu = \frac{\gamma Ho}{2\pi}$$

where γ is a nuclear constant related to its gyromagnetic properties.

γ is related to the spin number I and the magnetic moment μ by the expression

(B) $\quad \gamma = \dfrac{2\pi\mu}{hI}$

where h is Planck's constant.

From expression (A) it is evident that one can vary the magnetic field, Ho, or the irradiating frequency, ν, until resonance between the two orientations is achieved. When one examines a sample, either Ho or ν is systematically scanned. When one reaches a point where the injected electromagnetic radiation is absorbed, a nucleus in the sample is in resonance. The relationship of Ho to ν where resonance occurs is characteristic of the particular nucleus *in its environment in the molecule.* This is the fact which relates NMR to structure-identification work. Thus, for each magnetic nucleus in a given external field, there is a band of frequencies where resonance can occur. The specific frequency absorbed at resonance in a given magnetic field is related to the specific position of that nucleus in that molecule. In practice, a standard material, which absorbs radiation at a specific frequency, is used in the sample. The frequencies absorbed by the sample itself are then related to the frequency absorbed by the standard in the magnetic field being used. The difference in frequency between the sample absorption and the standard absorption is known as the *chemical shift.*

Chemical shift(s) can be expressed as parts per million, which is a dimensionless value. It is a ratio of the absorption frequency difference between the sample and the reference divided by the applied frequency. For example, if a sample shows an absorption peak at a frequency of 60 Hz away from the absorption peak of the standard, and if the applied frequency was 60 MHz, then

$$s = \dfrac{60}{60 \times 10^6} = 1 \times 10^{-6} \text{ or } 1 \text{ ppm}$$

Though s is dimensionless, it has a sign because shifts in frequency can occur in both directions from the reference. In the case of proton NMR, it has been found more desirable to use so-called τ value for chemical shift. This results in only positive values which just increase numerically. In proton NMR, when tetramethylsilane is used as a reference,

$\tau = 10.00 - s$

Figure 4-1 shows a table of various proton chemical shifts. Within the scope of this discussion, we may consider the chemical shift to be

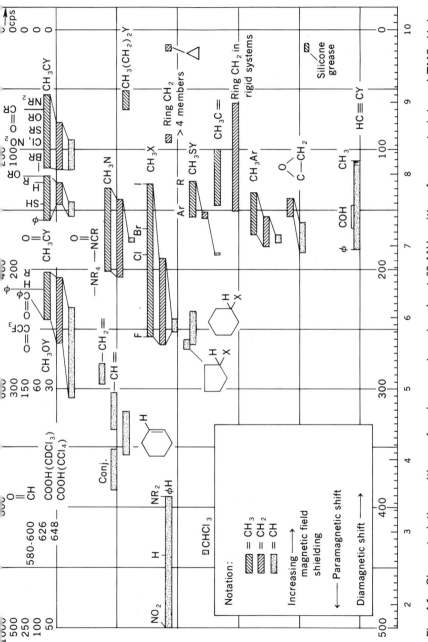

Fig. 4-1 Characteristic positions of various proton signals at 60 MHz with reference to internal TMS. Unless otherwise noted, the positions are those of aliphatic protons. *(Reprinted with permission from Roy H. Bible, Jr., "Interpretation of NMR Spectra," Plenum Press, New York, 1965.)*

governed by three factors:

1. Electron density in the vicinity of the nucleus under observation
2. Magnetic anisotropy arising from intramolecular electronic circulation
3. Hydrogen bonding

For the purpose of illustrating the effect of electron density, we use halogenated ethanes. Consider that the resonance of all hydrogens in ethane occurs around 0.87 ppm relative to tetramethylsilane. If one hydrogen were substituted with iodine, the hydrogens geminal to iodine would resonate at 3.20 ppm. On the other hand, if we substituted with bromine instead, the geminal hydrogens would resonate at 3.40 ppm. Chlorine would pull the resonance of the geminal hydrogens to 3.57 ppm. Thus, we see that the chemical shift is dependent on the electronegativity of the substituent. Conversely, we may use the chemical shift to give us information about substituents. In the case presented above, the chemical shift is sufficiently different to permit the identification of the halogens from the hydrogen spectrum. Other substituents, both elements and functional groups, that may be identified from the hydrogen spectrum are shown in Fig. 4-1.

Molecules with π bonding have electrons that are free to circulate. When these molecules are placed in a magnetic field, the field induces circulation of these π electrons. The electronic charge in motion generates a magnetic field which can oppose the applied field in some regions of the molecule and reinforce it in others. This effect is termed magnetic anisotropy. In acetylene, for example, the hydrogens are in a region where the generated magnetic field opposes the applied field, and consequently the hydrogen resonance occurs at a lower ppm value than would be expected from electron density considerations alone. Acetylenic hydrogens resonate around 3 ppm, whereas ethylenic hydrogens are found at about 5 ppm. The opposite case occurs with aromatic compounds. The ring current which is induced in the benzene ring generates a field which reinforces the applied field in the vicinity of the aromatic hydrogens, causing them to resonate at a higher (6.4 to 8.4 ppm) value than electron density considerations would suggest. This is quite fortunate, for this effect places aromatic hydrogens in a conspicuous range. The shift to higher values is even more pronounced in the case of aldehydes, which give resonance around 10 ppm. Hydrogen bonding causes hydrogens to resonate at higher values. Hydroxylic hydrogens appear between 2 and 5 ppm, whereas the more strongly bonded carboxylic hydrogens resonate around 10 ppm.

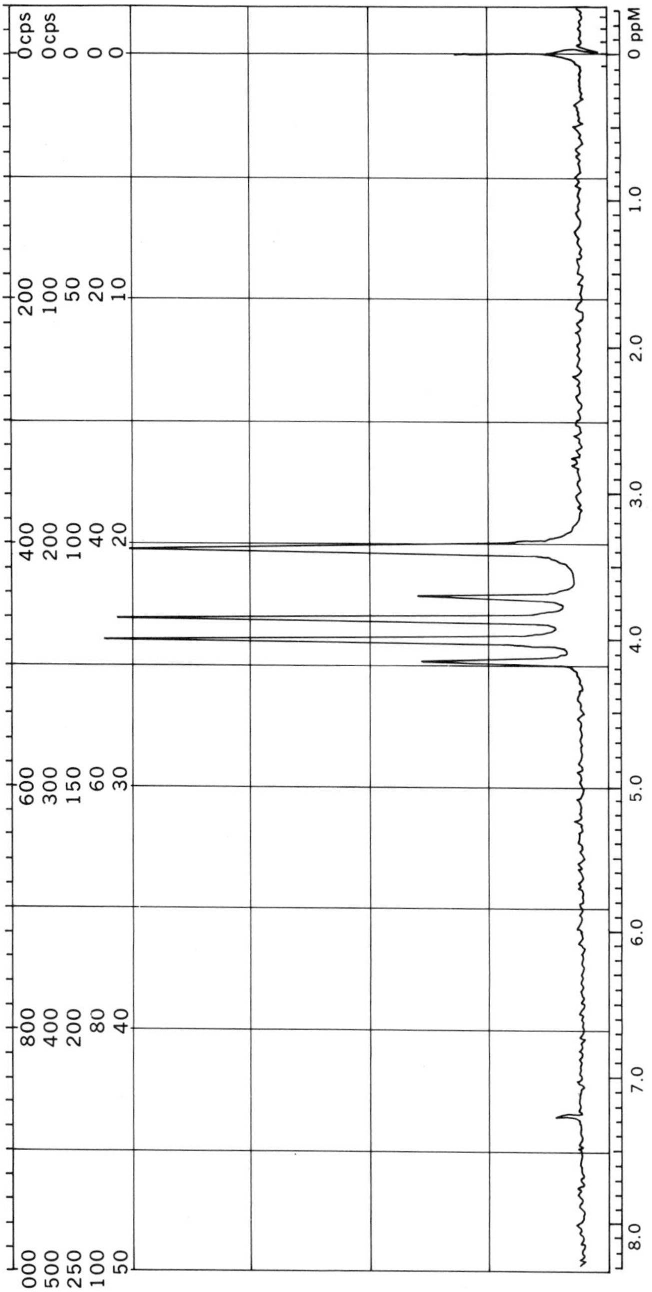

Fig. 4-2 2,2,2-trifluoro-ethanol spectrum. (From N. S. Bhacca, L. F. Johnson, and J. N. Shoolery, Varian Spectra Catalog, vol. I, Varian Associates, 611 Hanson Way, Palo Alto, Calif.)

The above-described NMR phenomenon is the simplest variety, where one species of magnetic atom is present per molecule. However, when several species are present, each species affects the orientation of the other in the external magnetic field and, as a result, multiple peaks

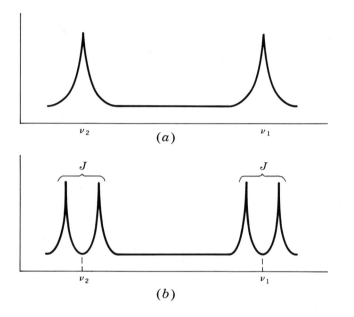

ν_2 (*a*) ν_1

ν_2 (*b*) ν_1

Fig. 4-3 (*a*) Uncoupled spectrum. (*b*) Spectrum with spin-spin coupling.

occur for each species. For example, in the compound

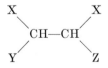

each proton would absorb different frequencies at resonance, since it is in a different environment. One would expect two peaks (see Fig. 4-3*a*). However, the spin of one proton couples with the spin of the other and results in two peaks for each proton (see Fig. 4-3*b*). This phenomenon is known as *spin-spin coupling*.

The distance *J* between the two peaks is known as the *coupling constant* and is characteristic of the relationship of the two coupled atoms to each other in the molecule. The above coupling occurs between atoms with only two combinations of spins. Multiple combinations of spins lead to multiple splittings with a separate peak for spin-spin coupling. Figure 4-4 shows a series of coupling constants for common proton species. Coupling can occur between different types of the same atom (i.e., protons in different configurations). This is known as *homo-*

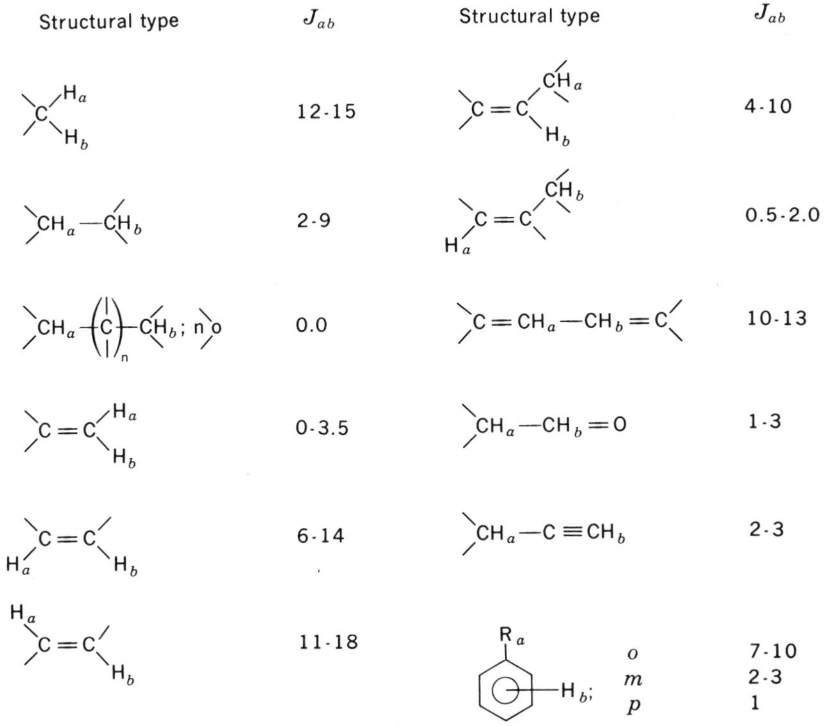

Structural type	J_{ab}	Structural type	J_{ab}
$\underset{}{\overset{H_a}{\underset{H_b}{C}}}$	12-15	$C = C \overset{CH_a}{\underset{H_b}{}}$	4-10
$CH_a - CH_b$	2-9	$C = C \overset{CH_b}{\underset{H_a}{}}$	0.5-2.0
$CH_a \left(C \right)_n CH_b ; n > 0$	0.0	$C = CH_a - CH_b = C$	10-13
$C = C \overset{H_a}{\underset{H_b}{}}$	0-3.5	$CH_a - CH_b = O$	1-3
$\underset{H_a}{C} = C \overset{}{\underset{H_b}{}}$	6-14	$CH_a - C \equiv CH_b$	2-3
$\overset{H_a}{\underset{}{C}} = C \overset{}{\underset{H_b}{}}$	11-18	$\overset{R_a}{\underset{}{}} - H_b;$ $\begin{array}{l} o \\ m \\ p \end{array}$	$\begin{array}{l} 7\text{-}10 \\ 2\text{-}3 \\ 1 \end{array}$

Fig. 4-4 Proton spin-spin coupling constants. (*Reprinted with permission from L. M. Jackmann, "Applications of Nuclear Magnetic Resonance Spectroscopy in Organic Chemistry," Pergamon Press, New York, 1959, p. 85.*)

nuclear coupling. Coupling can also occur between different magnetic atoms (i.e., proton to fluorine or to boron). This is known as *heteronuclear coupling.*

Coupling constants also give information pertinent to functional group identification, particularly in cases where hydrogen is neighbored by a functional group which contains magnetic nuclei of a different species. The spectrum of 2,2,2-trifluoroethanol (Fig. 4-2) illustrates this point. The spectrum shows the hydroxyl resonance at 3.38 ppm and the methylene resonance at 3.93 ppm. The methylene resonance is split into four lines separated by about 9 Hz. Now 9 Hz is the order of magnitude of the coupling constant of hydrogen with fluorine which is three bonds removed. Further, the four-line pattern indicates the presence of three fluorine atoms. Thus, the trifluoromethyl group is recognized from the hydrogen spectrum.

Quantitative functional-group determination is obtained through the intensity parameter. The intensity of NMR resonance at constant field is governed by:

1. Sensitivity of nucleus being observed
2. Number of nuclei per unit volume

Since we observe the spectrum of only one nucleus at a time, we obtain most of our quantitative information by comparing the intensities of resonances of the one nuclear species. Therefore, sensitivity may be considered constant. The second factor, number of nuclei per unit volume, is important and is dependent on the following:

1. Number of nuclei per equivalent functional group
2. Number of equivalent functional groups per molecule
3. Concentration of molecular species in solution.

The effect of (1) is demonstrated in the spectrum of ethanol (Fig. 4-5), in which the relative intensities of the peaks correspond to the number of hydrogens in the represented functional groups. An example of (2) is shown in the spectrum of isopropyl alcohol, Fig. 4-6. Note that the ratios of functional groups are obtained by dividing intensities by the number of nuclei per group. There are one hydroxyl and one methyne group, but two methyl groups. Thus, the methyl resonance is twice that expected for a single methyl. A mixture of acetonitrile and benzene illustrates (3) (see Fig. 4-7). The benzene and the methyl resonances are divided by 6 and 3, respectively (the number of nuclei per group or molecule). The ratio of resulting quotients (1.00 to 1.69) is the mole ratio of the two compounds. The percentages determined from the spectrum are 53.0 and 47.0 for benzene and acetonitrile, respectively. From the above considerations, we see that in the case of a totally soluble sample, ratios of functional groups are obtained from the peak intensities after they are corrected for the number of nuclei per group.

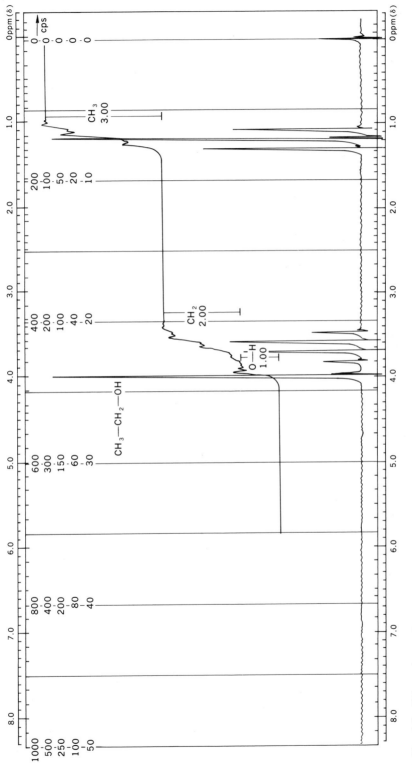

Fig. 4-5 Ethanol spectrum.

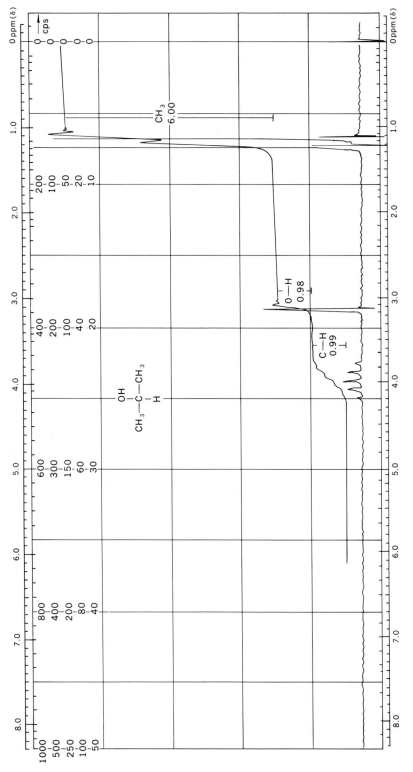

Fig. 4-6 Isopropyl alcohol spectrum.

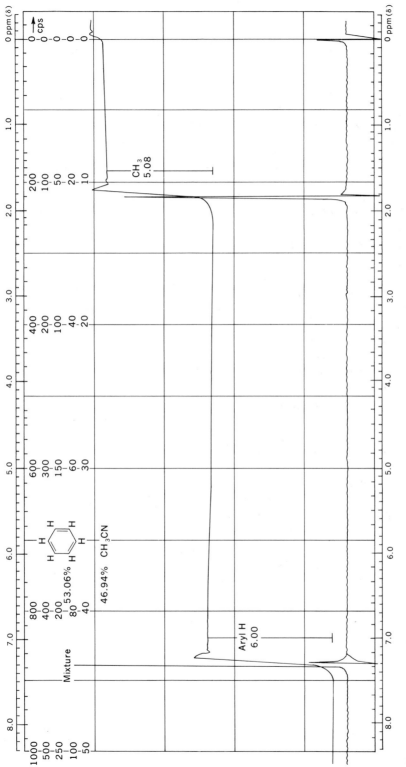

Fig. 4-7 Acetonitrile-benzene spectrum.

If necessary, the weight of each functionality may be obtained by comparing its intensity with the intensity of a weighed amount of some known compound which has been added to the solution.

ELECTRON SPIN (PARAMAGNETIC) RESONANCE (ESR, EPR)*

The measurement of the precession frequency of a free electron is accomplished in a manner similar to the method used in nuclear magnetic resonance spectroscopy. The spinning electron possesses a magnetic moment. When it is subjected to a strong magnetic field, it precesses with a frequency which is proportional to that field and to its magnetic moment. The observation of this phenomenon depends on the introduction of a rotating magnetic field whose frequency is equal to the precession frequency of the electron. The electron possesses a spin of $\frac{1}{2}$, the energy difference between the two spin states is related to the applied field, and the spin populations are given by the Boltzmann factor. The measurable quantity in the electron paramagnetic resonance experiment is the net magnetic moment. The precession frequency of a free electron is 2.8026 MHz/gauss, and the usual experiment employs microwave apparatus operating from 8,000 to 12,000 MHz/gauss with a magnetic-field strength of approximately 3,000 gauss.

Briefly, an EPR spectrometer consists of a magnet with suitable sweep capability, a klystron oscillator to supply radiofrequency energy to the sample, a means of modulating the field and supplying voltage to the phase detector, a detector system with suitable amplifiers, and a means of displaying the EPR signal.

Data important to molecular structure studies that are available from EPR spectra are the *g value, hyperfine interaction, observed line widths* and *electronic level splittings*. The *g* value and the hyperfine interaction are related to molecular structure and the line widths are environment-dependent. The *g* value is the spectroscopic splitting factor, which is about 2.0 for most radical species and is characteristic for a given species. Because the *g* value is dependent on field strength, increased field values may offer more data where materials are suspected of containing two different *g* values. In crystals where the orbital angular momentum of the electron is subjected to strong electrostatic fields and essentially quenched, the spin is relatively unperturbed and the *g* value is dependent on orientation of the crystal with

* Written by Harry Agahigian, Perkin-Elmer Corp., Norwalk, Conn.

respect to the magnetic field. The applications of the EPR technique to solid-state physics, crystallography and inorganic chemistry become obvious.

The interaction of electron and nuclear magnetic dipole moments is called the contact hyperfine interaction. Since the electron has to be in an S state, the extent of the interaction is a measure of the S character of the electron orbital. The interaction is invaluable in studies of paramagnetic ions, odd molecules and radicals. The study of the hyperfine interaction in π-electron systems yields information concerning orbital overlap and spin densities. The magnitude of the hyperfine splitting, therefore, will depend on the electron orbital and its proximity to the proton.

In its application to molecular structure, EPR has been extremely valuable to the physical-organic chemist and the biologist. The spectrum of 1,4-naphthoquinone is an example of the hyperfine interaction which is of value in studies of the 1,4-semiquinones. A basic triplet is present for the 2, 3 protons and for each triplet line, a quintet of lines, which is due to the 5, 6, 7, 8 protons.

One of the systems that has been studied has been semiquinones and substituted semiquinones. These can be produced by oxidation of hydroquinones. Some correlations can be made in semiquinone systems. The g value decreases as the number of aromatic rings increases. The g values of anthracene ion and phenanthrene ion differ, and seem to be related to the geometry of the various rings. The g values of semiquinones are also dependent on the substituents present. Halogen substituents show a consistent trend dependent on number and size and molecular geometry. Shifts in these g values can be due to temperature, solvent and concentration, but these variables are not as large in magnitude as the differences due to structural changes. The parameters and spectral considerations are somewhat analogous to those of nuclear magnetic resonance experiments. In studies on similar aromatic systems, the geometry of the substituents was considered in order to interpret the data, i.e., changes in line widths and splittings. Solvent-solute interactions also play an important role in these systems. Approximately 10^{-9} molar concentration of radicals is measured by the EPR experiment; it is a measure of the number of unpaired electrons.

The feature of electron paramagnetic resonance spectrometry is that the technique has applications in the fields of chemistry, physics and biology, and is challenging both for the experimentalist and the theoretician. Unpaired electrons, as found in free radicals, transition-element ions, rare earths, color centers, biradicals, etc., can be detected by the use of a suitable magnetic field and radiofrequency field. The reactions and the kinetics of biochemical systems have been studied by EPR. One-electron transfer oxidation-reduction reactions can be studied and the intermediates and the products readily identified, and the spectra will yield information concerning the bonding and spin density. The hyperfine splitting yields information concerning the occupied orbitals. Since the intermediates can be detected, reliable kinetic data are obtained by measuring changes in concentration as a function of time. The effects of inhibitors on oxidation processes, as well as of free radicals induced in polymers, can be studied by EPR spectrometry. Photochemical reactions and polarographic processes have also been studied. In biological fields, the monitoring of certain drug levels in the blood of patients has been successful.

The EPR data in free-radical studies are a measure of the shift of the g value from the g value at the unpaired electron, which is about 2. Enough studies have been made to enable one to predict the g values. As pointed out in the case of paramagnetic ions such as the transition elements, the g values differ markedly, and the values can be used to obtain detailed information concerning crystal geometry. The application of EPR studies to polymerization and radiation damage has been demonstrated. Solvent and temperature studies have also had much emphasis.

The scope of EPR for structure determination and identification is not as broad as that of NMR. EPR spectra are obtained on far fewer compounds. However, where EPR spectra can be obtained, data become available which generally could not be obtained by other means.

X-RAY DIFFRACTION

This approach can only be used for *complete identification and structure* work. The approach hinges on the crystal structure of compounds. Since crystal structure shows little or no correlation with general characteristics, the x-ray approach is of little value for *characterization* or *general identification* studies.

This x-ray approach involves the diffractive properties of crystals of chemical compounds. The distances between atoms in the crystal lattice act as the spaces of a diffraction grating. When x-rays pass through a crystal, they are diffracted, resulting in enhancement and extinction of light emerging from the crystal. X-rays are necessary, since the spacings are so small that short wavelengths are necessary for diffraction to occur. Figure 4-8 shows Laue patterns; these indicate the spots where enhancement has occurred. In the technique discussed so far, single crystals of the material in question are used. These crystals

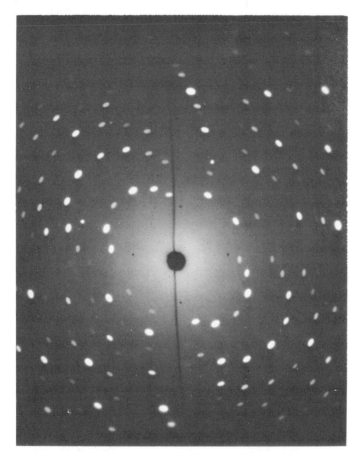

Fig. 4-8   Laue pattern of quartz (copper radiation).

are rotated in precise configurations; diffraction is measured while the crystal is in many different positions relative to the incident light. By mathematical analysis of the variation in Laue pattern with crystal position, one can obtain a "contour diagram" of the molecule in question showing areas of heavier electron density and, hence, location of the atoms in the structure. Figure 4-9 shows such a contour diagram for DL-isocrystopleurine methiodide.

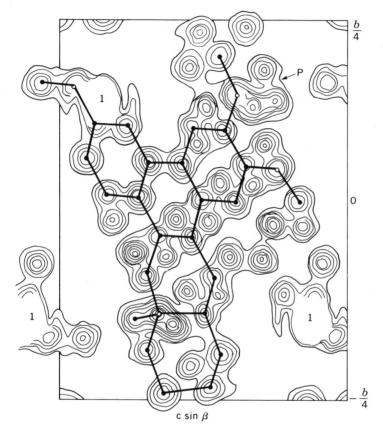

Fig. 4-9   Generalized projection of DL-isocrystopleurine methiodide. (*Reprinted with permission from M. J. Buerger, "Crystal-structure Analysis," John Wiley & Sons Inc., New York, 1960, p. 398.*)

The above x-ray technique is used only for *structure or complete identification* work. It is time-consuming to do a full study, and it requires a thorough knowledge of crystallography and mathematics. The time for a study has been shortened by the use of computers, but we are still speaking of days, weeks, even months, for a study. The job is made easier by the existence of heavy atoms in a molecule. These give large, intense areas on the contour diagram and act as a sort of focal point around which the rest of the structure can be built. This circumstance lessens the error in interpretation. The x-ray structure is interpretive in nature, and often, weak spots in the final structure must be bolstered by other approaches (i.e., NMR and mass spectrometry) or by examination of related compounds by x-ray methods.

In general, one finds complete identification or structure studies are established more easily and faster by NMR, mass spectrometry, infrared absorption, or a combination of these. X-ray methods are used, but the complexity of the mathematics, the frequent inability to get large enough crystals and the interpretive nature of the data result in rather limited application. X-ray diffraction, however, has been applied to structure determination of materials where all other approaches failed. For example, the identification of vitamin B_{12} and of proteins such as myoglobin and hemoglobin was thus accomplished.

There is an x-ray diffraction approach which is very useful for the "fingerprint" type of *complete identification*. This is the so-called powder diffraction technique. The single-crystal technique is difficult to use as a fingerprint method, because the crystals being compared have to be in identical orientations to the incident x-rays for identical patterns to be obtained. This is not only difficult to achieve, but if one knows the unknown crystal so well that he can position it properly, he essentially has already made the identification. The powder method, as the name implies, uses a ground sample of the unknown. A sample of this powder contains tiny crystals of the unknown in all possible positions with respect to the incident x-ray beam (or nearly so). Then, instead of obtaining single spots as in a Laue pattern, one obtains a series of concentric circles. These circles are really a summation of Laue spots of individual crystals in their various positions. Figure 4-10 shows such a photographic powder pattern for quartz. The diameter of each circle is a fixed parameter for each chemical material, and since there are usually several concentric circles, each is a parameter. These parameters fix the identity of the material, and the more circles present in this pattern, the more definite the result. The identification is made by comparing the parameters obtained on the powder diffraction pattern with those in the literature (the American Society for Testing Materials publishes an extensive file of x-ray diffraction data of known compounds. Figure 4-11 shows an example from the ASTM file). If a comparison cannot be found in the literature, one can obtain powder

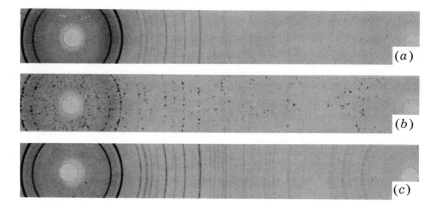

Fig. 4-10   Debye-Scherrer photographs prepared under different conditions. *(a)* Quartz powder, <5 microns, specimen stationary. *(b)* Quartz powder, 15 to 50 μ, specimen stationary. *(c)* Quartz powder, 15 to 50 μ, specimen rotating. *(Reprinted with permission from H. P. Klug and L. E. Alexander, "X-ray Diffraction Procedures," John Wiley & Sons Inc., New York, 1954, p. 196.)*

6-0040

d	8.26	2.76	5.45	9.44	$Fe_2(SO_4)_3 \cdot 9H_2O$
I/I₁	100	76	64	40	COQUIMBITE

Rad. Cu   λ 1.5418   Filter Ni
Dia.   Cut off   Coll.
I/I₁ DIFFRACTOMETER   d corr. abs.?
Ref. C.M. WARSHAW, GULF RESEARCH AND DEVEL.,
HARMARVILLE, PA.

Sys. HEXAGONAL   S.G. P3M,32 OR 3M
a₀ 10.92 b₀   c₀ 17.14   A   C 1.570
α   β   γ   Z 4
Ref. HOCART, IN UNGEMACH: BULL.SOC.MIN. 58 165
(1935) ALSO WARSHAW

εa 1.55 - 1.57 nωβ 1.54-1.55 εγ   Sign +
2V   D 2.11 mp   ColorLESS, TRANSPARENT
Ref. HOCART, IN UNGEMACH. ALSO DANA, VOL. II
P 532

MATERIAL FROM SZOMOLNOK, HUNGARY, U.S.N.M.
95729. ALSO FROM BORATE, SAN BERNARDINO,
CALIFORNIA, U.S.N.M. R-7661.

d Å	I/I₁	hkl	d Å	I/I₁	hkl
9.44	40	100*	1.858	26	414
8.52	20	002	1.821	28	330,406
8.26	100	101	1.780	18	421,332
6.34	6	102	1.767	14	415
5.45	64	110	1.701	6	423,407
4.72	22	200*	1.682	8	228,219
4.60	44	112			
4.55	12	201	*THESE LINES MAY SHOW		
3.64	42	203	ORIENTATION EFFECTS.		
3.58	14	210			
3.50	34	211			
3.36	62	114			
3.29	8	212			
3.10	26	301			
3.03	32	213			
2.759	76	303			
2.538	24	304			
2.383	12	313			
2.303	26	224			
1.941	14	413			

Fig. 4-11   ASTM card 6-0040 giving x-ray data and crystal parameters for coquimbite ($Fe_2[SO_4]_3 \cdot 9H_2O$). *(Reprinted with permission from ASTM collection.)*

diffraction patterns of known materials which are suspected. Comparison of the patterns of the knowns with the pattern of the unknown reveals the identity or lack of it.

Note in Fig. 4-10 the effect of particle size on the pattern. In (a) of Fig. 4-10, the particles are so small that the individual Laue spots merge to form smooth circles. In (b) of Fig. 4-10, the particles are so large that the individual spots that make up the circle can be seen. In (c) of Fig. 4-10, the spots have been eliminated by rotating the sample; the rotation has the effect of achieving infinite positions.

The powder pattern can be determined with a counter, instead of photographically as above. Figure 4-12 shows a counter plot for quartz powder. This should be compared to Fig. 4-10 which is the photographic pattern for quartz. Note the many parameters; these make for conclusive identification.

The powder diffraction analysis is quite rapid, seldom longer than 2 hr; and as stated above, an identity, once found, is quite absolute, because of the multiplicity of lines present. However, one drawback of this approach is that if identity is *not* found, the pattern gives no hint of what the unknown might be. Infrared, nuclear magnetic resonance, and mass spectrometry also can be used as fingerprint approaches, but in these cases, even if a positive match of spectra is *not* found, the spectrum of the unknown can give some clues as to its *general character or identity*. Another drawback is that the sample must be crystalline, or no x-ray pattern is obtained. In addition, some materials exist in several crystalline forms, so that a negative match does not always mean that a certain material is not present. One sample may be in a crystalline form different from that of the material on which the literature pattern was obtained.

The powder approach is much simpler to operate than the single-crystal technique, since no crystal alignment is needed and, of course, the intense mathematical computations are also not needed. The cost of equipment solely for powder diffraction work is approximately \$6,000 to \$10,000,* while that for single crystal work (also usable for powder work) is approximately \$8,000 to \$70,000 (without computer).*

RAMAN SPECTROSCOPY

This has been discussed on pp. 73–77 for functional-group analysis. What has been said there applies largely to structure and identification

* Courtesy of Henry Court, Phillips Electronics Corp., Mount Vernon, N.Y.

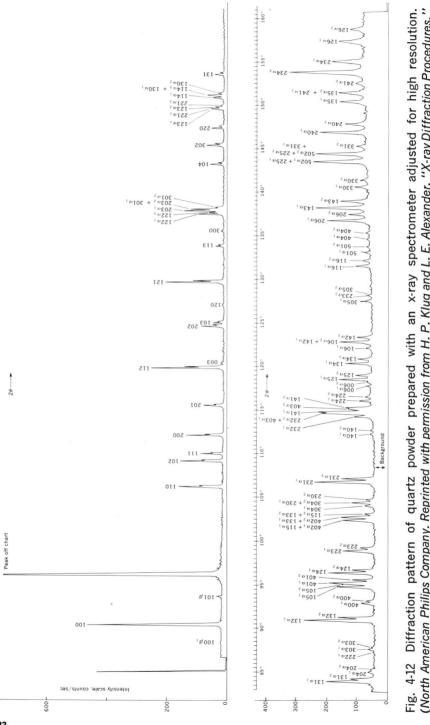

Fig. 4-12 Diffraction pattern of quartz powder prepared with an x-ray spectrometer adjusted for high resolution. (North American Philips Company. Reprinted with permission from H. P. Klug and L. E. Alexander, "X-ray Diffraction Procedures," John Wiley & Sons, Inc., New York, 1954, p. 258.)

work. It is a corollary to infrared absorption, since the approach relies on the vibrational and rotational energies in the molecule. However, because of the weak signals emitted, its range of application is small. Also, the high energy inputs required to overcome the weak signals cause photochemical reactions and/or decompositions which negate the results. Also, many materials fluoresce under these high energies, which makes analysis impossible. However, the newer instrumentation being made available at this writing promises to circumvent or minimize some of the existing problems. See pages 73–77 for a more complete discussion.

NUCLEAR QUADRUPOLE SPECTROSCOPY

Nuclear quadrupole spectroscopic resonance (NQR) is still in the development phase but holds much promise for structure work. It is based on the existence of electrostatic quadrupoles around certain nuclei which cause these nuclei to orient themselves when placed in an electric field. Thus a relationship to NMR can be seen, with the exception that only electrostatic instead of magnetic interactions are involved. The atoms possessing nuclear electrostatic quadrupoles are Al, N, Cl, Br, I, B. Hence, we see the applicability of this structure approach to molecules when NMR cannot normally be applied (that is, Al, N, Cl, Br, I). Also, NQR can be applied to solids, glasses, and very viscous liquids, whereas NMR cannot. Even in cases where both NQR and NMR can operate, both yield different (and often supplemental) information, since they are based on different types of interactions.

NQR is somewhat difficult to operate at present because of the broad range of resonance frequencies for each active atom. This makes the frequency scans very time-consuming. Also, since the field is not very well developed at present, interpretation is made difficult by lack of background information.

Most existing NQR devices are "homemade" at present, but manufactured models are beginning to appear.

MICROWAVE SPECTROSCOPY

The microwave portion of the electromagnetic spectrum extends from wavelengths of 1 m to 30 cm or from frequencies of 300,000 to 1,000 MHz, though the portion usable for identification purposes lies between 20,000 and 220,000 MHz. This region lies between the far infrared and the conventional radiofrequency regions. Application of microwave spectroscopy is almost exclusively involved with absorption work in gaseous samples.

In the visible and ultraviolet portions of the spectrum, the absorption wavelengths are characteristic of the transitions between electronic energy states. The rotational and vibrational energies of portions of the molecule are measured only as perturbation effects. In the infrared region, the vibrational energies of portions of the molecule (i.e., functional groups) are measured directly, and the rotational energies of the molecules are measured as perturbation effects. In the microwave region, transitions between rotational energies are observed as characteristic of the molecule as a whole, with nuclear interactions as first-order perturbations. In the radiofrequency portion of the spectrum, the nuclear interactions are directly observable (that is, NMR).

The approach lends itself to identification problems by comparison of unknown with known spectra. Microwave spectra are generally very specific since they are a result of the properties of the molecule as a whole. Also, the frequency of spectral lines can be very accurately measured. One can resolve two lines 0.25 MHz apart and, since the general region scanned extends from 17,000 to 40,000 MHz, then 92,000 separate microwave-absorption lines can be resolved with a single sample. Thus, even complex mixtures can be qualitatively analyzed. The limiting factor in microwave spectroscopy is not interference (see Fig. 4-13). However, the low intensity of absorption is a limitation. While some materials such as water, ammonia, or methanol can be detected in parts-per-million quantities, more complex molecules can barely be detected, even in 10% concentrations.

Quantitative analysis is not easily accomplished with microwave spectroscopy. This is mainly due to the fact that the rotational motion of a molecule in a mixture is affected by the other components of the mixture. Hence, it cannot be assumed that peak height is directly proportional to concentration. One may calibrate a system, but that calibration will hold only for that qualitative composition at that quantitative level. There are methods which make quantitative analysis possible, but all involve measurement of parameters other than just frequency and absorption. These other measurements increase the sources of error, sometimes very significantly.

Microwave spectroscopy has not found wide usage, since most analyses possible by this approach are possible by other, less expensive, and more readily available approaches which are easier to use (e.g.,

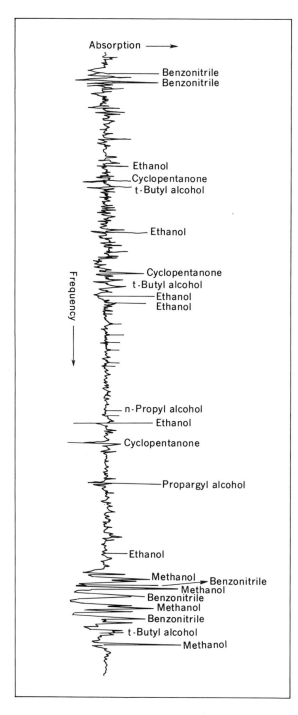

Fig. 4-13 Microwave spectrum of a mixture. (Reprinted with permission from "Modern Methods of Research and Analysis," Dow Chemical Co., 5th rev., Chemical Physics Research Laboratory, Midland, Mich. Jan., 1966.)

gas chromatography). The current cost of the equipment ranges from $20,000 to $150,000.*

OPTICAL ROTATORY DISPERSION

Organic materials containing certain asymmetric structures have the ability to rotate the plane of polarized light when such light is passed

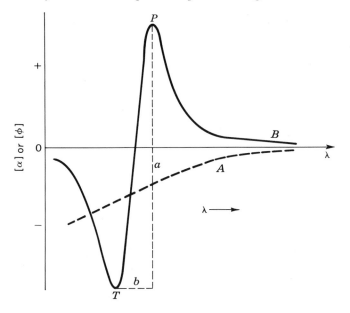

Fig. 4-14 Typical optical rotary dispersion curves. Curve A, negative plain curve. Curve B, positive Cotton effect curve with peak P, trough T, amplitude a, and breadth b. [*Reprinted with permission from G. G. Lyle and R. E. Lyle, "Determination of Organic Structures by Physical Methods," vol. 2, F. C. Nachod, and W. D. Phillips (eds.), Academic Press Inc., New York, 1962, p. 4.*]

through them. The change in the degree of this rotation with the wavelength of the light used is known as optical rotatory dispersion. The resultant angle of rotation is dependent on the degree of asymmetry of the molecule and on the relationship of the wavelength of the plane-polarized light to the wavelength of the absorption maximum of a

* Courtesy of Stanley Klainer, Tracerlab, Boston, Mass.

chromophore in the vicinity of the asymmetric center. As the wave-length of the polarized light is decreased, an increase in the numerical value of the angular rotation usually occurs. If the rotation is plotted versus wavelength, and if no absorption of light occurs, a curve such as *A* in Fig. 4-14 is obtained. This is known as a *plain curve.* Anomalous rotatory dispersion curves are given by many compounds, however. These curves contain positive peaks, negative peaks, and sometimes both positive and negative peaks as seen in Fig. 4-15. Such a curve with positive and negative peaks is known as a *Cotton effect* curve *(B)* (Fig. 4-14). The peak and trough of the wave are known as *extrema* of the wave of a curve. The vertical distance between the peak and the trough is called the *amplitude a,* and the distance *b* is known as the *breadth* of the curve. The point between the peak and the trough at which the curve crosses the zero axis generally occurs at the same wavelength at which an absorption maximum occurs in the ultraviolet or visible regions. If a compound has a rotatory (asymmetric) center in the vicinity of a chromophore (ultraviolet or visible absorption) which has an absorption maximum of relatively low intensity, the optical rotatory dispersion curve can be expected to be anomalous. In many cases, the optical opacity of the samples decreases the light to such a degree that rotatory effects cannot be measured.

Some chromophores which give anomalous curves are carbonyl, azide, xanthate, nitrite, dithiocarbamate, conjugated double bonds, carbocyclic and heterocyclic aromatic groups. Chromophores which absorb at shorter wavelengths, such as carboxyl, amide, nonconjugated double bonds, and saturated groups such as OH, NH, CH, do not show Cotton effect curves in the region of the spectrum usable with current instruments.

The structures of optically active compounds can be determined in three ways: (1) comparison of the rotatory dispersion curve of the unknown with curves of analogous compounds whose absolute config-urations have been established; (2) deduction of the structure from theoretical considerations (so-called octant rule or axial haloketone rule); (3) preparation of a derivative of a functional group located on the asymmetric center, which, in conjunction with the chromophore produced by the derivatizing agent, governs the sign of the rotatory dispersion curve.

With optical rotatory dispersion alone, it would be difficult to arrive at the structure or identity of a material. Generally, previous knowl-edge about the material or its analogs, or information gained by nuclear magnetic resonance, mass spectrometry, and/or absorption spectroscopy is generally needed. The approach is quite limited in general utility, primarily by the need for an optical rotatory center and a chromophore, but also by the need for auxiliary information on the sample or on analogous compounds in order to make an accurate interpretation.

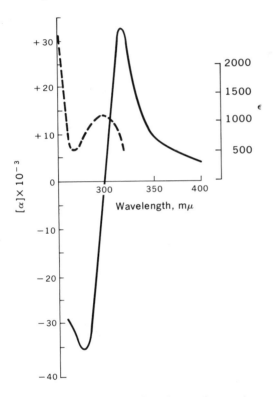

Fig. 4-15 The ultraviolet absorption spectrum (. . . .) and the optical rotary dispersion curve(—) of parasantonide (T) in ethanol. [S. Mitchell and K. Schwarzwald, J. Chem. Soc., p. 889 **(1939)**. Reprinted with permission from G. G. Lyle and R. E. Lyle, "Determination of Organic Structures by Physical Methods," vol. 2, F. C. Nachod and W. D. Phillips (eds.), Academic Press Inc., New York, 1962, p. 6.]

MÖSSBAUER SPECTROSCOPY

There are different levels of energy involved in the emission of a gamma ray from a nucleus. Some emitted gamma rays are so energetic (greater than 1 Mev) that they will cause the parent atom to be torn

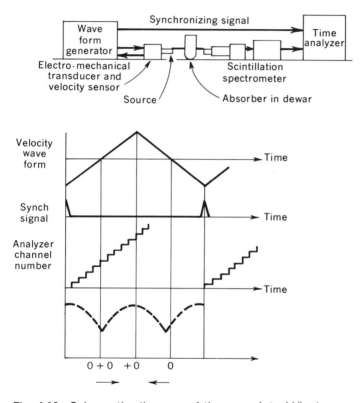

Fig. 4-16 Schematic diagram of the complete Mössbauer effect spectrometer. [*Reprinted with permission from G. K. Wertheim, Science,* 144:256 (1964).]

from its molecule or from its lattice site by the recoil. Emitted gamma rays of intermediate energies (150 Kev to 1 Mev) also tend to cause the same effects. However, with gamma rays of energies below 150 Kev, it becomes possible to achieve emission of these without enough recoil to excite the lattice; the entire energy goes into the gamma ray. These lower-energy gamma rays are reabsorbable by other atoms without disruption of the absorbing atom. Hence the lower-energy gamma rays exhibit a resonance behavior of emission and reabsorption. This behavior is the basis of the Mössbauer effect.

Mössbauer spectroscopy depends on the fact that the absorbing atom in different molecular configurations in a molecule or under other influences by other atoms will absorb gamma rays of slightly different energies. To achieve a band of energies from a gamma-emitting source,

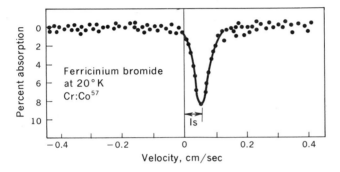

Fig. 4-17   Isomer shift. Effect of the electric monopole interaction is to shift nuclear levels without separating magnetic sublevels. Shifts are very small compared with the total energy of the gamma ray, 10^{-12} E. [*Reprinted with permission from G. K. Wertheim, Science,* 144:257 (1964).]

advantage is taken of the Doppler effect. Namely, the source (or sample) is vibrated, and the rate at which the source and sample approach or recede from each other results in different energy levels. The energy of a gamma ray emitted by a moving source is expressed by the term $E\nu/C$ where ν is the velocity component. The experimental measurement is the determination of absorption of gamma rays as a function of Doppler velocity. Figure 4-16 shows a schematic diagram of a Mössbauer spectrometer.

There are several types of structural information that can be obtained from a Mössbauer spectrum. One is the *isomer shift,* an example of which is seen in Fig. 4-17. This shift in energy is due to the electrostatic interaction between the nucleus and the surrounding electron-charge cloud. For instance, two valence states of the same element will exhibit different isomer shifts. Similarly, since the isomer shift measures the electronic charge density at the nucleus, it is directly sensitive to the S electrons and indirectly sensitive to the other electrons which may be involved in chemical bonds. The most extensive chemical investigations utilizing isomer shift involve the elements iron and tin, mainly because the different oxidation states of these metals have a pronounced effect on isomer shift.

Quadrupole splitting is another type of information obtainable from a Mössbauer spectrum. The quadrupole splitting results from the interaction of the nuclear quadrupole moment with the electric field gradient outside the nucleus. In structure determination, the absence of quadrupole splitting is an indication of a cubic or near cubic arrangement (i.e., octahedral or tetrahedral).

Magnetic hyperfine splitting information is also made available by Mössbauer spectroscopy. This information, however, is of little value with relation to molecular structure and is used mainly in the study of alloys, especially the magnetic alloys.

Mössbauer spectroscopy is in its infancy at present, the effect itself having been first discovered in 1958, and hence is of little practical utility as yet. Outside of tin and iron compounds, little work has been done, though Mössbauer effect has been observed with some 45 elements. The instrumentation is not complex or expensive. The basic Mössbauer spectrometers range in price from $2,000 to $5,000.* An analyzer unit adds an additional $5,000 to $70,000.* A working total unit can be purchased for $8,500.*

OTHER STRUCTURAL CONSIDERATIONS

Structure as discussed above is the molecular or chemical structure of a material. However, the physical structure and identity is also of importance, and measurements are needed to elucidate this structure. Crystallinity, for example, is such a physical structure parameter. Some materials exist in different crystalline and/or amorphous forms. Sulfur is such a material, as are many of our polymers. Some materials, such as polymers, have different configurations or degrees of cross-linking, each of which must be detected. Other materials exist as different hydrates or solvates, and still other materials exist in associated form as dimers, trimers, etc.

This topic is included in the *structure and identity* section because, even though the chemical moiety is known, its character may be

* Values obtained from Technical Measurements Corp., North Haven, Conn.

variable, and this must also be pinned down for the exact nature of the material to be known.

X-ray diffraction (see pages 116–121), will of course resolve the different polymorphic crystalline forms of a material. It will also resolve different hydrates or solvates if these are crystalline. The technique is fast and absolute, though it cannot quantitate the amount of each form present with any high precision or accuracy. X-ray analysis is of no value with amorphous materials, but it will yield valuable data on the degree of crystallinity in an apparently amorphous material such as a polymer.

Infrared absorption is of some help in this area of physical structure and identification, since the absorption will often detect differences in physical characteristics. For example, different crystalline forms of the same material sometimes show absorptions at different wavelengths when examined in the solid state; or, at least, the peak shapes vary somewhat. The approach will also detect hydrates and solvates by the absorption of the attached water or solvent. It may detect different degrees of hydration or solvation, but this is made possible by quantitating the water and solvent absorptions. Crosslinking may be detected if a new linkage is created in the crosslinking operation or if a functional group is consumed; for example, in crosslinking via sulfur bonds, mercaptans are consumed to form disulfides.

$$\left.\right|\!-\text{SH} + \text{HS}\!-\!\left|\quad \rightarrow \quad \right|\!-\text{S}\!-\!\text{S}\!-\!\left|\right.$$

Dimers and trimers are often detectable by infrared, though the bulk of the sample may still exist as monomer. For example, 2,4-toluene diisocyanate exhibits a dimer which is normally difficult to detect, since the dimer will revert back to monomer on heating; however, infrared will detect it.

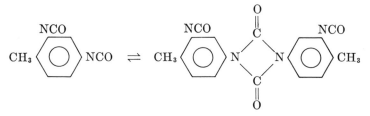

One of the strongest tools in the elucidation of physical structure details and identity is thermal analysis. Whether the differences being

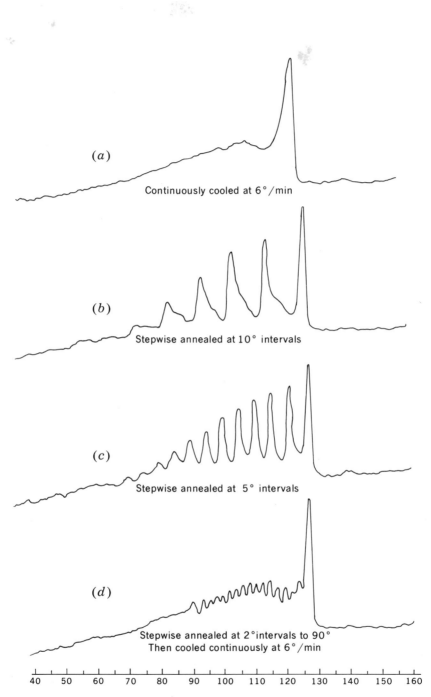

Fig. 4-18 Polyethylene fusion curves. Same sample, but different thermal histories, 11E-1, 6.65 mg. Scanning rate 18°/min. [*Reprinted with permission from A. P. Gray and K. Casey, Polymer Letters*, **2**:381–388 (1964).]

sought are due to crystallinity, hydration, association, crosslinking, or other factors, there usually is a separate heat effect for each mode present. The heat effects can be followed with *thermogravimetry* and with *differential thermal analysis*. These heat effects can be endothermal or exothermal, and they can be quantitatively measured by conventional calorimetry or, more conveniently, by *differential scanning calorimetry.**

Thermogravimetric analysis (TGA), as the name implies, is the change in weight with change in temperature. TGA is of limited application in physical structure work, because a change in weight is needed with each thermal event. Many structural changes take place thermally without change in weight, for example, change in crystalline form, melting, glass transitions, dissociation. TGA will not detect such details, but *differential thermal analysis* (DTA) will. Figure 4-18 shows a striking case where the same polyethylene was given different thermal treatments in processing. The use of DTA makes possible the detection of the different treatments and the curves show the number of different physical "species" present in the system. The curves in Fig. 4-18 were obtained on a Perkin-Elmer differential scanning calorimeter (DSC) which is a "quantitated DTA." In DTA, the sample is placed in one container, and an inert reference is placed in a second container. Both are heated simultaneously. The temperature of each will rise uniformly with no temperature difference between sample and reference until a physical or chemical change takes place in the sample. Changes either absorb heat (endothermal) or emit heat (exothermal). The recorder then registers the temperature difference between sample and reference. The number and magnitude of thermal events that occur and the temperatures at which they occur are characteristic of the material in question. The DSC operates like a DTA device except that, instead of just recording the temperature difference between sample and reference (as sample and reference vary in temperature), the DSC feeds in power to keep both sample and reference at the same temperature. By knowing the amount of applied power, the *quantity* of heat involved in the thermal event can be determined. The ability to quantitate makes possible the measurement of specific heats, heats of fusion and vaporization, and heats of reaction or decomposition. Though these data do not contribute much structural information, they are valuable physical constants and also can often be used to identify unknown species in a sample. For example, a heat of fusion of 80 cal/g usually means water.

* Perkin-Elmer Corp., Norwalk, Conn., has introduced this approach and supplies an instrument.

Table 4-2 Identification and structure determination—summary evaluation of available methods

Approach	Characterization problems*	General identification problems*	Complete identification and/or structure problems*		Destructive or nondestructive	Cost of equipment†	State of development
			Fingerprint type	Deductive type			
Chemical tests	Good	Fair to poor	Poor	Poor	D	Low	Past its prime and declining
Ultraviolet and visible absorption	Poor	Poor	Fair to poor	Poor	ND	Low to high	Developed
Infrared absorption	Good	Excellent	Very good	Fair	ND	Low to high	Developed
Mass spectrometry	Fair	Very good	Excellent	Excellent	D	High	Developed but still growing
Nuclear magnetic resonance	Fair	Excellent	Excellent	Excellent	ND	High	Developed but still growing
X-ray (single crystal) diffraction	Poor	Poor	Excellent (but difficult and not recommended)	Excellent	ND	High	Developed
X-ray diffraction (powder)	Poor	Poor	Excellent	Poor	ND	Moderate to high	Developed
Electron paramagnetic resonance	Poor	Poor	Poor	Poor	ND	High	Still developing

Table 4-2   Identification and structure determination—summary evaluation of available methods (continued)

Approach	Characterization problems*	General identification problems*	Complete identification and/or structure problems*		Destructive or nondestructive	Cost of equipment†	State of development
			Fingerprint type	Deductive type			
Raman spectroscopy	Poor	Fair	Fair	Fair	ND	High	Not new but still not optimally developed
Nuclear quadrupole‡ spectroscopy	Poor	Poor	Fair to poor	Fair to poor	ND	High	Rather new and undeveloped
Microwave spectroscopy	Poor	Poor	Fair to poor	Fair to poor	ND	High	Rather new and undeveloped
Mössbauer effect	Poor	Poor	Fair to poor	Fair to poor	ND	Moderate to high	Rather new and undeveloped
Optical rotatory dispersion	Poor	Poor	Fair to poor	Fair to poor	ND	Moderate to high	Developed but not widely used
Vacuum ultraviolet	Poor	Poor	Poor	Poor	ND	High	Developed but not widely used

* See pp. 95 and 96 for definition of each type of problem.
† Low denotes <$5,000; moderate denotes $5,000 to $15,000; high denotes >$15,000.
‡ Techniques are very new and need more development to determine applicability.

Suggested Readings

General Structure Determination

Freeman, S. K.: "Interpretive Spectroscopy," Reinhold Publishing Corporation, New York, 1965. (Text covering spectroscopic techniques as used in a coordinated manner for structure determination.)

Silverstein, R. M., and G. C. Bassler: "Spectrometric Identification of Organic Compounds," 2d ed., John Wiley & Sons, Inc., New York, 1967. (Introductory-level text.)

X-ray Diffraction

Klug, H. P., and L. E. Alexander: "X-ray Diffraction Procedures," John Wiley & Sons, Inc., New York, 1954.

Lipscomb, W. N.: Physical Methods, in A. Weissberger (ed.), "Technique of Organic Chemistry," 3d ed., vol. 1, pt. 11, Interscience Publishers (Division of John Wiley & Sons, Inc.), New York, 1960, pp. 1643–1736. (Comprehensive survey chapter.)

Lonsdale, K.: "Crystals and X-rays," D. Van Nostrand Company, Inc., Princeton, N.J., 1949.

Lonsdale, K. (ed.): "X-ray Crystallographic Technology," Hilger and Watts, Ltd., London, 1952.

Electron Paramagnetic Resonance Spectroscopy

Bard, A. J.: "Standard Methods of Chemical Analysis," 6th ed., vol. 3, pt. A, F. Welcher (ed.), D. Van Nostrand, Company Inc., Princeton, N.J., 1966, pp. 616–635. (Brief introduction to the subject.)

Bersohn, R.: "Determination of Organic Structures by Physical Methods," vol. 2, F. C. Nachod and W. D. Phillips (eds.), Academic Press Inc., New York, 1962, pp. 563–614. (Comprehensive survey.)

Blois, M. S., Jr.: "Free Radicals in Biological Systems," Academic Press Inc., New York, 1961, chaps. 2, 5, 8, 9, 19–21.

Drago, Russell S.: "Physical Methods in Inorganic Chemistry," Reinhold Publishing Corporation, New York, 1965, pp. 328–356. (Rather theoretical discussion of subject.)

Flett, M. St. C.: "Physical Aids to the Organic Chemist," American Elsevier Publishing Company of New York, 1962, pp. 224–254. (Good, not too theoretical survey chapter.)

Ingram, D. J. E.: "Free Radicals as Studied by ESR," Butterworth Scientific Publications, London, 1958.

Ingram, D. J. E.: "Spectroscopy at Radio and Microwave Frequencies," Butterworth Scientific Publications, London, 1955, chaps. 2–4.

Pake, G. E.: "Paramagnetic Resonance," W. A. Benjamin, Inc., New York, 1962, chaps. 1–3, 5, 8.

Varian Associates Staff: "NMR & EPR Spectroscopy," Pergamon Press, New York, 1960. (Collection of papers at Varian Workshop.)

Wertz, J. E.: Nuclear and Electron Spin Magnetic Resonance, *Chem. Rev.,* **55**:829 (1955).

Nuclear Quadrupole Spectroscopy

Drago, R. S.: "Physical Methods in Inorganic Chemistry," Reinhold Publishing Corporation, New York, 1965, pp. 315–323.

O'Konski, C. T.: "Determination of Organic Structures by Physical Methods," vol. 2, F. C. Nachod and W. D. Phillips (eds.), Academic Press Inc., New York, 1962, pp. 661–727.

Microwave Spectroscopy

Dailey, B. P.: "Physical Methods in Chemical Analysis," W. G. Berl (ed.), Academic Press Inc., New York, 1956, pp. 281–301.

Wilson, E. B., and D. R. Lide: "Determination of Organic Structures by Physical Methods," vol. 1, E. A. Braude and F. C. Nachod (eds.), Academic Press Inc., New York, 1955.

Optical Rotatory Dispersion

Crabbe, P.: "Optical Rotatory Dispersion and Circular Dichroism in Organic Chemistry," Holden-Day, San Francisco, Calif., 1965.

Djerrassi, C.: "Optical Rotatory Dispersion," McGraw-Hill Book Company, New York, 1960. (Detailed text.)

Lyle, G. G., and R. E. Lyle: "Determination of Organic Structures by Physical Methods," F. C. Nachod and W. D. Phillips (eds.), Academic Press Inc., New York, 1962, pp. 1–62. (Survey chapter.)

Thermal Methods

Wendlandt, W. W.: "Standard Methods of Chemical Analysis," vol. 3, pt. A, 6th ed., F. Welcher (ed.), D. Van Nostrand Company, Inc., Princeton, N.J., 1966, pp. 644–668. (Brief introduction to the subject.)

Wendlandt, W. W.: "Thermal Methods of Analysis," Interscience Publishers (Division of John Wiley & Sons, Inc.), New York, 1964. (Complete text.)

Mössbauer Effect

Fluck, E.: The Mössbauer Effect and Its Application in Chemistry, in H. J. Emeleus and A. G. Sharpe (eds.), "Advances in Inorganic Chemistry and Radio Chemistry," vol. 6, Academic Press Inc., New York, 1964.

Wertheim, G. K.: "Mössbauer Effect: Principles & Applications," Academic Press Inc., New York, 1964. (Detailed text.)

Wertheim, G. K., *Science,* **144**: 253–259 (1964). (Lucid, elementary survey.)

Nuclear Magnetic Resonance

Bible, R. H.: "Interpretation of NMR Spectra," Plenum Press, New York, 1965.

Flett, M. St. C.: "Physical Aids to the Organic Chemist," American Elsevier Publishing Company of New York, 1962.

Foster, H.: "Standard Methods of Chemical Analysis," vol. 3, pt. A, 6th ed., F. Welcher (ed.), D. Van Nostrand Company, Inc., Princeton, N.J., 1966, pp. 598–615. (Good brief introduction to subject.)

Jackman, L. M.: "Applications of Nuclear Magnetic Resonance Spectroscopy in Organic Chemistry," Pergamon Press, New York, 1959. (Comprehensive text.)

Pople, J. A., W. G. Schneider, and H. J. Bernstein: "High Resolution Nuclear Magnetic Resonance," McGraw-Hill Book Company, New York, 1959. (Comprehensive text.)

Silverstein, R. M., and G. C. Bassler: "Spectrometric Identification of Organic Compounds," 2d ed. John Wiley & Sons, Inc., New York, 1967. (Good introductory material.)

Varian Associates Staff: "NMR and EPR Spectroscopy," Pergamon Press, New York, 1960. (Descriptive material.)

Chemical Methods: See **Suggested Readings,** Chap. 3.

Mass Spectrometry: See **Suggested Readings,** Chap. 3.

Raman Spectroscopy: See **Suggested Readings,** Chap. 3.

Absorption Spectroscopy: See **Suggested Readings,** Chap. 3.

FIVE
MOLECULAR WEIGHT AND MOLECULAR WEIGHT DISTRIBUTION

MOLECULAR WEIGHT

Avogadro's law is one of the most important generalizations that have had the effect of making chemistry a systematic science. The idea that, when reduced to standard conditions of temperature and pressure, the same volumes of different gases have the same number of constituent particles, or molecules, has given meaning to the quantitative relations observed for gaseous reactions. To provide a definition of molecular weight, this idea can be expressed by the familiar equations □

$$n = \frac{W}{M} = \frac{PV}{RT}$$

or

$$M = \frac{WRT}{PV}$$

where n = number of moles
W = weight
M = molecular weight
P = pressure
V = volume
T = absolute temperature
R = gas constant

The values obtained in this manner are approximate. When it was seen that the results become more consistent as the pressure of the gas examined is lowered, it became apparent that the principle as formu-

□ Paragraphs in this chapter designated by the box have been reprinted in whole or in part, with the permission of the publishers, from R. V. Bonnar, M. Dimbat, and F. H. Stross, "Number Average Molecular Weights, Fundamentals and Determination," Interscience Publishers (Division of John Wiley & Sons, Inc.), 1958, pp. 1–15.

lated holds only under ideal conditions, thus leading to the concept of the perfect gas. Under nearly all real conditions, the departures from the perfect gas become so large that the resulting error cannot be tolerated in modern scientific practice. Nevertheless, in many cases, it has been possible to extrapolate observed behavior to ideal conditions; an example is found in the accuracy attained by the limiting density method for determining atomic weights.□

Analogously, it was established in systems involving solutions instead of gases that freezing-point lowering, boiling-point elevation, vapor-pressure lowering, generally, and osmotic pressure are, in the limit at infinite dilution, proportional to the number of molecules present. Molecular weight values obtained by the use of these principles were essential in establishing the stoichiometric relationships on which the laws of physical and organic chemistry rely.□

Departures from ideal behavior are caused by the normal physical interactions between molecules in simple systems; moreover, many substances show additional effects, such as hydrogen bonding, leading to association and dissociation. These departures are a factor in measurements on single-component systems (e.g., measurements of vapor densities) and on binary and multicomponent systems (solution-type methods). As a result of these effects, experimental measurements require correction by amounts that are functions of the concentration, in order to represent ideal conditions. It is often possible to make this correction by extrapolating to zero concentration results obtained at a series of finite concentrations. The values so obtained have served as a sound basis for evaluating industrial processes, for designing equipment, for interpreting chemical reactions, for classifying molecular types in hydrocarbon mixtures, and for many other purposes.□

USES FOR MOLECULAR WEIGHT DETERMINATIONS

Molecular weight determinations are useful for five general purposes:□

1. To establish the formula of a compound
2. To characterize fractions from separation processes
3. To determine the degree of polymerization
4. To determine relative amounts in a mixture of given homologs
5. To convert weight to molar concentrations

To establish the formula of a compound. The elemental analysis yields the proportions of the various kinds of atoms present (pages 39–40). The lowest proportion yielding integral numbers for all atoms present represents the empirical formula. The determined molecular weight will normally be equal to the rational weight or to an integral multiple thereof; from the latter, the formula of the compound is deduced. If the purity of the sample tested is known to be high, the accuracy required for the experimental molecular weight determination is only moderate; because the formula of the compound must have integral values for each constituent atom, no greater accuracy is required than is sufficient to determine the multiple of the rational weight that represents the molecular weight. However, high purity in the sample may not be obtainable, so that a high accuracy in the molecular weight determination is needed to account for the discrepancies between the elemental analysis and the determined molecular weight which arise from the impurities. In laboratory practice, the molecular weight may be the first clue to indicate that the sample tested does not have the composition expected from the preparative method used. □

To characterize fractions from separation processes. This use is especially important to the petroleum industry, which relies heavily on distillation methods for separating crude petroleum into useful components. In this industry, the use of molecular weights for description purposes has become nearly equivalent to the use of boiling points; in the higher-boiling fractions, for example heavy lubricating stocks and residues, molecular weights are probably more representative of the materials obtained than are boiling points. A special use of molecular weight characterization peculiar to the petroleum industry is the "n-d-M method" for calculating the relative amounts of the different hydrocarbon types present in a petroleum distillate [1]. Other industries that deal with naturally occurring products or with replacement or general synthesis reactions may well have similar applications in dealing with the composition of mixtures. A further example of the use of characterization by molecular weight determinations may be found in the study of polymer fractions. When dealing with wide-range polymers, it is sometimes useful to separate the material into a series of fractions having much shorter ranges and an ascending progression of molecular weights. The accuracy required in the characterization of these fractions depends upon the closeness of the neighbors in the polymer series that are separated by the fractionation. Where the fractionation procedure is effective for separating adjacent numbers of a series, the required accuracy of the molecular weight determination becomes high. □

To determine the degree of polymerization. In the preparation or manufacture of polymeric materials, the measurement of the extent to which the polymerization reaction has progressed is essential for process control purposes. Furthermore, in the case of high polymers, the engineering properties of the product and intermediates are frequently correlated with the molecular weight, which thus gives a useful basis for specification of the degree of polymerization. This concept may be extended into association polymers, such as soaps and detergents, where the size of the micelle is one of the factors leading to an understanding of the behavior of the material.□

The use of number-average methods is usually limited to molecular weights of 1,000 or below; however, ebullioscopic, vapor pressure, and osmotic pressure methods are continuing to find widespread use as range, accuracy, and instrumentation are improved. Currently, other methods, such as light-scattering techniques and gel permeation chromatography, are increasingly used.□

To determine relative amounts of homologs in a mixture. If the molecular weights of the components of a binary mixture are known, then, by determining the molecular weight of the mixture, the proportion of the two components can be found. This procedure is useful where it is not practicable to purify completely a reaction product, but where the principal impurity is known. The commonest example is in the separation of homologs by physical methods applied either directly or to derivatives made from the original reaction product. For this type of procedure, the accuracy of the molecular weight determination must be the best obtainable. Impurities or solvents of substantially lower molecular weight must be removed lest, even when present in small quantities, they cause serious errors.□

NUMBER-AVERAGE MOLECULAR WEIGHT METHODS

The following methods give number averages for the molecular weights of mixtures: cryoscopic, ebullioscopic, vapor-pressure lowering (isothermal), osmotic pressure, gas density, and end-group analysis.

Survey of the Cryoscopic Methods

The cryoscopic methods are based on the measurement of the depression of the freezing point of a solvent that occurs as a result of the addition of the sample. Cryoscopic methods use the following types of freezing-point measurement: warming curve, cooling curve, steady state, and equilibrium. In the first three methods, the measurements are made as follows: (1) the freezing point of the initial solvent is measured, (2) a known weight of sample is added, and (3) the freezing point of the solution is measured. Steps 2 and 3 are usually repeated several times with successive additions of sample substance to establish the dependence of the results upon concentration. In the case of equilibrium cryoscopic methods, the partially frozen system is carefully held at constant temperature, and the sample concentration in the liquid phase is determined by analysis. Since the cryoscopic methods are comparatively simple, they have been extensively developed, and may well be the methods that are most widely known. This is discussed in more detail on pages 246–251 where the freezing-point determination is discussed. □

The application of cryoscopic methods is advantageous if the samples to be measured are mixtures of volatile and nonvolatile components, or are unstable, reactive, or in some way hazardous to handle by other methods. Straight-run gasolines, Stoddard solvents, and the lighter kerosenes are examples of the first type which are best measured cryoscopically. Examples of the second type are olefinic or acetylenic compounds, acyl chlorides or acid anhydrides, and peroxides. For nearly all molecular types, solvents can be found that have freezing points at or below room temperatures; therefore, the use of cryoscopic procedures is widely applicable. □

Boiling-point elevation methods are less desirable since the boiling point is more difficult to measure than the freezing point (see page 252). Also, with mixtures, the sample fractionates on boiling, yielding inconsistent figures. Boiling also increases the instability of some compounds, causing breakdown during analysis. Three solvents, benzene, dioxane, and water, are suitable for by far the larger part of the organic compounds commonly encountered. However, control methods of reduced accuracy but higher convenience may utilize special solvents.

The general limitations of the cryoscopic method are discussed below.

Solubility of Sample

The sample must be soluble in the chosen solvent at and below the freezing point of the latter. This is the most restrictive limitation of the cryoscopic method. When a nearly pure sample is being measured, no further change in the freezing point occurs once the solubility limit of the sample is passed. When a mixture is being tested, the solubility limit for one component may be exceeded after one or two data points have been measured; this may result in large, undetected errors in the measurements. For this reason samples must be soluble to the extent of about 20% at a temperature within 1 to 2°C above the solvent freezing point.□

Solid Solutions

The sample must not form a solid solution with the chosen solvent. If it does, the molar depression of the freezing point will be too low. When the solubility of the sample is the same in the solid as in the liquid solvent, no freezing-point depression occurs on addition of sample, and the situation is easy to recognize. The freezing point may even be raised instead of lowered, if the sample is more soluble in the solid than in the liquid solvent. The situation is more difficult to recognize if the sample is only slightly soluble in the solid phase of the solvent, for instance to an extent of 5 to 10% of the amount present. The error in the freezing-point depression thus caused is small enough so that it may go undetected, but it will, nevertheless, give misleading results. The best practical method for excluding solid-solution effects, other than by tests on a known sample of the material to be analyzed, is the comparison of measurements obtained in two different solvents. Solid-solution formation should be considered possible (but by no means inevitable) when the molar volumes (molecular weights divided by the densities) of the solvent and sample differ from each other by a factor of less than 2; for such samples, measurements in a second solvent should be considered.□

Interference with Crystallization

The sample must not interfere with the crystallization of the chosen solvent. Various surface-active samples, for example the asphaltene and resin fractions from some petroleum sources, will interfere with crystallization rates. The effect of such interference is most serious for cryoscopic methods that depend on cooling the solution, i.e., the cooling-curve and steady-state methods. It then causes high and erratic freezing-point depressions. Interference with crystallization may also be detected by comparing cooling-curve or steady-state freezing-point depressions with warming curve results. It is not certain whether samples that interfere with crystallization also interfere with melting processes to any extent; accordingly, when interference with crystallization is noted, it may be best to abandon at least the particular solvent, if not the cryoscopic method, for the sample in question.□

Transitions in the Solid Solvent

The chosen solvent must not have a solid-solid phase transition within or near the range of freezing-point depressions to be measured. Should such a transition occur within the range of a measurement, the cryoscopic constant—the depression in freezing point per mole of sample—would undergo an apparent change as the freezing point dropped below the transition temperature.

Association of the Sample

Neither the sample nor any of its important components may associate in the solvent, nor may components of the sample react in the solvent to form complexes. Such behavior results in molecular weights that are too high. It may be difficult to distinguish between association and solid-solution effects, since both have similar effects on the molecular weight measurements. Examples of self-association are given by the phenols or the carboxylic acids in hydrocarbon solutions; an example of unwanted interaction is that between weak acids and tertiary amines in nonpolar solvents. Association behavior is best detected and corrected by comparing results obtained in a polar and in a nonpolar solvent, for instance in dioxane and in benzene.□

Magnitude of Molecular Weight

The molecular weight of the sample must not be too high. Increasing weight concentrations of sample substance must be used with increasing molecular weight in order to obtain the same freezing-point depressions, and we are dealing with increasingly imperfect solutions. Nevertheless, by utilizing highly sensitive thermometric devices and thermistors, cryoscopic measurements have been made on substances with molecular weights as high as 50,000, and these measurements have shown satisfactory agreement with others using different methods [3, 4]. Ordinarily, however, the best measurements involve molecular weights of up to 1,000, and not exceeding 3,000 by too much. Also, with these large sample additions, the effects of traces of low-molecular-weight contaminants, e.g., of solvent, become marked. On the other hand, should the difficulties of sample preparation or purification be overcome and solvents of sufficient solvent power be used, these working limits could be revised upward.□

Heat of Fusion of Solvent

A final practical limitation on the choice of solvents is that the heat of fusion of the solvent should not be too low. There exists a temptation to utilize solvents with a low heat of fusion and, consequently, a large freezing-point depression per mole of sample. However, the large freezing-point depression is offset by large random errors in the measurements, with little or no net gain in the accuracy of the molecular weight, since the stability, and hence, the precision, of the freezing-point measurements depend upon having an adequate heat of fusion for the solvent. □

Calculations

The calculations for the cryscopic methods are as follows [2]:

$$M_2 = K_F \frac{1,000 w_2}{\Delta T_F w_1}$$

where M_2 = molecular weight
K_F = freezing-point depression constant
w_2 = weight of solution
w_1 = weight of solvent
ΔT_F = lowering of freezing point

Further information is shown on pages 246–251. The derivation of this equation can be found on pages 632–636 of Ref. 2.

Survey of the Ebullioscopic Methods

In these methods, the elevation of the boiling point of a solvent, resulting from the addition of sample, is the quantity measured. A wide variety of ebullioscopic apparatus has been reported for this purpose (see suggested readings). The principal limitations of the ebullioscopic methods are discussed below.

Solubility and Stability

The sample must be soluble and chemically unreactive at the boiling point of the solvent. In general, the solubility of the sample can be determined by observing the behavior in the ebulliometer in which the boiling-point elevation is being measured. There are special cases where it may be better to make an independent test of the solubility before selection of the solvent. The first case can be exemplified by polymeric materials which dissolve slowly and then only in specific solvents. In such a case, the solubility of the sample should be tested by refluxing a few tenths of a gram of sample with about five volumes of solvent. The use of such a test avoids the long tie-up of an ebulliometer, with possible difficulty in cleaning the apparatus should the solubility prove insufficient. In practice, it may be found necessary to test as many as eight or ten solvents before finding one suitable for quantitative measurements. The second special case occurs with dark samples such as residues or still bottoms, where the dark color may conceal important deficiencies in solubility. □

In addition to being soluble, the sample must also be stable under the test conditions. Usually, the solubility of the sample must be tested and found adequate before the stability of the sample can be ascertained. In order to reach a final, steady temperature reading, the sample must not be changing in structure while the measurement is being made, which, for slowly soluble samples, may require the better part of a working day. Consequently, the more slowly the sample dissolves, the more important is its chemical stability; slow changes in composition can be masked by slowness in dissolving. For samples that are readily soluble, chemical instability can be detected by slow changes in the boiling-point elevation that continue past the time normally required to establish constant reading. Furthermore, since the rates of decomposition or polymerization reactions may depend on the sample concentration, the temperature drifts that indicate chemical instability may not be detected until after several changes of sample have been added to the ebulliometer. Usually, a mere change of solvent will not improve chemical stability sufficiently. A change to much lower temperatures, such as are obtainable with the cryoscopic methods, is required. □

Vapor Pressure of Solute

The sample must have a low vapor pressure at the boiling point of the solvent. If the sample contributes to the total vapor pressure of the solution, the boiling point of the solution, and hence the boiling-point elevation, will be lowered to an extent depending on the vapor pressure contribution of the sample. Traditionally, a difference in boiling points of sample and solvent of 150°C has been regarded as a proper requirement [5]. This rule is most conservative; samples of xylene can be determined in benzene solution, where the difference in boiling points is about 55°C, with satisfactory accuracy. A boiling-point difference of 100°C is surely adequate; if the difference in boiling points is smaller, it should be established experimentally whether or not the vapor pressure of the sample is sufficiently high to cause interference. In ebulliometers using highly sensitive thermometers, samples with high vapor pressures cause temperature instability. □

Minimum-boiling Mixtures

None of the samples may form minimum-boiling mixtures with the solvent. This is a much more limiting restriction than the vapor pressure requirement. For example, nearly all the common oxygenated solvents, such as alcohols or ketones, and some ethers, form minimum-boiling point with water, with the result that when water is present the boiling point of the solution is less than it should be. Boiling-point depressions instead of boiling-point elevations have been observed for some combinations of water content, molecular weight, and solvent. This anomaly in ebullioscopic measurements is analogous to the anomalous freezing-point elevation caused by certain solid solutions in the cryoscopic methods. In cases where the contaminating solvent cannot be removed from the sample, for example in samples of esterification polymers, where water removal methods might change the degree of polymerization, it has been possible to use as the ebullioscopic solvent an azeotrope having the contaminant as one component. The tetrahydrofuran-water azeotrope has been found useful for this purpose; however, the precision of the measurement is not quite as good as for a pure solvent. □

Magnitude of the Molecular Weight of the Sample

The molecular weight of the sample must not be too high. The limitations and reasoning considered for the cryoscopic methods apply also to the ebullioscopic methods; whereas recent advances in design and temperature measurement have extended the molal-weight level conveniently reached to about 20,000 [6, 7], the simple versions of ebullioscopic apparatus that are used for large-scale routine analysis are most reliable up to a level of about 3,000. □

Association of the Sample

As with the cryoscopic method, the sample must not form association complexes in the chosen solvent. In order to surmount this limitation, it may be necessary to utilize a variety of solvents. For example, benzene and cyclohexane, which are preferred solvents for hydrocarbon samples, are unsuitable for samples with hydrogen-bonding groups, e.g., phenols, carboxylic acids, amines, imines, or imidazoles. Polymer samples having molecular weights higher than 400 to 600 sometimes exhibit peculiar solubility characteristics. They will often be completely and ideally soluble in one solvent, but may be completely insoluble or form nonideal solutions in another solvent quite similar in structure or polarity. Ethanol, when adequate for dissolving the sample, is one of the most practical solvents for hydrogen-bonding samples. Benzene has proved to be a satisfactory solvent for ketones, esters, ethers, and their sulfur-containing analogs, as well as for most petroleum fractions, provided that no hydrogen-bonding compounds are present; many hydroxyl compounds have been measured satisfactorily in benzene solutions, but such successes are individual rather than typical. Toluene has proved to be useful for many petroleum fractions that dissolve in benzene with difficulty, but its use with petroleum residues is not universal; for residues from some crudes, it is a poorer solvent than benzene. For more polar compounds, 1,2-dichloroethane, ethanol, tetrahydrofuran and its water azeotrope, and, occasionally, methyl ethyl ketone have proved satisfactory.□

Calculations

Molecular weights by boiling-point elevation methods are calculated as follows:

$$M_2 = K_b \frac{1,000 w_2}{\Delta T_b w_1}$$

where M_2 = molecular weight of solute
$\quad\quad\ K_b$ = boiling-point elevation constant
$\quad\quad\ w_2$ = wt of solute
$\quad\quad\ w_1$ = wt of solvent
The derivation of this equation can be found on pp. 624–627 of Ref. 2.

Survey of the Vapor-pressure-lowering Methods

By vapor-pressure-lowering methods, we mean those in which the solution of the sample and either a portion of pure solvent or a reference solution are held at exactly the same temperature, and some function of the vapor pressure of the solvent is observed. Historically [8], this method was used to determine the activity of the solvents in solution, and it was directly compared with the pure solvent.□

These methods take three forms: (1) the direct comparison of the vapor pressures of solution and solvents [9], (2) the isopiestic method, in which the solvent is partitioned by evaporation between the sample and a known standard, and (3) the thermo-osmotic, or Hill-Baldes method [10], in which the evaporation rates of a standard and an unknown solution are compared through the raising of the sample temperature.□

The vapor-pressure-depression technique was not commonly used until relatively recently. The freezing-point-depression method enjoyed the greatest popularity and the boiling-point elevation was next. However, in the past few years a vapor-pressure device which utilizes the Hill-Baldes approach has been developed; it is very widely used and very simple to operate (manufactured by Hewlett-Packard, Avondale, Pa.). The device uses thermistors to record the differential cooling effect between pure solvent and solution. The sensitivity of the thermistors permits accurate, precise results and also permits sensitivity such that molecular weights as high as 10,000 to 50,000 can often be measured. Coleman Instruments also manufactures a similar instrument, claiming determinability of molecular weights up to 100,000.

Calculations

Molecular weight determination by vapor-pressure depression is based on the following equation:

$$\frac{p^0 - p}{p} = \frac{w_2}{M_2} \cdot \frac{M_1}{w_1}$$

where w_2 = weight of solute of molecular weight M_2
  w_1 = weight of solvent of molecular weight M_1
  p^0 = vapor pressure of pure solvent
  p = vapor pressure of solution

The derivation of the above equation can be found on pp. 615–618 of Ref. 2.

Survey of the Osmotic-pressure Methods

The scope of the osmotic-pressure methods, i.e., the methods that measure the hydrostatic pressure necessary to maintain isothermal equilibrium between a solution of the sample and the pure solvent, is limited for practical reasons to samples of macromolecules. A practical upper limit is 500,000, since in the neighborhood of this value, the osmotic pressure of solutions dilute enough to give interpretable results becomes too low to give a useful discrimination between samples. A lower limit is fixed by the nature of the membrane material used; all membrane materials permit the diffusion of the smaller sample molecules from the solution into the solvent, but the size of the smaller molecules thus diffusing depends on the type of material. Gel cellophane membranes have been used for samples having molecular weights in the range of 15,000 to 25,000. Recently, sintered Teflon and hydrolyzed polyvinyl acetate membranes have been reported usable for molecular weights as low as 1,500, and the Hepp osmometer even for sucrose, i.e., in the molecular weight range around 350.□

When dealing with macromolecules, the choice of a suitable solvent is much more specific than it is for ordinary low-molecular weight compounds. The sample must form a true solution with the solvent; the formation of a dilute gel instead of a true solution must be avoided. Often more ideal solutions are obtained by the use of solvents with less than maximum solvent power, provided true solutions are formed. One basis for choice of solvents, other things being equal, is their viscosity, since lower solvent viscosity reduces the time per determination.□

Temperature considerations also enter into the choice of solvent for osmotic-pressure measurements. It is desirable to measure osmotic pressures at the highest temperature that can be used without damage to the sample or membrane and at which the desired temperature control can be maintained. Since the usual osmometer has the physical construction of a very sensitive liquid-expansion thermometer, constancy of the temperature is important. Temperature constancy may be required for days. Consequently, it is desirable to select operating temperatures that are easily controlled. The solvents used should not be so volatile at the operating temperature as to cause errors in concentration or liquid levels over the period of time required for the tests; ordinarily, the solvents should have boiling points 50 to 60°C above the working temperature, if special precautions are not taken to minimize solvent losses.□

It should further be pointed out that solvents for osmotic-pressure measurements should be quite reproducible.□

Dynamic Osmometry

A dynamic osmometric measurement has also recently been adopted to determine molecular weight. This measures the change in pressure with time (device manufactured by Hewlett-Packard, Avondale, Pa.).

This approach is said, at this writing, to be very broadly applicable, and certainly is much faster than the equilibrium approach. The device is also said to be easy to manipulate.

Calculations

These calculations are for the static, equilibrium method only.

$$M_2 = \frac{w_2 R T}{\pi V}$$

where w_2 = weight of solute of molecular weight M_2
$\quad\quad \pi$ = osmotic pressure
$\quad\quad T$ = absolute temperature
$\quad\quad V$ = volume of solution
The derivation of this equation is shown on pages 659 to 664 of Ref. 2.

Survey of the Gas-density Methods

Gas-density measurements are perhaps the oldest form of molecular weight determination. The measurements may be the weight of a fixed volume of gas, the volume displaced by a known weight of sample, or the buoyant effect of the sample gas on an object of known volume. To determine the volume of the gas at standard conditions, the volume, temperature, and pressure of the gas must be observed. The following limitations apply.□

Volatility of Sample

The sample must be completely volatile at the temperature of measurement. Results accurate to within 1% have been obtained at temperatures as high as 207°C; attempts to work at higher temperatures have been less successful. Most of the more volatile compounds not otherwise unsuitable, if nearly pure, are measurable within this temperature limit. On the other hand, many samples of straight-run gasolines have enough higher-boiling material so that gas-density methods are not properly applicable.□

Temperature of Measurement

The sample must be a nearly perfect gas at the temperature of measurement. For most substances that are sufficiently volatile, this requirement is met if the end point of the sample boiling range is more than 25°C below the temperature of measurement. Some small gas imperfections may be tolerated when they can be corrected for by measurements at several pressures and extrapolation of the product of the pressure and volume per unit weight to zero pressure. As an example of substances restricted by this limitation, one may take the carboxylic acids, which are known to dimerize partially in the gas phase. □

Ethylen amine

Stability of Sample

The sample must not decompose or polymerize at or below the temperature of measurement. Such reactions give greater or smaller gas volumes than intended. A second, practical difficulty with such samples is that they present hazards to the apparatus, either through violence of reaction or formation of deposits that are difficult to remove. Gas-density methods should not be applied to samples that are likely to be even slightly unstable at the test temperature; common examples of structures that should be avoided or given special care are acetylenes, olefins, and ketones. □

For samples having molecular weights under 100, the gas-density method should be considered first, unless one of the above limitations is encountered. Many of the perfluoro compounds, examples of compounds of higher molecular weight, may also be measured by gas density. □

Calculations

The relationship between weight and gas density is as follows:

$$M = \frac{wRT}{PV}$$

where w is the weight of the gas of volume V (gas density) at pressure P and absolute temperature T. A discussion of this equation is given on pp. 300–303 of Ref. 2.

Survey of the Functional-group Methods (End-group Analysis)

Any chemical method that determines one and only one kind of atom or functional group can be used to determine the molecular weight of a sample in which every molecular species present has the same number of the atoms or functional groups to which the chemical method responds. This method has been used on polymer samples in which some particular chain-terminating groups are present or may be introduced, hence the name "end-group analysis." □

Some such polymers are the polyalkylene glycols, such as

$$HO(CH_2CH_2O)_xH$$

with a hydroxyl group on each end. Also the polyamide polymers

$$HOOC(CH_2)_x(\overset{\overset{\displaystyle O}{\|}}{C}NHCH_2)_yNH_2$$

with carboxyl groups and/or amino groups on the ends. Analysis of these groups readily yields the molecular weight.

Polyfunctional Impurities

Since the method requires that each molecular species have the same number of measured atoms or groups, the molecular weight calculated from the chemical analysis will be too low if extra atoms or groups are introduced into some molecular species, as by replacement reactions or chain branching. Other things being equal, the comparison of end-group and osmotic-pressure results on polymers might be used to evaluate branching of the polymer chain. □

Reactivity

Especially when functional groups are being measured, the higher members of a homologous series may be less reactive than the lower members, so that the larger molecules are only partially counted. In this event, the results of end-group methods will yield too high a molecular weight. □

Impurities

If nonreactive impurities are present, or if the measuring reaction is inhibited, end-group methods will yield too high a molecular weight. Similarly, impurities that consume the measuring reagent will give too low a result. □

All molecules must have the same terminal group. It must be known that the desired number of measurable atoms or groups are introduced into each molecular species formed. If the measured atom or group results from a chain-terminating process, no other chain-terminating process can be tolerated in the preparation of the sample to be measured. □

MASS SPECTROMETRY

A commonly used method for molecular weight determination, and one of the most accurate, is mass spectrometry (see pages 31–33; 100–102). In the mass spectrum of a material, there is often a peak which represents the parent molecule. The molecule has lost an electron in the bombardment and has become positively charged. The mass number of this peak then represents the molecular weight. In some cases, this molecule is so unstable that it fragments completely and no molecular ion is visible. Thus one cannot always take the largest mass peak and assume this to be the molecular ion.

A more certain approach to molecular weight using mass spectrometry is the effusion method. This technique depends on the rate of effusion through the small orifice (molecular leak) of the mass spectrometer. This rate is inversely proportional to the square root of the molecular weight (Graham's law). The orifice is first calibrated by measuring the rate of effusion of a material of known molecular weight. Calculations may be carried out by means of Eq. (1).

$$\frac{r_u}{r_k} = \frac{\sqrt{M_k}}{\sqrt{M_u}} \tag{1}$$

where M_k = molecular weight of known
$\quad\quad r_k$ = rate of effusion of known
$\quad\quad M_u$ = molecular weight of unknown
$\quad\quad r_u$ = rate of effusion of unknown

X-RAY DIFFRACTION

Since x-ray diffraction methods can yield the dimensions of a unit cell d, from the Bragg equation (I), the volume V of the unit cell can be determined. Single crystals of 0.1 to 1 mm are usually required. Having this volume and the density p of the material, the mass M of the material can be calculated [Eq. (II)]. Multiplying this mass by Avogadro's number N_0 yields the mass of the unit cell in molecular weight units.□ (See suggested readings.)

(I) $\quad nr = 2d \sin \theta$
(II) $\quad M = pVN_0$

where n = order of the spectrum
$\quad\quad r$ = wavelength of the x-rays
$\quad\quad \theta$ = angle of incidence of x-ray beam to capital plane

However, the actual molecular weight of a compound is not known until the number of molecules in the unit cell is known. The true molecular weight is then obtained by simple division. The most usual approach to the true molecular weight is to determine the approximate molecular weight by one of the cryoscopic or other methods. Then the proper integer becomes apparent, and the exact molecular weight is obtained.

The main limitation in molecular weight determination by x-ray is that the density value is not too easy to obtain on the single, small crystals used for x-ray work. Usually a density-gradient tube (pages 181–182) can be used, if suitable nonsolvents for the crystal are available. A pycnometer density measurement can be made (see page 181) on the solid if enough is available. The x-ray measurements, and hence the determination of unit cell size, can be carried out with linear measurements possible to ± 1 part in 20,000.

In view of the simpler molecular weight methods, the x-ray technique is not often used.

TYPES OF MOLECULAR WEIGHT VALUES FOR MIXTURES

Number-average molecular weight, $\bar{M}_n$, is obtained by adding the number of molecules of each species, each multiplied by its molecular weight, and dividing by the total number of molecules of each species [11].

$$\bar{M}_n = \frac{\sum_i N_i M_i}{\sum_i N_i}$$

where N_i = number of molecules of i and M_i = their molecular weight.

The boiling point, freezing point, vapor pressure, and osmotic pressure yield number-average molecular weight values.

Weight-average molecular weight, $\bar{M}_w$, is obtained by adding the product of the weight g_i and molecular weight (M_i) of each fraction and dividing by the total weight [11].

$$\bar{M}_w = \frac{\sum_i g_i M_i}{\sum_i g_i}$$

Light-scattering and ultracentrifugation methods yield weight-average molecular weight values.

Z-average molecular weight, $\bar{M}_z$, is defined as [11]:

$$M_z = \frac{\sum_i N_i M_i^3}{\sum_i N_i M_i^2}$$

This type of molecular weight is rarely used and is obtainable by ultracentrifugal techniques. So far, the different molecular weights can be compared as follows [11].

$$\bar{M}_n = \frac{\sum_i N_i M_i}{\sum_i N_i} \qquad \bar{M}_w = \frac{\sum_i N_i M_i^2}{\sum_i N_i M_i} \qquad \bar{M}_z = \frac{\sum_i N_i M_i^3}{\sum_i N_i M_i^2}$$

If a sample is completely homogeneous, then $\bar{M}_n = \bar{M}_w = \bar{M}_z$. If it is not homogeneous, then $\bar{M}_n < \bar{M}_w < \bar{M}_z$.

Viscosity-average molecular weight is that average molecular weight determined by measuring the intrinsic viscosity $[\eta]$. This is usually applied to polymers (See Ref. 11, pages 407 to 412).

$$[\eta] = KM^a$$

where K and a are constants for the particular solute in a particular solvent and at specific temperatures

ULTRACENTRIFUGATION

Equilibrium Sedimentation Method

In this approach, the solute molecules are caused to sediment by a centrifugal force (usually up to 10,000 g). However, Brownian motion and diffusion of the solute oppose the sedimentation and tend to keep the molecules dispersed. In the proper centrifugal field, an equilibrium between the two opposing forces is set up so that a continuum of solute concentration exists across the cell (see Fig. 5-1). In an ideal system, the molecular weight relationship can be written as follows: (See **Suggested Readings,** under *Ultracentrifugation;* Braude and Nachod, page 42.)

$$M = \frac{2RT \ln (C_2)/(C_1)}{(1 - \bar{v}p)w^2(X_2^2 - X_1^2)}$$

where C_1 and C_2 = respective solute concentrations at distances X_1 and X_2 from the axis of rotation
$\bar{v}$ = partial specific volume of solute
p = density of solution
w = angular velocity of rotation

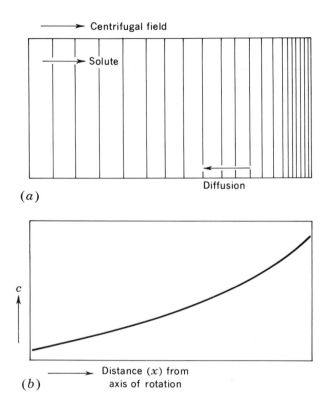

Fig. 5-1 *(a)* Opposing sedimentation and diffusion processes in the ultracentrifuge cell. *(b)* Distribution of solute concentration in sedimentation equilibrium (diagrammatic). [*Reprinted with permission from P. Johnson, "Determination of Organic Structures by Physical Methods," E. A. Braude and F. C. Nachod (eds.), Academic Press Inc., New York, 1955, p. 41.*]

With a mixture of molecular weights (a polydisperse system such as a polymer), the higher-molecular weight fractions will concentrate at the larger distances from the axis of rotation, provided that p for the solute is greater than p for the solvent. By choosing X_1 and X_2 so that they are at the extremities of the cell, the molecular weight obtained becomes the average molecular weight in polydisperse systems. If one chooses several values of X across the cell, increasing values of M will be obtained with increasing values of X. These values give some idea of the polydispersity (molecular weight distribution) of the system.

With this technique, molecular weights in the range of from 1,000 on up can be determined. Results have been reported for molecular weights less than 1,000 but these require specialized techniques. Best results are generally obtained for molecular weights above 5,000.

Dynamic Sedimentation Method

This technique involves the measurement of sedimentation velocity based on the fact that all solute particles of a given molecular weight in the solution move at the same velocity v in the direction of the centrifugal field. Thus, after time t, pure solvent is left near the surface and a boundary appears between solvent and solution. In Fig. 5-2, c is the concentration and x is the distance from the axis of rotation. If the system is a mixture of two monodisperse solutes, two boundaries (peaks) will appear as seen in Fig. 5-2. These boundaries will move through the cell at the velocity of sedimentation of each molecule in question.

The width and shape of each boundary are related to diffusion, which opposed the formation of a concentration-gradient boundary. Solutes whose components have similar but not exactly the same molecular weight will also cause broadening of the peaks, since the approach can only resolve boundaries with molecules whose sedimentation constants vary by more than about 15%.

In practice, the centrifugal field varies across the cell since each point x is at a different distance from the axis of rotation. The sedimentation of a given boundary is characterized by the sedimentation constant S, defined as the velocity of sedimentation under unit centrifugal field. (See **Suggested Readings,** under *Ultracentrifugation;* Braude and Nachod, page 47.)

$$S = \frac{dx}{dt} \frac{1}{w^2 x}$$

If a molecule sediments steadily through the solvent, uninfluenced by neighboring solute molecules, the centrifugal and frictional forces acting on it are mutually opposing and can be equated. The frictional forces can be assumed to be proportional to the linear velocity, dx/dt, through the solvent.

(I) $\dfrac{\text{Frictional force}}{\text{Molecule}} = f \dfrac{dx}{dt}$

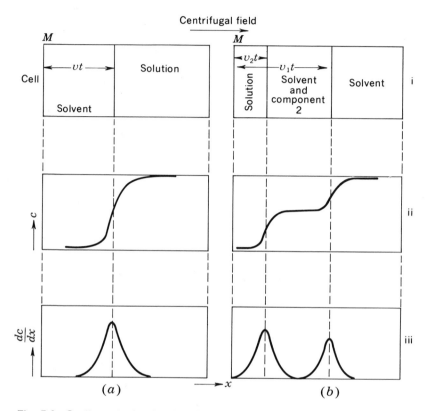

Fig. 5-2   Sedimentation in the ultracentrifuge cell: *(a)* Monodisperse solute. *(b)* Mixture of two monodisperse solutes. *(Reprinted with permission from P. Johnson, "Determination of Organic Structures by Physical Methods," E. A. Braude and F. C. Nachod (eds.), Academic Press Inc., New York, 1955, p. 46.)*

where f is the frictional constant per molecule. The centrifugal force per molecule is given by Eq. (II).

(II)   (Molecular volume) $\times$ (density difference between solute and solvent) $\times$ (centrifugal field)

$$= \left(\frac{M}{N \cdot p_{solute}} \right) \times (p_{solute} - p_{solvent}) \times (w^2 x)$$

$$= \frac{M}{N} (1 - \bar{v} p_{solvent}) w^2 x$$

where N is Avogadro's number and the other symbols are as defined on pages 159–161.

Equating (I) and (II) (omitting the subscript *solvent*)

(III) $M = \dfrac{Nf}{(1 - \bar{v}p)} \cdot \dfrac{dx/dt}{w^2 x} = \dfrac{FS}{(1 - \bar{v}p)}$

where F is the molar frictional constant. The frictional constant in sedimentation can be identified with that in diffusion. From diffusion theory. (See **Suggested Readings,** under *Ultracentrifugation;* Braude and Nachod, page 49.)

(IV) $F = \dfrac{RT}{D}$

where D is the diffusion constant. Finally, Eq. (V) is obtained.

(V) $M = \dfrac{RTS}{D(1 - \bar{v}p)}$

This is the fundamental equation used in determining molecular weight from sedimentation measurements. (See **Suggested Readings,** under *Ultracentrifugation;* Braude and Nachod, page 49.) The values for S and D must be determined under identical conditions of temperature and solvent viscosity. In the derivation of Eq. (V), it was assumed that solute molecules migrate independently without interaction. To achieve this condition as much as possible, the values for S and D are determined for low concentrations of solute and extrapolated to zero concentration.

The shape of the molecules affects the value of f. If the molecules of solute are spherical, Stokes' law can be applied and $f = 6\pi r \eta$ where η is the viscosity of the solvent and r is the radius of the spheres. Then F becomes

$6\pi N \eta \left(\dfrac{3M\bar{v}}{4\pi N}\right)^{\frac{1}{3}}$

and M can be calculated from Eq. (III) without using the diffusion term. With the dynamic sedimentation method, the limits of molecular weight measurement are about the same as for the equilibrium method.

LIGHT SCATTERING

If a light wave passes through a solid, liquid, or gas, it produces forced vibrations of the negative-charge clouds around and between the atoms. This causes the atoms to act as light sources, scattering light in directions different from the direction of the incident beam. The scattering of the primary wave can be interpreted at a certain turbidity τ of the medium. (See **Suggested Readings,** under *Light Scattering;* Mark and Tobolsky, page 54.)

$$\frac{I}{I_0} = e^{-\tau l}$$

where $I_0 =$ intensity of incident light
$\quad\quad I =$ intensity of light after it has passed through a length l of the scattering medium

According to the electrodynamics of Lord Rayleigh [12], the turbidity of an ideal gas containing n molecules of polarizability α is (see **Suggested Readings,** under *Light Scattering;* Mark and Tobolsky, page 54)

$$\tau = \frac{8\pi}{3}\left[\frac{2\pi}{\lambda}\right]^4 n\alpha^2$$

where λ is the wavelength of the scattered light.

Einstein and Raman showed that the turbidity of a solution varies with fluctuations of solute concentrations, and hence is related to osmotic pressure. Debye [13] utilized this effect to determine the molecular weight and shape of organic macromolecules.

He introduced van't Hoff's law for osmotic pressure and found that the turbidity of a solution, where the solute molecules are small compared to the wavelength of the scattered light, is connected with the molecular weight M_p of the solute of concentration c. (See **Suggested Readings,** under *Light Scattering;* Mark and Tobolsky, page 55.)

(I) $\quad \tau = HM_pc \quad$ where $\quad$ (II) $\quad H = \frac{32\pi^3}{3}\frac{\gamma^2 n^2}{\lambda^4}\frac{1}{N_{av}}$

$$\gamma = \frac{\partial n}{\partial c}$$

where $N_{av} =$ Avogadro's number
$\quad\quad n =$ reference index of the solvent
$\quad\quad c =$ solute concentration

In the case of macromolecules it is necessary to use a more complicated relationship between osmotic pressure and molecular weight

(III) $\quad \dfrac{Hc}{\tau} = \dfrac{1}{M_p} + \dfrac{2B}{RT}c$

where B is a characteristic value for a given solute-solvent system at a given temperature. (See **Suggested Readings,** under *Light Scattering;* Mark and Tobolsky, page 56.)

Equation (III) has been used to determine molecular weights of macromolecules, with fair agreement with other methods such as osmotic pressure and sedimentation.

Light scattering has been used to determine the molecular weights of mainly macromolecular materials. Though it has been reportedly used to determine molecular weights of about 200, it is most applicable in the molecular weight range from about 1,000 to about 5,000,000.

MOLECULAR WEIGHT DISTRIBUTION

We have seen above in the discussion of ultracentrifugation one technique for determining the molecular weight distribution of a mixture. However, there are techniques with higher resolving power to give better data concerning this distribution. By far the biggest use for molecular weight distribution data is in the area of vinyl and condensation polymers. However, there is some need in the area of hydrocarbon waxes and greases as well as natural polymers such as the celluloses, starches, and proteins. The techniques are diverse.

Gas Chromatography

This technique is an ideal one if the total mixture can be vaporized and put through a column. It is ideal in that separate peaks, each representing one component or one molecular weight, can be obtained. Success was obtained with this technique in the laboratory of the author on polyglycol ether samples. For example, detergents were examined consisting of an alkyl phenol onto which had been added ethylene oxide. Single, separate peaks were obtained for each adduct from 1 mole of ethylene oxide per mole of alkyl phenol to 8 moles of ethylene oxide per mole of phenol [14] (see Fig. 5-3). The CCl_4 peak represents solvent and the DBF peak an internal standard, dibutyl fumarate. Polypropylene glycols were also tested, and successful distributions were obtained up to molecular weights of 500 to 600, also with single peaks for each adduct. Figure 5-4 shows a chromatogram for polypropylene glycol whose average molecular weight is 630.

The necessity for volatility, of course, severely limits this approach.

Fractional Precipitation Methods

This is the oldest method for determination of molecular weight distribution. In this case, the material is dissolved in a solvent, and non-

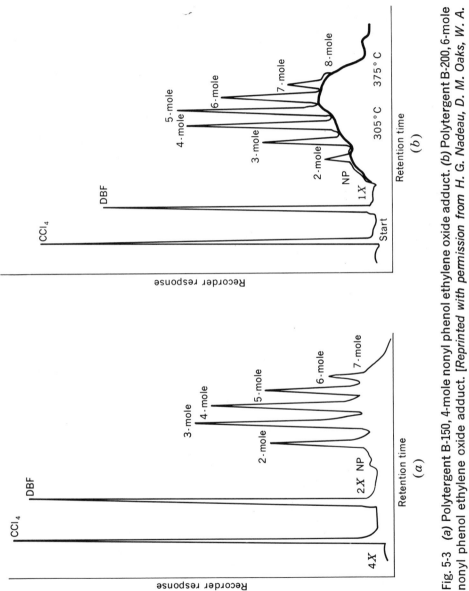

Fig. 5-3 (a) Polytergent B-150, 4-mole nonyl phenol ethylene oxide adduct. (b) Polytergent B-200, 6-mole nonyl phenol ethylene oxide adduct. [Reprinted with permission from H. G. Nadeau, D. M. Oaks, W. A. Nichols, and L. P. Carr, Anal. Chem., **36**:1915 (1964).]

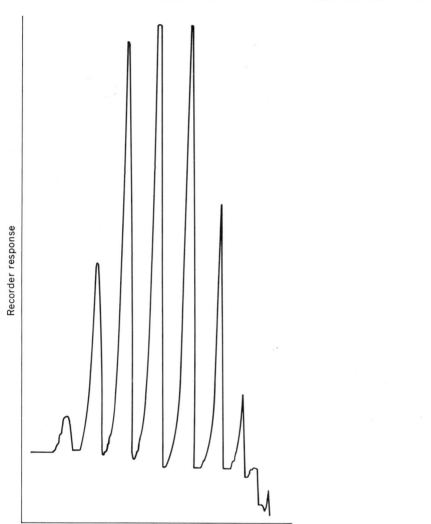

Retention time 1600X

Fig. 5-4   Gas chromatogram of polypropylene glycol.
(Courtesy of Olin Mathieson Chemical Corporation.)

solvent is added to the system to the point of incipient precipitation. Then further small increments of nonsolvent are added very slowly with as violent agitation as possible; a fraction will precipitate which usually represents the highest molecular weight portion. The non-solvent is added slowly and violent agitation is used to avoid localized high concentration of nonsolvent which would result in poor fractionation. The precipitated fraction is removed by filtration or centrifugation. To the filtrate is added another increment of nonsolvent, precipitating a second fraction. The process is repeated until as much of the sample has been precipitated as possible. Usually, the very low molecular weight material will remain in solution and must be isolated by evaporating the filtrate after the last precipitation.

Another fractional precipitation technique uses temperature to achieve the precipitation. In this case, the sample is dissolved in a solvent and the material is brought to incipient precipitation with a nonsolvent. Then the temperature of the system is changed, usually lowered, to force a fraction out of solution (a few polymers are less soluble in certain solvents at higher temperatures). The fraction is isolated as above and the temperature of the filtrate is changed further to precipitate out the second fraction. The process is repeated as above. This temperature precipitation method has the advantage that the temperature can be very gradually changed uniformly over the entire system. Generally, the flask containing the sample solution is immersed in a bath which is gradually cooled or heated. Thus, the precipitating conditions are distributed over the surface of the flask in contact with the solution. This achieves a slower precipitation than is generally possible by addition of a nonsolvent, where a drop of precipitant hits one spot of the solution. However, this more gradual precipitation results in higher resolution of the fractionation (cf. homogeneous precipitation). One operational drawback is that the filtration or centrifugation must be carried out rapidly, so that the temperature of the system does not substantially change during the process and upset the equilibrium.

Needless to say, the precipitation methods of fractionation are time-consuming because of all the manipulations. Also, the need to dry all the fractions and especially to evaporate the final filtrate to retrieve the most soluble fraction adds to the time. In addition, the precipitation achieves only a separation of fractions. A separate molecular weight analysis by one of the methods discussed in this chapter must be run on each of the fractions. The gas chromatographic method described above and the gel permeation method described below both fractionate and indicate the molecular weight of the fractions obtained. In addition, the precipitation methods generally lack precision and accuracy. However, in their prime such techniques were very widely applied, since they were the only diagnostic approaches available. They still remain among the best fractionation methods for preparing rather large quantities of fractionated species.

Gel Permeation Chromatography

Gel permeation chromatography is a relatively new technique whereby molecular aggregates, especially polymeric systems, are separated in accordance with their molecular size. The process is closely related to liquid-elution chromatography in that the sample is dissolved in a suitable solvent and the solution eluted through several feet of column packed with specific sorbtive media. The packing is normally polystyrene or related polymers which have undergone controlled polymerization to give a definite particle or "bead" size, and which also have been crosslinked so as to give the beads a microscopic grid or pore system. Through proper polymerization techniques, the grid dimensions can be controlled to give a desired size within narrow ranges. Pore diameters of 10 to 10^6 Å can be attained as desired.

Although the general theory is still in the formative stage, it is believed that as the sample molecular-aggregate solution is passed through the column by the eluting solvent (and since the "beads" exhibit a definite range of porosity), the smaller molecules will find a greater number of pores into which they can "permeate" whereas the larger molecules tend to "slip" over the smaller pores. This process allows the larger molecules to elute faster than the smaller molecules, which are retained due to the greater degree of "permeation," and therefore a concentration gradient is established as a function of molecular size. Since size is generally a direct function of molecular weight within a homologous series, a number-average molecular weight distribution is achieved.

As the eluting solvent leaves the partitioning column, it passes through a detection system, which is normally a differential refractometer. The refractive index of the polymer-eluant solution is compared to that of the pure eluant, the difference being translated into an electrical signal, which is in turn transmitted to a strip-chart recorder. The ordinate of the chart trace records the differential index of refraction which, if the index of refraction is assumed constant over the molecular weight range, then becomes a measure of the relative amount of polymer eluted at a particular time. The abscissa becomes the time axis and is often reported as a function of eluted solvent or "retention volume," since the separation technique is dependent on flow and eluted volume.

If proper standards are chosen, a calibration curve can be drawn relating retention volume to molecular size or molecular weight. The recorder trace normally does not show each molecular weight fraction as being resolved, but instead resembles a distribution curve (Fig. 5-5) which would approach gaussian shape for an ideal system. The distribution curve is then manually separated into segments equispaced along the abscissa, and a pseudo-integration is carried out by measuring the heights of the segments. If the heights are multiplied by the molecular weight of the segment as determined from the calibration curve, and the products summed, a cumulative mole percent (Fig. 5-6) for

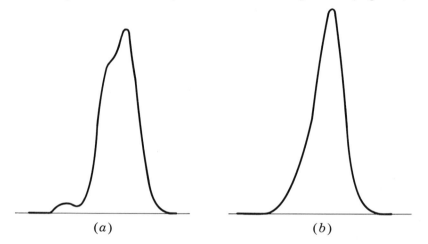

(a)   (b)

Fig. 5-5 Gel permeation chromatograms of polypropylene glycols; (a) shows multiple species present; (b) single specie present. (Permission of Olin Mathieson Chemical Corporation.)

each segment is obtained. Further calculation can yield number-average molecular weight, weight-average molecular weight, and molecular dispersion factors. It is well to note that polymer samples (a) and (b) in Fig. 5-5 were prepared in an identical manner yet performed differently in use. They are shown to have different distributions.

These molecular distribution factors represent data previously obtainable only by very tedious and time-consuming laboratory analysis. When properly utilized, the gel permeation technique allows the polymer chemist to add another dimension to molecular weight calculations. Whereas older instrumentation gave only bulk molecular weight figures, this new technique provides the molecular distribution in addition to average molecular weight.

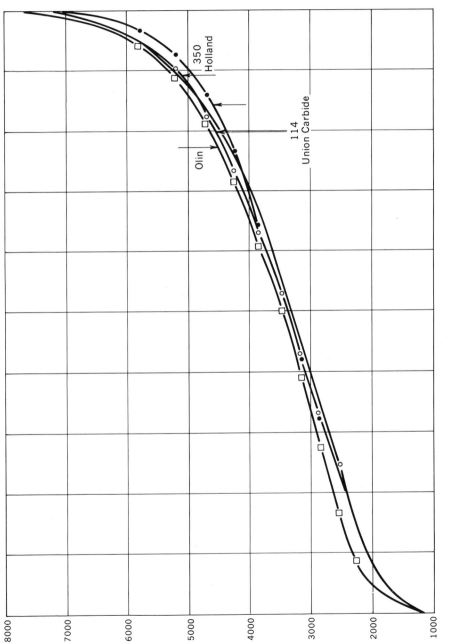

Fig. 5-6 Cumulative gel permeation plot. (*Permission of Olin Mathieson Chemical Corporation.*)

Table 5-1 Molecular weight—summary evaluation of available methods

Approach	Approximate general* applicability, mol wt range	Ease of determination	Cost of equipment†	Destructive or nondestructive	Remarks
Freezing point	Up to 1,000	Easy	Low	ND	Widely used
Ebulliometric	Up to 3,000	Easy to difficult	Low	ND	Rarely used; main problem is super-heating difficulties
Vapor pressure	Up to 10,000§	Easy	Low	ND	Widely used with modern instrumentation. Possibly the most widely used of colligative methods
Osmotic pressure	10,000 to 500,000	Moderate to difficult	Low to moderate	ND	New dynamic osmotic pressure instrumental method (see pp. 153–154) has greatly simplified this technique, and use of this instrumentation is growing rapidly
Gas density	Unlimited except by volatility of sample	Easy	Low	ND	Used widely for gases and low boiling liquids, also used as adjunct to gas chromatographs
End-group analysis	Unlimited except by sensitivity of chemical method for specific element or group	Easy	Generally low	D	Widely used
Mass spectrometry	Up to 500 to 6,000‡	Moderate	High	D	Widely used

Table 5-1 Molecular weight—summary evaluation of available methods (continued)

Approach	Approximate general* applicability, mol wt range	Ease of determination	Cost of equipment†	Destructive or nondestructive	Remarks
X-ray diffraction	Unlimited	Difficult	High	ND	Requires crystalline material; not widely used
Ultracentrifugation	2,000 and higher	Difficult	High	ND	Moderately used; used mainly in the biomedical area
Light scattering	1,000 to 5,000,000	Easy to difficult	Moderate to high	ND	Moderately used
Gas chromatography		Easy to moderate	Low to moderate	ND	Applicable to only completely volatile samples
Fractional precipitation		Easy to difficult	Low	ND	Widely used
Gel permeation chromatography		Easy to moderate	High	ND	Rather new but growing very rapidly

* These ranges are the *general* ranges. Isolated works report limits outside these approximate ranges.
† Low denotes <$5,000; moderate denotes $5,000 to $15,000; high denotes >$15,000.
‡ Depending on specific instrument used and volatility of compounds.
§ Newer devices are reporting 100,000, but data are too recent for validation.

Literature Cited

1 J. C. Vlugter, H. I. Waterman, and H. A. van Western, *J. Inst. Petrol. Technol.*, **18**:735 (1932).
2 S. Glasstone, "Textbook of Physical Chemistry," D. Van Nostrand Company, Inc., Princeton, N.J., 1940, p. 636.
3 K. G. Schon and G. V. Schulz, *Z. physik. Chem.*, **2**:197 (1954).
4 G. V. Schulz and H. Marzolph, *Z. Elektrochem.*, **58**:211 (1954).
5 B. J. Mair, *J. Res. Natl. Bur. Std.*, **14**:345 (1935).
6 N. H. Ray, *Trans. Faraday Soc.*, **48**:809 (1952).
7 K. G. Schon and G. V. Schulz, *A. Physik. Chem.*, **2**:197 (1954).
8 R. E. Gibson and L. H. Adams, *J. Am. Chem. Soc.*, **55**:2679 (1933).
9 I. E. Puddington, *Can. J. Res.*, **27B**:151 (1949).
10 A. P. Brady, H. Huff, and J. W. McBain, *J. Phys. & Colloid Chem.*, **55**:304 (1951).
11 C. Tanford, "Physical Chemistry of Macromolecules," John Wiley & Sons, Inc., New York, 1961, pp. 145–150.
12 Lord Rayleigh, *Phil. Mag.*, **1871**:41, 107, 274, 477.
13 P. Debye, *J. Applied Phys.*, **15**:338 (1944); *J. Phys. & Colloid Chem.*, **51**:18 (1947).
14 H. G. Nadeau, D. M. Oaks, W. A. Nichols, and L. P. Carr, *Anal. Chem.*, **36**:1915 (1964).

Suggested Readings

Cryoscopic, Ebullioscopic, Vapor Pressure, Osmotic Pressure, Gas Density, Functional End-group Methods

Bonnar, R. V., M. Dimbat, and F. H. Stross: "Number Average Molecular Weights, Fundamentals and Determination," Interscience Publishers (Division of John Wiley & Sons, Inc.), New York, 1958.

Mass Spectrometry

Beynon, J. H.: "Mass Spectrometry and Its Applications to Organic Chemistry," American Elsevier Publishing Company of New York, 1960, pp. 323–324. (Effusion methods only.)
Biemann, K.: "Mass Spectrometry: Organic Chemical Applications," McGraw-Hill Book Company, New York, 1962. (Parent mass methods for molecular weight, pp. 50–58; Effusion methods, pp. 173–176.)
Eden, M., B. G. Burr, and A. W. Pratt: *Anal. Chem.*, **23**:1735 (1951). (Effusion only.)

Light Scattering

Mark, H., and A. V. Tobolsky: "Physical Chemistry of High Polymeric Systems," 2d ed., Interscience Publishers (Division of John Wiley & Sons, Inc.), New York, 1950, pp. 54–62. (Short summary.)

Tanford, C.: "Physical Chemistry of Macromolecules," John Wiley & Sons, Inc., New York, 1961, pp. 275–316. (General survey.)

X-ray

Robertson, J. M.: "Determination of Organic Structures by Physical Methods," E. A. Braude and F. C. Nachod (eds.), Academic Press Inc., New York, 1955, pp. 468–469.

Ultracentrifugation

Braude, E. A., and F. C. Nachod: "Determination of Organic Structures by Physical Methods," Academic Press Inc., New York, 1955, pp. 41–59. (Summary article.)

Nichols, J. B., and E. D. Bailey: Physical Methods, in A. Weissberger (ed.), "Technique of Organic Chemistry," 3d ed., vol. 1, pt. A, Interscience Publishers (Division of John Wiley & Sons, Inc.), New York, 1960, pp. 1008–1136. (Detailed chapter.)

SIX

PHYSICAL
PROPERTIES

In chemistry, and especially in analysis, we tend to look upon matter as chemical, and thus the chemical properties occupy most of our thinking. However, knowledge of the physical properties of materials is needed in order to properly handle, produce, transport, treat, and use these materials. One of the biggest functions of an analytical department is to gather these physical-property data. These are used in all facets of the industry: research, development, production, and sales. Each section below outlines some of the applications of each type of physical-property data.

DENSITY

Density d is defined as the mass m per unit volume v of material at a specified temperature t

$$d^t = \frac{m}{v}$$

The value of density is often referred to the density of water at 4°C. The density of water at 4°C is 1.0000. In this case, therefore, $d^t = d_4{}^t$. This differentiates density from specific gravity, which is the mass m of a material per unit volume v at temperature t when compared to the mass m_w of an equal volume of water at the same temperature. Thus, specific gravity is $d_t{}^t$. Both density and specific gravity are used for the same purpose, namely to establish a weight to volume relationship.

There are two general purposes for obtaining density measurements; one is for calculating other parameters of the material under study. For example, the molecular weight can be determined from gas density. Also, the determination of molecular weights of crystalline solids by x-ray diffraction requires a value for density. In addition, the evaluations of molar refraction, parachor, surface tension, and dipole moments require density. Density is also a valuable parameter in the handling of materials. The size of plant and packaging equipment, for example, requires the knowledge of how much volume is associated with a given mass. Also, in practice, materials are often transferred by volume but react in certain weight relationships, so a density value is needed. The second purpose of density measurement is exemplified when density is used to analyze and monitor binary systems; the composition of radiator antifreeze is monitored this way, as are gas mixtures in the chemical industry. Since the manipulative techniques for measuring the densities of gases, liquids, and solids are somewhat different, each is discussed separately.

Gas-density Measurement

Gas densities can be used to calculate molecular weight using the ideal gas law

$$M = \frac{d}{p} RT$$

where M = molecular weight
d = density
p = pressure
R = gas constant
T = absolute temperature
This is a very convenient method, though the nonideality of most systems must be compensated for in most cases for optimum accuracy.

Gas density is also used to monitor binary gas mixtures.

1. The *variation in buoyancy* with density is one method of determining the density of gases. So-called gas-density balances are used for this determination. In these devices, a sealed bulb is suspended in the gas in question and buoyancy is measured by the amount of weight or force needed to counterbalance it. Laboratory gas-density balances are available [1]. Gas-density balances are also available for use directly in chemical processing equipment. These use the same basic principle of the sealed bulb in the gas, but have an automatic counterbalancing system that records the density directly onto a dial and/or recorder [3].

2. There are also gas-density balances [1] based on the fact that the *ratio of densities of two gases equals the inverse ratio of pressures* necessary to bring the balance to equilibrium.

The relationship between density and pressure just mentioned is also applied to process, on-stream densitometers [3, pp. 28–33]. In these cases, two rotary blowers are used on a common shaft, one blower acting on the sample and one on a reference gas (generally air). Both blowers rotate at the same speed but each will generate a pressure related to the density of the gas. In other on-stream devices [3, pp. 28–

33], the same principle is applied in reverse. The two rotary blowers are on different shafts. Sample gas is led onto one rotor and the reference gas onto the second rotor. Both gases are at atmospheric pressure. The incoming gases rotate the rotors to different extents depending on their densities.

3. *Flow through a capillary* is also used to monitor gas density. The rate of flow (or pressure drop across the capillary) is related to density. This technique is widely used in the gas-density detectors for gas chromatography (see pages 235 and 237). Here there are two capillaries, one for reference gas and one for the chromatographic eluent. When reference gas is passing through both capillaries, the net difference is zero. However, when a fraction is eluting and is in the sample stream, the balance will pick up the density difference.

Liquid-density Measurement

1. *Weighing a known volume* of a liquid is one of the common methods of determining its density. For fast results, though not optimal in accuracy, one can merely introduce a known volume of liquid via pipette or burette into a tared weighing bottle and weigh it. For nonvolatile liquids, densities good to three decimal places can be obtained. Of course, the density obtained is at ambient temperature. For the most accurate work, and to determine density at specific temperatures, constant-temperature baths and pycnometers are used. A pycnometer is merely a weighing vessel of calibrated volume, equipped for accurate volume-reading and constructed to eliminate or minimize evaporation. There are many types of pycnometers [1, pp. 148–154], some of which permit density determinations to $\pm 5 \times 10^{-6}$ units, but most of which measure to $\pm 2 \times 10^{-4}$ units.

The measurement is made by placing the liquid in the pycnometer. The pycnometer is then placed in the constant-temperature bath until temperature equilibrium has been attained. Then the volume is either read off the calibrations or automatically adjusted by the pycnometer itself. The pycnometer is then weighed. With this weight and the volume calibration of the pycnometer, the density can be calculated. Since the volume of the liquid is generally larger than the volume of the weights used in the mass determination, the buoyant effect of the air on the liquid must be taken into account.

Automatic pycnometers for continuous density measurement in process equipment are available [3, pp. 42–44]. In these devices, the pycnometer is a vessel of fixed volume through which the test liquid passes continuously. The vessel is suspended on a balance mechanism to record changes in weight. The liquid inlet and exit on the test vessel are spiral tubes, to permit the vessel to rise and fall with density and yet maintain a closed system.

2. *The buoyant effect* of the liquid can also be used to determine liquid density. The ordinary *hydrometer* utilizes this principle. In this case, a weighed, sealed glass plummet is floated in the liquid. It will sink down to a depth dependent on the buoyancy of the liquid, leaving its calibrated glass stem above the liquid. The level to which the plummet sinks is read off the glass stem. This reading is usually calibrated directly in density or specific-gravity units.

Automatic hydrometers exist for in-process density measurements [3, pp. 44–48]. In these cases the position of the plummet is indicated electrically. Inside the plummet a magnetic core is sealed. A differential transformer is arranged outside the test vessel. As the plummet rises and falls in the test vessel, it varies the length of the magnetic core between the coils of the transformer. This causes variation of output voltage with density.

The *Mohr-Westphal balance* utilizes the same buoyancy principle as the hydrometer, only in this case a sinker is allowed to be completely submerged in the liquid. The balance weighs the sinker in air and then in the liquid. The density is calculated by the equation

$$d = \frac{W_A - W_l}{V}$$

where
$$W_A = \text{weight in air}$$
$$W_l = \text{weight in liquid}$$
$$W_A - W_l = \text{mass of displaced liquid}$$
$$V = \text{volume of sinker and hence, volume of displaced liquid}$$

Automatic Mohr-Westphal-type balances also exist for process density measurement [3, pp. 40–42]. These are balances with two sinkers, one on each end of a balance arm. One sinker is immersed in a reference liquid and the other in the test liquid which is continuously flowing. The balance will shift position as the density changes; the shift can be read off a dial.

3. *Hydrostatic pressure* is also used to measure density [1, pp. 173–174]. Hydrostatic pressure is defined as hdg, where h is the height of liquid, d is its density, and g is the force due to gravity. The measurement is made by using a gas under known pressure emanating a tube calibrated in length. The tube is inserted in the liquid to the point

where bubbles just cease to come out. The depth of immersion of the tube is read and, knowing the gas pressure, the density of the liquid is calculated.

Automatic densitometers exist based on this principle also [3, pp. 35-37].

4. *Gamma-ray absorption* can be used for density measurements since the amount of radiation absorbed is a function of the density of the material through which it passes. This technique is used mainly for continuous, in-process measurement [3, pp. 48-52]. The gamma-ray source is located on one side of a pipe and the detector is located on the other side of the pipe. The variation in density of the liquid flowing between the source and the detector causes variation of the transmitted radiation.

Density Measurements on Solids

1. *Gamma-ray absorption* as described above for liquids is also used for solids as powders or slurries. The principle and operation are identical to those described above.

2. *Liquid displacement* is another technique used. This is very similar to the pycnometer method for liquids (page 179). In the case of solids, the solid is weighed in the pycnometer. Then liquid of known density is put into the pycnometer, and the whole is placed in a constant-temperature bath. A liquid should be used in which the solid is completely insoluble. When the volume has equilibrated and is determined, the pycnometer is weighed. The weight difference is due to the liquid added. Knowing the weight of liquid added and its density, the volume of added liquid V_l can be determined. Knowing the total volume of the pycnometer V_t, the volume of the solid V_s can be determined:

$$V_s = V_t - V_l$$

Then, knowing the weight of the solid, its density can be calculated. Of course, the buoyant effect of air should be taken into account, as in the case of liquids (page 179). Also, in the case of powders, care must be taken to displace trapped air, or the results will be greatly in error. Liquids of low surface tension should be used to "wet" all the particles, thus avoiding trapped air. In addition, by applying vacuum and/or ultrasonic external agitation, air pockets can usually be dislodged.

3. *Density-gradient* tubes can be used to measure the density of solids. These consist of tubes containing liquids of known density. In long tubes of these liquids, the density will vary from top to bottom

because of hydrostatic compression. The density at any height in the tube can be calculated. A solid sample dropped into these tubes will sink to a level where its density equals the density of the surrounding liquid. Of course, the solid must be completely insoluble in the liquid. This is a very rapid, simple, and effective method.

VISCOSITY

Liquids

Viscosity in a liquid may be considered as the resistance to any forces tending to induce differential motion between adjacent layers of the fluid [4, p. 691]. Viscosity data are useful in two ways: one is to enable calculation of other parameters such as the molecular weights of polymeric materials, rheological (flow) parameters, and sedimentation parameters. Secondly, viscosity is a widely applied physical property in the handling, treatment, manufacture, and use of chemical materials. The viscosity of a system dictates items such as diameter of pipe, size of agitator and power requirements for agitator drive, temperature of handling and shipping, type of production vessel, and shipping container. Viscosity is also used to monitor production parameters such as concentration of solute in solvent, degree of polymerization in polymer manufacture, and solid content of slurries.

It should be mentioned that there are two types of viscous flow behavior, Newtonian and non-Newtonian. A Newtonian fluid is one whose viscosity at a given temperature and pressure remains constant, regardless of the rate of shear applied or of other experimental conditions. All other liquids are non-Newtonian. Actually, most liquids are non-Newtonian, and one will get different viscosity values with different measuring techniques, even though the temperature and pressure are the same in every case. This means that there are factors in viscosimetric measurements which do not appear in the general equations cited below. For example, *turbulence* will affect flow along with viscosity; so will *thixotropy*, since it is defined as the change in viscosity with applied shear (e.g., some of our common household paints are thixotropic to prevent running. When they are stationary, they are almost gels. However, when brushed, the applied shear liquefies them, making them spread easily). The *wetting effect* of the liquid on different surfaces also will affect the viscosity as measured by different techniques. All in all, viscosity of bulk materials is a rather empirical measurement. The viscosity of dilute solutions, however, can often be kept closer to

Newtonian behavior, since solvents and concentrations can be chosen accordingly.

1. *Capillary flow* is one method for determining the viscosity of liquids. The liquid is placed in a U tube, one arm of which is a capillary. There are several designs of capillary viscometers; these can be found in Ref. 4, pages 702, 703, 722. The equation describing flow through a capillary is as follows:

$$\text{(I)} \quad \eta = \frac{\pi r^4 P t}{8V(l + nr)} - \frac{mpV}{8\pi(l + nr)t}$$

where η = absolute viscosity
$\quad r$ = radius of capillary
$\quad P$ = mean effective pressure drop through the capillary
$\quad V$ = volume of flow in time t
$\quad l$ = length of capillary
$\quad m, n$ = coefficients associated with flow at the ends of the capillary
$\quad p$ = absolute density of the liquid

This equation, known as the modified Poiseuille equation, is very unwieldy for most applications. To simplify the measurement, the viscosity of the unknown is compared to a material of known viscosity. In this manner, most of the terms of the equation cancel out and others become insignificant.

$$\text{(II)} \quad \frac{\eta_1}{\eta_2} = \frac{P_1 t_1}{P_2 t_2}$$

Since P is hydrostatic pressure and equals hdg (height, density, and force due to gravity), substitution in Eq. (II) results in Eq. (III).

$$\text{(III)} \quad \frac{\eta_1}{\eta_2} = \frac{hd_1 g t_1}{hd_2 g t_2} = \frac{d_1 t_1}{d_2 t_2}$$

The capillary method is by far the viscosimetric method most widely used in the laboratory. In on-stream process application, the capillary method is used, but the rotating cylinder approach described later is more popular. The U-tube approach is not practical in plant on-stream viscometry, because of the inability to automate it. However, a capillary is used through which liquid is forced at constant velocity. The pressure drop across the capillary is a measure of the viscosity [5, pp. 68–73].

2. *Drag on a rotating cylinder* is another viscosimetric approach. A rotating body in a liquid medium is slowed down by the viscous resistance of the liquid. The relationship of viscosity to the drag on rotation

is shown by the expression below, which describes the rotation at constant velocity of a cylinder relative to a coaxial stationary cylinder [4, pp. 705, 706].

$$G = 4\pi l \frac{a^2 b^2}{b^2 - a^2} \eta \Omega$$

where G = instrumental couple required to maintain the cylinder in motion

l = length of cylinders

a = radius of inner cylinder

b = radius of outer cylinder

Ω = angular velocity of the moving cylinder

η = viscosity

Though the expression derived is based on two cylinders, the manufactured viscometers of this type usually use only one cylinder. The viscosity is read directly from a dial, applying a factor for the specific rotating cylinder used (these viscometers use shapes other than cylinders for specific uses). In the laboratory this approach is not used to any great extent on materials of relatively low viscosities (1 to 1,000 cp). This is due to the fact that the capillary methods can be used in these cases and are generally more accurate and precise than the rotating-cylinder method. However, for more viscous materials, the rotating-cylinder method is preferred since these materials will not flow well through capillaries. The relatively poor accuracy and precision of the rotating-cylinder approach are due to several factors: the nature of the cylinder surface has to be the same from cylinder to cylinder; corrosion, dents, nonlinearity of shaft (yielding wobbly rotation) all alter the viscous effect on the cylinder. Also, the wetting properties of the fluid for the cylinder are a factor.

The rotating-cylinder approach enjoys popularity in on-stream, in-process analysis, however [5, pp. 58–61]. Even in these systems, it is used mainly in the more viscous media such as polymerization media, glue solutions, paint, starch solutions, and the like.

3. The *damping of the oscillations* of a vibrating probe is also used for viscosity measurements. The probe is made to oscillate by an electrical impulse. The rate of decay of the oscillation is a function of the viscosity of the medium. The effect can be compared to ringing a bell in a liquid; the ring dies away faster the more viscous the medium. Even though the mathematical theory behind this approach is not clearly defined, however, the approach is used to some degree, especially in on-stream, in-process analysis [5, pp. 53–57]. It is applied in polymeri-

zation systems, oil refining, manufacture of soaps, margarine, glues, and the like.

4. *The resistance to a falling body* exerted by the viscosity of a liquid is another measure of viscosity. In this case a sphere is used and Stokes' law applied [4, pp. 707–709].

$$W = 6\pi\eta r v$$

where W is the resistance to motion of a sphere of radius r moving at uniform velocity v. For the steady state under the action of gravity, the equation simplifies to

$$\eta = \frac{2}{9} r^2(\sigma - p) \frac{g}{v}$$

where σ and p = densities of sphere and liquid, respectively
g = force due to gravity
r = radius of sphere

As in the case of viscosity measurement with the rotating cylinder and vibrating probe, the theory here does not always hold up in practice, and the actual measurements, based on liquids of known viscosity, become somewhat empirical. The falling-ball method, however, does enjoy a fair amount of laboratory application, though generally only among the higher-viscosity media.

The falling-body approach is also used on a continuous, in-process basis, though in this case the falling body is generally not a sphere [5, pp. 61–68; 70–73]. In one case, the falling body is a piston which fits loosely in a cylinder. The piston is allowed to fall free into the cylinder containing the liquid. The time of fall is related to viscosity. In another approach, the body is not allowed to fall, but the fluid is moved up in a tube containing a solid body which tends to fall to the bottom. The upward velocity of fluid needed to maintain the body in one position is related to viscosity.

5. There are some special viscometers used for special cases of non-Newtonian viscosities in materials. For example, a *cone and plate viscometer* is used [4] to measure the viscosity of very viscous or even plastic fluid materials. This is really an application of the rotating-body approach. The fluid is placed between the cone and the plate, and the cone is rotated (the cone is actually almost a plate, having an angle of only a fraction of a degree).

Also, *consistency meters* exist for measuring the apparent viscosity of slurries. In this case, not only the viscosity of the liquid phase figures in the measurement; the particle size and shape of the solid and the solid content of the system also are involved. A "capillary" approach exists for this measurement, except that the "capillary" is usually rather wide-bore tubing [5, pp. 73–75]. The rotating-cylinder approach is also used for consistency measurements [5, pp. 60, 61]. Examples of materials in which these techniques are used to measure consistency are dispersions of flour, paper pulp, pigments, crystals; also food slurries such as catsup, tomato puree, applesauce, and baby foods.

Gases

Gases also exhibit viscosity. In these cases the viscosity arises from the transport of momentum between adjacent layers of gas [6]. Equation (II) shown on page 183 for the flow of liquids through capillaries simplifies for gases to

$$\frac{\eta_1}{\eta_2} = \frac{t_1}{t_2}$$

since the pressure drop for the two gases is kept constant. Hence, capillary flow is a simple, useful method for measuring gas viscosity. A gas viscometer is shown in Ref. 4.

REFRACTIVE INDEX

When light passes from one isotropic medium, m, to another, M, it undergoes a change in wave velocity ($V_m \to V_M$); and its direction also changes (Fig. 6-1), unless the ray is perpendicular (NL) to the boundary between m and M. The relation between the angle of incidence, i_m, and the angle of refraction, r_M, is expressed in Snell's law of refraction,

(I) $n' = \dfrac{\sin i_m}{\sin r_M}$

where n' is the refractive index of medium M relative to medium m, and is equal to V_m/V_M [7, p. 1140]. The refractive index as it is normally used is referred to air as medium m resulting in Eq. (II),

(II) $n = \dfrac{V_{air}}{V_M} = \dfrac{\sin i_{air}}{\sin r_M}$

It is seen that n is a dimensionless number. However, absolute refractive indexes are referred to vacuum. Refractive index is quite temperature-dependent and also depends on the wavelength of the light used; thus, in giving refractive-index figures, both these conditions need to be stated; for example, n_D^{15} for benzene is 1.5044. This means that the refractive index was measured at 15°C using sodium D light.

Refractive-index values are used for several reasons: (1) to take advantage of certain optical properties (opaqueness or transparency, birefringence), (2) as a parameter, to identify materials, (3) to determine the quantitative composition of binary mixtures, and (4) to calculate other parameters, such as molar refraction.

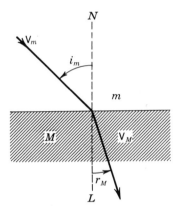

Fig. 6-1 Refraction of a light ray for isotropic media. [*Reprinted with permission from N. Bauer, K. Fajans, and S. Z. Lewin, Physical Methods, in A. Weissberger (ed.), "Technique of Organic Chemistry,"* 3d ed., vol. 1, pt. 2, *Interscience Publishers (Division of John Wiley & Sons, Inc.), New York,* 1960, p. 1141.]

Immersion Methods

The refractive index of a transparent solid can be easily determined by placing the solid in a known liquid of approximately the same refractive index as the solid and in which the solid does not dissolve. The system is then heated or cooled until the solid is no longer visible; at this point, the solid and liquid have the same refractive index. This index can be determined from a predetermined plot of refractive index versus temperature for the liquid.

The refractive index of liquids can be determined in the same way, but only transparent, insoluble solids of known refractive index are used.

Critical-angle Measurements

These measurements are those most commonly used for laboratory refractive index measurements. Both the Abbe and Pulfrich refractometers utilize this approach [7, p. 1232]. The relationship between critical angle and refractive index can be seen from Eq. (II) on page 186. At the critical angle, $r = 90°$, and since $\sin r = 1$, Eq. (II) becomes

$$n = \frac{\sin i}{1}$$

where angle i is now the critical angle.

These devices can be used with monochromatic or white light and by far outnumber all other types of refractometers.

Differential Refractometry

This method is based on the comparison of the refractive index of a known reference liquid with that of an unknown. In these cases, the light does not pass from air (or vacuum) into the sample, but from a liquid reference into the liquid sample. Thus, the angles of refraction are smaller and more accurately measured than the air-liquid refraction angles. Also, the reference and unknown can be more easily kept at the same conditions, making sensitive measurements possible. Where refractive indexes using the critical-angle measurements can seldom be obtained to better than $\pm 10^{-4}$ units, those by differential methods can be obtained to precisions of $\pm 10^{-5}$ to $\pm 10^{-6}$ units.

Differential refractometry is not often applied to general laboratory work, but it is used where accuracy and precision are needed. It is used as a detector in gel permeation chromatography where the eluent from a column is monitored (pages 169–170). The pure solvent acts as reference and the column eluent acts as the unknown. When just solvent is emerging from both, no signal is recorded, but as soon as a chromatographic fraction begins to appear in the column eluent, the refractometer detects the difference in refractive index.

Interference Refractometry

This type of measurement is basically a differential refractometric measurement, except that interference fringes are used to compare the refractive index of the reference liquid to that of the sample liquid. In this case, two intersecting light beams from the same source are made to produce a set of interference bands at the place of intersection. If the test substance of index n is placed in one beam and a reference material of equal length but of different index n_0 is placed in the other beam, a shift in the interference bands occurs. This shift is related to refractive index according to the expression

$$(n - n_0) = \frac{\lambda N}{L} \qquad [8, \text{ p. } 444]$$

where N = number of interference bands involved in the shift
λ = wavelength of light used
L = length of material traversed

Where differential refractometry as described above was sensitive to $\pm 10^{-6}$ units, interferometric-differential refractometry can extend to $\pm 10^{-7}$ to $\pm 10^{-8}$. These sensitivities permit the determination of the refractive indexes of gases [7, pp. 1274, 1275].

Image-displacement Method

This technique actually measures the angle of refraction as related to the angle of incidence (pages 186–187); displacement of the refracted ray at a fixed distance from the sample is measured, using a fixed angle of incidence. In these measurements, the sample itself is the prism (if solid) or is contained in a hollow prism (if liquid). The light is generated, passed through the prismatic sample, and the image is located with a telescope on a swivel that pivots about the sample; the displacement is thus measured. In the case of solids fabricated into prisms, refractive indexes good to 1×10^{-6} can be obtained.

Microscopic Methods

The *immersion method* described on page 187 can be used to determine the refractive index of liquids or solids, except that it can be done with small samples viewed under a microscope. One advantage of the microscopic method is that, with anisotropic solids which possess more than one refractive index, each refractive index can be obtained. This is accomplished by aligning the crystals so that one vibration plane is observed, and the refractive index in this direction is determined by the immersion method, using liquids of known refractive index. The crystal is then rotated to its other vibration planes and the process is repeated.

Image displacement is also used microscopically. A mark is scratched on a microscope slide and a compartment to hold liquid is constructed above this mark. Another mark is made on the slide outside the cell. The microscope is focused on the scratch outside the cell; then the slide is moved over, positioning the cell filled with liquid under the microscope. The scratch under the liquid will appear out of focus, and refocusing is necessary. The amount of refocusing is measured on the micrometer. The thickness of the cell (liquid) is measured. The refractive index is measured as follows [9, p. 376]:

$$n = \frac{\text{true measured thickness, } \Delta}{\text{apparent thickness}}$$

$$n = \frac{\Delta}{\Delta^- \text{displacement}}$$

Reference 9 is excellent for details on microscopic methods.

Continuous, On-stream Refractometry

Refractometry is used on-stream to monitor the composition of process streams. The *image-displacement method* employing the hollow prism (page 189) is used in some cases. The approach is amenable to measurements on viscous semitransparent materials such as inks and jellies. The fact that much light is absorbed is of no consequence as long as some light gets through. An ordinary 6-volt bulb is used, and monochromatic light is not needed. The optimum sensitivity attained is 10^{-5} units. The sample cell requires temperature control, often to $\pm 0.02°C$.

The *critical-angle measurement* is also used for on-stream measurements. In these cases, the emergent light is photoelectrically detected. A light beam is split into two beams, one which acts as reference and one which passes through the sample. The light is adjusted so that the intensities of the beams are equal, and each beam is interrupted to fall on a phototube in turn. If the refractive index of the liquid remains constant, the light intensity of each beam remains constant and no signal is generated. However, if the refractive index of the sample changes, the sample light beam will shift position and its intensity on the phototube will change. The phototube detects the difference that now exists between the two beams and converts it to an electric current. The current is amplified and operates a servomotor. This motor positions a mirror until both beams again record the same intensity. The positioning of the mirror is a measure of the refractive index.

Differential refractometers are also used directly in process lines. These are exactly as described on page 188, except that operation is automated. This type of refractometer has one advantage for in-plant use, and that is due to the fact that rigid temperature control is not generally needed, since the measurements are differential in type and both reference and sample are always close to the same temperature.

Reference 10 is a source for details on continuous, in-process refractometers.

VAPOR PRESSURE

Vapor pressure is not a very characteristic property of a chemical material, yet it is very important in the practices of the chemical profession. Many materials are distilled; the design of distillation columns and equipment is based on the vapor pressure–temperature relationships of the materials in the system. Also, the vapor pressure of a material governs its packaging for shipment; this is especially true of lower-boiling materials. The container, or tank car, must be constructed accordingly, and the degree to which it is filled is also dependent on the vapor pressure of the contents. Materials which are explosive require a full knowledge of vapor pressure to ensure that explosive limits are not reached.

The vapor-pressure measurement is nothing more than the measurement of the pressure attained with a material held at a given temperature. However, there are several techniques for measuring this pressure-temperature relationship.

The *isoteniscope* is one instrument for vapor-pressure measurement. This is simply a U-tube device which is shown in Fig. 6-2. The sample is held in bulb E; the U tube D contains a liquid in which the vapor is not soluble (usually mercury). The appendage C holds all the mercury to be used in D. The sample is distilled into E by submerging E in Dry Ice, liquid nitrogen, or other refrigerant while vapor is allowed to enter. When enough liquid is in E, the mercury from C is allowed to flow into D by tilting the apparatus. E is then heated to boiling while the system is kept under slight vacuum through A. A manometer is included in the system beyond A to measure the pressure therein. This expels air from the space between E and D. When no more air bubbles through the mercury, the apparatus is brought to the desired temperature, and air is allowed to enter through A until the levels of the mercury in the U tube are equal. The pressure of the system is read off the manometer. The boiling process may have to be repeated several times to ensure removal of all air from between E and D and also to remove any dissolved gases from the sample. Several consecutive readings are usually made; when the readings become constant, this is taken as the result [11, pp. 434–439]. Of course, the technique described above is applied to the determination of vapor pressures of pure materials. With impure materials, disproportionation of the sample occurs in E, with resulting continual change in vapor pressure as material is boiled off. However, the vapor pressure of a pure material is often required, and the isoteniscope approach is very simple to apply.

The *boiling-point method* is another vapor-pressure measuring technique. This approach depends on the fact that at the boiling point, the vapor pressure of the liquid equals the pressure exerted on the system. In this case the liquid is kept at the desired temperature, vacuum (or pressure) is applied until the liquid boils at equilibrium, and the pressure is read; or, conversely, a fixed pressure is applied to the system, the temperature is varied until equilibrium is achieved, and the temperature is read. Figure 6-3 shows a typical ebulliometric device. The main problem in ebulliometric measurements is the minimization of

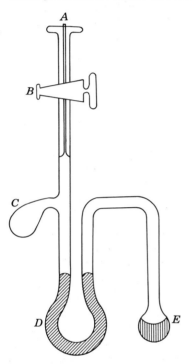

Fig. 6-2   Modified isoteniscope. [*Reprinted with permission from G. W. Thompson, Physical Methods, in A. Weissberger (ed.), "Technique of Organic Chemistry,"* 3d ed., vol. 1, pt. I, *Interscience Publishers (Division of John Wiley & Sons, Inc.), New York, 1959, p. 437.*]

superheating, since this causes temperature fluctuations. To accomplish this, boiling chips, sealed capillaries (see Fig. 6-3), and/or glass wool are placed in the liquid. Also, all liquids must be boiled or otherwise degassed for accurate measurement. This is usually accomplished by boiling the sample in the apparatus at the lowest pressure attainable. Then the pressures are gradually raised into the ranges of the desired measurements. It is well to note that boiling temperatures are all measured in the space above the liquid. This yields the best liquid-vapor equilibrium temperature with minimum effects from superheating [11, pp. 439–446].

A *gas-saturation method* also exists. This consists of efficiently bubbling a known volume of inert gas through the test liquid at the desired temperature. Saturation should be achieved. After saturation, the

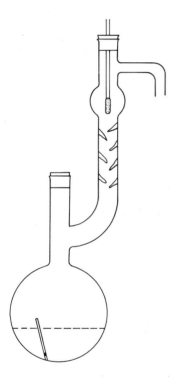

Fig. 6-3 Boiling-point apparatus. The exit tube is connected to a condenser, receiver, cold trap, manometer, surge tank, and manostat; heating unit and insulation are not shown. [*Reprinted with permission from G. W. Thomson, Physical Methods, in A. Weissberger (ed.), "Technique of Organic Chemistry," 3d ed., vol. 1, pt. I, Interscience Publishers (Division of John Wiley & Sons, Inc.), New York, 1959, p. 443.*]

amount of liquid evaporated is measured by collecting by efficient condensation, by chemical analysis, or by the decrease in weight of the saturator (bubble tower). The calculation, based on Dalton's law, is given in Eq. (I).

(I) $\dfrac{\text{Vol}_{\text{vapor}}}{\text{Vol}_{\text{gas+vapor}}} = \dfrac{\text{vapor pressure of material}}{\text{total pressure of gas + vapor pressure of liquid}}$

The volume of vapor is determined from the ideal gas laws, which relate the weight of material to volume of its vapor at specific conditions. The volume of gas is known, having been measured, and the pressure of the gas used in the saturator is known, since it is controlled (usually atmospheric pressure) [11, pp. 446–451].

There are several micromethods for the determination of vapor pressure. Most of these are scaled-down versions of the methods outlined above. However, some also exist for measuring vapor pressures in the low ranges, others exist for measuring the vapor pressures of metals by effusion. These methods are described in Ref. 11, pages 453 to 471.

FREEZING (MELTING) POINT

Freezing-point measurement is used for molecular weight determinations (pages 144–148). It is also used for assaying the purity of high-purity materials (pages 246–251) and for calculating heats of fusion (pages 202–203). It can also be used to determine the composition of binary systems much as density and refractive-index measurements are used; standard curves are made by freezing mixtures of known compositions. When an unknown mixture is frozen, its composition is determined from the curve. Of course, the freezing (melting) point is also required to know at what temperature the material is solid or liquid. This is needed so that manufacturing, storage, transportation, or packaging conditions can be adjusted for the desired state of the material. The freezing (melting) point is also used as a parameter in identifying materials.

The measurement of the freezing (melting) point can be determined simply with the Thiele apparatus shown in Fig. 6-4. The sample is placed in the capillary shown next to the thermometer D. The bath is heated electrically at E (a flame can also be used). The liquid on the heated side rises, with the stirrer also pitched to draw the liquid up. The stirrer makes the temperature throughout the liquid uniform as it passes by. The liquid then descends over the capillary and thermometer, transferring its heat to these. The sample is observed visually.

An electrically heated metal block can also be used where the sample is placed on a spot on the metal. A thermometer is contained in a hole drilled into the block. As the temperature is raised, the sample can be observed visually or with the aid of a magnifying glass or microscope.

The above techniques are good for melting points which can vary a degree or more. For more accurate freezing (melting) point determinations, more sensitive temperature-measuring devices are needed, and these are immersed in the sample itself. These techniques are discussed

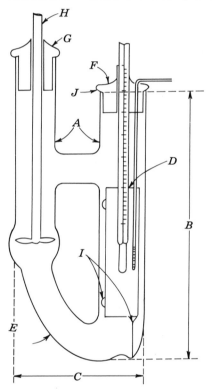

Fig. 6-4 Melting point apparatus— the Markley-Hershberg modification of the Thiele apparatus. [Reprinted with permission from E. L. Skau, J. C. Arthur, Jr., and H. Wakeham, Physical Methods, in A. Weissberger (ed.), "Technique of Organic Chemistry," 3d ed., vol. 1, pt. I, Interscience Publishers (Division of John Wiley & Sons, Inc.), New York, 1959, p. 322.]

in more detail on pages 246–251, where they are used to determine purity of materials via the change in freezing or melting temperatures.

BOILING POINT

The boiling point of a material is the temperature at which the vapor pressure of the material is equal to the pressure exerted on it. For example, the boiling point of a material in an open container is the temperature at which its vapor pressure equals the barometric pressure.

Boiling point, like freezing point, is used to calculate molecular weights (pages 148–151) and purity of materials (page 252). Its determination is also used to measure other parameters such as the heat of vaporization and vapor pressure (pages 191 and 193). Like the freezing point, the boiling point is used to determine the composition of binary systems, using boiling-point-versus-composition curves established with known mixtures. The boiling point of a material is also a characteristic parameter and is used to identify materials.

A typical ebulliometer is shown on page 193 (vapor pressure). There are several designs of ebulliometers; these can be found in Ref. 12, pages 369 to 381.

It is well to state that boiling points are much more difficult to determine than are freezing points. With freezing points, the temperature-measuring device is placed in the sample itself or in the medium in which the sample is. With boiling points, the temperature-measuring device cannot generally be placed in the liquid for the best measurements. This is because superheating causes erratic and/or erroneous values. If the temperature probe is placed in the vapor, good readings are obtained, but these measure the condensation temperature, which is the boiling temperature of the distilling portion of the material. However, if the sample is impure, the condensate has a composition different from that of the boiling liquid, and hence the condensation temperature will generally be lower. In fact, the difference between these two temperatures is an index of purity (see page 252).

SURFACE TENSION

This physical property is not generally required, except in certain fields where it then becomes a key property. The area of surface-active agents (detergents, soaps, emulsifiers, and the like) is one such field; in these cases, the degree of surface activity of the material is assessed by the surface tension of its solutions. These materials affect surface tension so greatly that this measurement is one of the best ways to measure the effectiveness of these agents. Also, surface tension is a good way to determine if waters contain these agents as impurities. In dealing with solid powders or porous solids, the penetration of liquids into these materials is governed by the surface tension of the liquid (among other factors); hence surface tension measurements aid in selection of the proper liquid.

Surface tension is defined [13, p. 306] as the force in the interface between a liquid and gas phase that opposes an extension of the surface. It is measured along a line perpendicular to the surface and is expressed in units of dynes per centimeter.

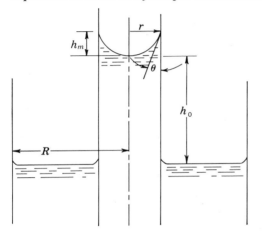

Fig. 6-5 Diagram for discussion of the capillary-rise method. [*Reprinted with permission from M. Dole, "Physical Methods in Chemical Analysis," vol. II, W. G. Berl (ed.), Academic Press Inc., New York, 1951, p. 308.*]

The *capillary-rise method* is one of the most popular methods for surface-tension measurement. Figure 6-5 illustrates the rise of a liquid in a capillary; the higher the surface tension of the liquid, the higher it will rise in the capillary. The force drawing the liquid up is as follows: a tension acting on the circumference of the capillary $2\pi r$ with a vertical component proportional to $\cos \theta$, where θ is the so-called contact angle. The contact angle is the angle between the capillary wall and a tangent to the meniscus at the point of contact. Since most liquids easily "wet" a clean glass capillary, θ is usually zero and can be eliminated; hence the force upward $= 2\pi r\gamma$, where γ is the surface tension. The force downward is due to the weight of the column of liquid which is $\pi r^2 hd$, where πr^2 is the volume of the cylinder of liquid and d is the density;

the force downward then becomes $\pi r^2 hdg$, where g is the force of gravity. At equilibrium, the force up equals the force down and

$$\gamma = \tfrac{1}{2} rhgd$$

This measurement is quite simple; however, the capillary must be scrupulously clean, or significant errors can be incurred. This is because, with an unclean capillary surface, the contact angle cannot be ignored in the equation. Also, the capillary rise is usually not great and is best

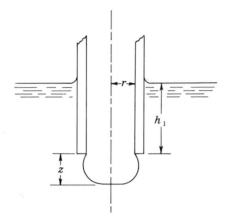

Fig. 6-6 Diagram for discussion of maximum-bubble-pressure method. [*Reprinted with permission from M. Dole, "Physical Methods in Chemical Analysis," vol. II, W. G. Berl (ed.), Academic Press Inc., New York, 1951, p. 317.*]

measured with a cathetometer, and the capillary radius is best determined by measuring the weight and length of a slug of mercury placed in the capillary. The density of the liquid can be measured by any of the methods given on pages 179–181. There are numerous capillary designs; Ref. 13 is a good source for descriptions of these.

The *maximum-bubble-pressure* method is another method for measuring surface tension. Figure 6-6 illustrates the approach. It is based on the pressure required to form a bubble of gas in the liquid whose surface tension is desired. As pressure is applied to the capillary, the pressure will increase as a bubble forms. A maximum pressure is reached beyond which the pressure drops while the bubble continues to expand. At maximum pressure, the bubble is assumed to be hemispherical, the contact angle is zero, and the total pressure in the capillary is given by the equation

$$P_{total} = \frac{2\gamma}{r} + gh_l(d_l - d_v)$$

where γ = surface tension
$\quad\quad r$ = capillary radius
$\quad\quad h_l$ = depth of immersion of the capillary
$\quad\quad g$ = gravitational force
$\quad\quad d_l, d_v$ = densities of liquid and vapor, respectively

The maximum-bubble-pressure method is a popular one and is usable in systems where other techniques are difficult to employ. For example, molten phosphorus or other corrosive liquids, and molten alloys or metals, can be measured in this way [13, p. 317].

Another surface-tension-measuring technique is the *drop-weight method;* as the name implies, this measurement is based on the maximum weight of a drop. The surface tension relationship is as follows:

$$\gamma = \frac{mgF}{r}$$

where m = drop weight
$\quad\quad r$ = radius of the capillary from which the drop falls
$\quad\quad F$ = constant factor for the material in question

The F factor is related to the ratio $r/V^{1/3}$, where V is the volume of the drop. From the density of the liquid and the weight of one drop, V and thus $V^{1/3}$ can be calculated. F factors can be found in the literature or determined with liquids of known surface tension, and then substituted in the above equation after the drop weights have been determined. The drop weight is measured by weighing multiple drops and dividing by the number of drops. Of course, weight losses by evaporation must be avoided.

The drop-weight method is not widely used for surface tension, though it is used to some degree to measure interfacial tensions.

The *pendant-drop method* is a rarely used one since the instrumentation is rather complex. This approach studies a hanging drop by magnifying it and measuring the relationship of the diameter at its equator to the diameter at another plane (i.e., the narrowest diameter). This approach also utilizes factors which must be obtainable in the literature or by separate surface tension measurements.

The *ring methods* are possibly the most popular methods, since equipment is available from instrument supply houses and the measurements are easy to perform. This approach involves the force required to rupture the air-to-liquid interface. If a wire ring were raised through the surface of a liquid (see Fig. 6-7), the ring would support a hollow cylinder of liquid. At the point that the film is broken, the force on the ring would be

$$mg = 4\pi R\gamma \qquad \text{or} \qquad \gamma = \frac{mg}{4\pi R}$$

It has been found, however, that if one takes rings of different dimensions r and R (see Fig. 6-7), the weight of supporting liquid is greater than would be predicted by the above equation. Hence, correction

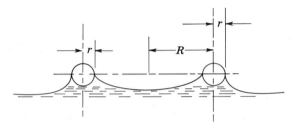

Fig. 6-7 Schematic diagram of the ring method. [Reprinted with permission from M. Dole, "Physical Methods in Chemical Analysis," vol. II, W. G. Berl (ed.), Academic Press Inc., New York, 1951, p. 326.]

factors are required after having measured the r and R dimensions of the ring. The purchased instruments, such as that in Fig. 6-8, have tables of such factors (F). True surface tension thus becomes

$$\gamma = \frac{mg}{4\pi R} F$$

The devices used in this approach are essentially balances; that shown in Fig. 6-8 is a torsion balance. A known weight is placed where the ring is (no liquid), and torsion is applied to the wire until balance is achieved. The readings on the dial are thus related to mass. The ring is then thoroughly cleaned and flamed, and the pull of the film is measured by the applied torsion of the wire. This is the m term of the equation.

Miscellaneous other methods [14, pp. 809–810] for surface tension measurement also exist. One of these depends on the *sensile drop*, or measurement of the shape of a drop of the test liquid on a plate (or of the shape of bubbles under a plate immersed in the liquid). Another method depends on the *pull on a vertical plate* as measured by a balance, as in the ring method described above. *Surface potential* measure-

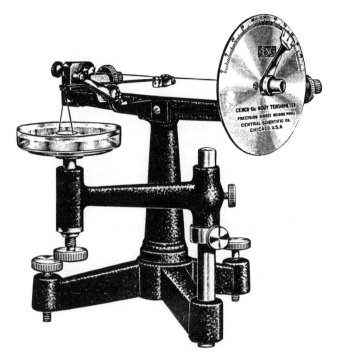

Fig. 6-8 *Cenco Du Noüy tensiometer. [Central Scientific Co. Reprinted with permission from M. Dole, "Physical Methods in Chemical Analysis," vol. II, W. G. Berl (ed.), Academic Press Inc., New York, 1951, p. 326.]*

ments have also been used, as has the *spreading of oil films* in aqueous systems. The *velocity of propagation* of ripples on a surface is used in still another method.

INTERFACIAL TENSION

This parameter is measured in a manner analogous to those mentioned above for surface tension, with slightly modified computations, since the interface is between two liquids. Since this measurement is rarely required, the reader is referred to either of the suggested references [13, 14] for details.

MISCELLANEOUS PHYSICAL PROPERTIES

There are other physical properties which can be measured, but these are required so seldom that a discussion in a book of this type is not warranted. However, a mention for the sake of completeness is in order.

Electrical Properties

Electrical properties such as *conductivity (resistivity)* and *capacitance* are occasionally required. One application of conductivity for determining purity of materials is shown on pages 256–257. Conductivity is also used to monitor small amounts of acids, bases, salts or other ionic media in aqueous solutions. Capacitance is occasionally used to monitor binary mixtures in which each component has a capacitance quite different from that of the other. For example, mixtures of 2,4-toluene diisocyanate and 2,6-toluene diisocyanate are monitored in this way, as is the amount of acetic acid in acetic anhydride; also monitored in this way are small amounts of water (high dielectric constant) in organic media (low dielectric constant).

Both conductivity and capacitance find a fairly wide application in continuous, in-process, automatic analysis [15].

Of course, in the manufacture of materials used in electric components, the measurement of these electrical physical properties becomes of importance.

Thermal Properties

Thermal properties also are occasionally measured, such as *specific heat, thermal conductivity, heat of fusion, heat of vaporization*, and *heat of reaction. Specific heat* is measured calorimetrically, one example appearing on page 134. This value is needed for some thermodynamic calculations. Also, this value is needed to determine how much heat must be put into or taken out of a system in order to transfer it from one temperature level to another.

Thermal conductivity is most commonly used to analyze binary mixtures in which one component has a different thermal conductivity from the other. The application of thermal conductivity to gas chromatography to monitor column effluents is in this category. However, direct analysis of mixtures is also accomplished by this method [16]. Mixtures of hydrogen and nitrogen in ammonia synthesis are monitored in this way since the hydrogen has a much higher thermal conductivity than the nitrogen. Mixtures of oxygen and ethylene oxide also are analyzed in this way.

Heat of fusion can be determined by calorimetry (see page 134) or by measuring the change in melting (freezing) point with pressure, using the Clapeyron-Clausius equation [17]:

$$\log \frac{P_2}{P_1} = \frac{L_F(T_2 - T_1)}{2.303RT_2T_1}$$

where L_F = heat of fusion

         T_1, T_2 = melting points at pressures P_1 and P_2

Heat of fusion has applications in determining the heat (or refrigeration) requirements to convert an amount of material from solid to liquid or vice versa. This is often needed in production and shipping, where material is bought, sold, or shipped in one physical state and used in another. Heat of fusion also has some value in identification of materials.

Heat of vaporization can be determined by measuring the vapor pressure (pages 190–194) at two temperatures and then applying a corollary of the Clapeyron-Clausius equation shown above

$$\log \frac{P_2}{P_1} = \frac{L_v(T_2 - T_1)}{2.303RT_2T_1}$$

where L_v = heat of vaporization

      P_1 and P_2 = vapor pressures at temperatures T_1 and T_2

              R = gas constant

This value can be determined calorimetrically, one method being shown on page 134. The heat of vaporization is often required in production, so that the heat (or refrigeration) required to evaporate or condense (i.e., distillation) the materials under study will be known.

Heat of reaction is often needed for calculations to elucidate reaction mechanisms. This value is measured by means of calorimeters.

Magnetic Properties

Magnetic susceptibility is a property measured to determine the magnetic properties of materials (paramagnetic or diamagnetic). This can be measured with a balance from which the sample is suspended in a magnetic field of known strength. The difference in "weight" when the magnetic field is on and off quantitates the magnetic effect. These measurements are used to determine molecular configurations of certain organic, metallo-organic, and coordination compounds [18].

pH and pK

The reader may question whether pH and pK are physical properties. However, since no chemical reactions are involved, the author has chosen to call them physical properties.

pH

The pH of a material or, rather, of a solution of a material, is often required since acidity and basicity often control or affect most properties of chemical materials such as reactivity, stability, performance, appearance, fluidity, etc. The pH can be said to be one of the most commonly measured parameters in the chemical laboratory. By definition it applies only to aqueous solutions, since it is based on the dissociation constant of water as 10^{-14}. However, in actual practice, "pH values" are determined in nonaqueous solvents as well. These nonaqueous "pH values" can only be classed as "apparent pH" and have no real basis; however, they are useful nonetheless because they generally do qualitatively relate to acidity and basicity. Also, they are reproducible values, and hence can be used to control a product.

pH is an expression of the degree of acidity or alkalinity of an aqueous solution of a material. It was proposed by Sörensen [19] and is based on the ion product for water $[H^+] \times [OH^-] = 10^{-14}$ at 20°C. Since 10^{-14} is a constant (K_w), it can be used as the basis of an acidity measurement. Expressing acidity as hydrogen-ion concentration, $[H^+]$, is cumbersome since the value is so small. Sörensen proposed the logarithmic expression for convenience. The logarithm was made negative so that we could deal with positive values. Hence

$$pH = -\log [H^+]$$

As is obvious from the above discussion, we can also speak of pOH where

$$pOH = -\log [OH^-]$$

Actually pH and pOH are tied together by the constant K_w; from $[H^+] \times [OH^-] = 10^{-14}$, it becomes obvious that

$$pH + pOH = 14$$

Hence, the division of the pH scale into 14 units is clear, and the dependency on the aqueous system is apparent.

The measurement of pH is taken as a routine thing, and familiarity has made us often too complacent. A *good* pH value requires care in its determination. (1) The quality of the water used for the solution must be good. Pure water must have a pH of 7.00 at 20°. However, in practice, even distilled water seldom meets this requirement. Dissolved carbon dioxide lowers the pH, and dissolved ammonia (from organic contamination) raises the pH. Distillation alone does not always rectify this condition, unless other steps are also taken, such as deionization or purge of the distilling system with nitrogen. (2) The condition of the electrodes of a pH meter is important. The electrodes often are affected by use, for example, and may have adsorbed or absorbed impurities, etched surfaces, or corroded connections. (3) Temperature should not be taken for granted for precise and accurate pH values. Proper temperature corrections should be applied. (4) It should also be remembered that most pH electrodes have an optimum range of operation. Outside these limits, corrections must be applied, and at certain pH limits the electrodes may have little utility at all for accurate work. (5) One should also be on guard against spurious effects. An improperly grounded pH meter can give irreproducible values. Other electrodes with the pH electrodes in the solution being tested will very often cause erroneous and irreproducible pH values.

The above may seem like an inconsequential discussion, but anyone who has had to control a material, a process, or a reaction within narrow pH limits knows the difficulties involved in measuring pH to ± 0.02 units. In addition, the sensitivity of some systems to pH has necessitated determination of pH values to ± 0.005 or even 0.002 units. There are now pH meters to achieve this, but the possible complications above become more pronounced at these sensitivities.

The reader is referred to the suggested readings for different methods of pH measurement and for a more detailed discussion.

pK

The pK value refers to the degree of dissociation of an acid (pK_a) or a base (pK_b). As in the case of pH, the negative logarithm approach is used for convenience of expression. The dissociation constant is expressed as

$$
(I) \quad
\begin{aligned}
HA &\rightleftharpoons H^+ + A^- & XOH &\rightleftharpoons X^+ + OH^- \\
K_a &= \frac{[H^+][A^-]}{[HA]} & K_b &= \frac{[X^+][OH^-]}{[XOH]}
\end{aligned}
$$

Though the values of pK are not of such general interest as those of pH, they have a very distinct utility. The pK will indicate the basicity or acidity (pH) to be expected when the material is dissolved in water. In material control for example, since a certain pH is required for optimum reaction, appearance, fluidity, stability, etc., the proper acid or base can be selected from a knowledge of the pK_a or pK_b of existing materials.

A knowledge of the pK of different acids or bases present in mixtures can foretell whether it would be possible to discriminate between the components by a potentiometric or indicator titration. Proper solvents, titrants, and indicators (or electrodes) can be selected to accomplish the desired task.

In addition, pK values give leads as to the type of acid or base present in an unknown system. Table 6-1 gives some examples of the variation of pK_a with different substituents in aliphatic and aromatic compounds. Aliphatic carboxylic acids have a pK_a of approximately 5; mineral acids a pK_a of about 1; phenols a pK_a of about 10; mononitrophenols a pK_a of 4.

The pK can be determined by using Eq. (I) on page 205 and by determining the concentrations shown in the expressions. The simplest approach is to titrate potentiometrically to the point where half of the acid or base is neutralized. At this point (see Eq. I), $[HA] = [A^-]$ and $[XOH] = [X^+]$, since half the acid or base is present as the salt. At this point then, $K_a = [H^+]$ and $K_b = [OH^-]$, or $pK_a = pH$ and $pK_b = pOH$. Hence, reading the pH at the point of half-neutralization will yield a good estimation of the pK values. The approach is most accurate where the dissociation constants are somewhat small; it is only in these cases that $[HA] = [A^-]$ and $[XOH] = [X^-]$. Where the dissociation constants are large, there is little undissociated acid or base in the system; the exact amount is not determinable except with effort.

Table 6-1   Substituted acetic acids

Acetic acid	pK_a	Acetic acid	pK_a	Acetic acid	pK_a
H—	4.76	HON=	*3.01*	CH_3S—	3.72
O_2N—	1.68	F_3C—	3.07	i-C_3H_7S—	3.72
$(CH_3)_3N^+$—	1.83	N_3—	*3.03*	$C_6H_5CH_2S$—	3.73
$(CH_3)_2NH^+$—	*1.95*	I—	*3.12*	C_2H_5S—	3.74
CH_3NH^+—	*2.16*	C_6H_5O—	*3.12*	n-C_3H_7S—	3.77
NH_3^+	2.31	$C_2H_5O_2C$—	*3.35*	n-C_4H_9S—	3.81
CH_3SO_2—	2.36	C_6H_5S—	3.52	HO—	3.83
NC—	*2.43*	CH_3O—	*3.53*	^-O_3S—	4.05
$C_6H_5SO_2$—	*2.44*	NCS—	*3.58*	$(C_6H_5)_3CS$—	4.30
HO_2C—	2.83			C_6H_5—	4.31
C_6H_5SO—	*2.66*	CH_3CO—	3.58	CH_2=CH—	4.35
F—	*2.66*	C_2H_5O—	*3.60*	CH_3—	4.88
Cl—	2.86	n-C_3H_7O—	*3.65*	^-O_2Se—	5.43
Br—	*2.86*	n-C_4H_9O—	*3.66*	^-O_2C—	5.69
		sec.-C_4H_9O—	*3.67*		
		HS—	3.67		
		i-C_3H_7O—	3.69		

SOURCE: Reprinted with permission from H. C. Brown, D. H. McDaniel, and O. Häfliger, "Determination of Organic Structures by Physical Methods," E. A. Braude, and F. C. Nachod (eds.), Academic Press Inc., New York, 1955, p. 577. Italics indicate apparent pK_a, uncorrected for activities. Bold type indicates corrected pK_a, calculated from thermodynamic considerations.

Table 6-2 **Monosubstituted benzoic acids**

Benzoic acid	In water			In 50% ethanol	
	o	m	p	m	p
H—	4.20	4.21		5.73	
$(CH_3)_3N^+$—	*1.37*	*3.45*	*3.43*	4.22	4.42
O_2N—	2.17	3.45	3.44	4.66	4.53
NC—		3.60^d	3.55	4.85	4.70
CH_3CO—				5.21	5.10
HO_2C—	2.95	*3.54*	*3.51*		
CH_3SO_2—		3.64	3.52	4.78	4.68
F_3C—		*3.79*		5.11	4.95
CH_3S—				5.53	5.74
HO—	2.98	4.08	4.58	5.61^a	6.13^a
HS—				5.42^a	5.56^a
I—	2.86	3.86			
Br—	2.85	3.81	4.00	5.22	5.35
Cl—	2.94	3.83	3.99		
F—	3.27	3.87	4.14		
$(CH_3)_3Si$—		4.24	4.27	6.01	5.85
CH_3O—	4.09	4.09	4.47		6.07
C_2H_5O—	4.21^c	4.17^c	4.45		
$n\text{-}C_3H_7O$—	4.24^c	4.20^c	4.46		
$i\text{-}C_3H_7O$—	4.24^c	4.15^c	4.68^c		
$n\text{-}C_4H_9O$—		4.25^c	4.53		
$n\text{-}C_5H_{11}O$—			4.55		
C_6H_5O—	3.53	3.95	4.52		
C_6H_5—	3.46				
CH_3—	3.91	4.24	4.34		5.94
CH_3CH_2—	*3.77*		4.35		
$(CH_3)_2CH$—			4.35		
$(CH_3)_3C$—	*3.46*	*4.28*	4.40		
$^-HO_3P$—	*3.78*	*4.03*	*3.95*	5.29	5.36
$^-HO_3As$—			*4.22*		
^-O_3S—		*4.15*	*4.11*		
^-O_2C—	5.41	4.60^b	4.82^b		
H_2N—	*4.98*	*4.79*	*4.92*		
CH_3NH—	*5.33*	*5.10*	*5.04*		
$(CH_3)_2N$—	*8.42*	*5.10*	*5.03*		

^{a} 20–22°C, 48.9% aqueous ethanol. ^{b} 18°C. ^{c} 20°C. ^{d} 3.68^{100}.
SOURCE: Reprinted with permission from H. C. Brown, D. H. McDaniel, and O. Häfliger, "Determination of Organic Structures by Physical Methods," E. A. Braude and F. C. Nachod (eds.), Academic Press Inc., New York, 1955, p. 588. Italics indicate apparent pK_a, uncorrected for activities. Bold type indicates corrected pK_a, calculated from thermodynamic considerations.

A more exact method for pK involves the use of emf measurements and the Nernst equation (method of H. S. Harned as described in Ref. 6, pages 963 and 964).

Literature Cited

1   N. Bauer and S. Z. Lewin, Physical Methods, in A. Weissberger (ed.), "Technique of Organic Chemistry," 3d ed., vol. I, pt. I, Interscience Publishers (Division of John Wiley & Sons, Inc.), New York, 1959, pp. 131–190. (General reference, mainly for laboratory methods of measurements.)

2   I. Kirshenbaum, Density and Specific Gravity, in B. E. Kirk and D. F. Othmer (eds.), "Encyclopedia of Chemical Technology," 2d ed., vol. 6, Interscience Publishers (Division of John Wiley & Sons, Inc.), New York, 1965, pp. 755–777. (Excellent brief survey.)

3   S. Siggia, "Continuous Analysis of Chemical Process Systems," John Wiley & Sons, Inc., New York, 1959, pp. 27–52. (Automatic continuous in-process methods of measurement.)

4   J. F. Swindells, R. Ullman, and H. Mark, Physical Methods, in A. Weissberger (ed.), "Technique of Organic Chemistry," 3d ed., vol. I, pt. I, Interscience Publishers (Division of John Wiley & Sons, Inc.), New York, 1959, pp. 689–726. (General discussion, all-inclusive except for in-process, on-stream, automatic methods.)

5   Siggia, *op. cit.*, pp. 53–75. (On-stream, continuous, automatic methods only.)

6   S. Glasstone, "Textbook of Physical Chemistry," D. Van Nostrand Company, Inc., Princeton, N.J., 1940, pp. 272–277.

7   N. Bauer, K. Fajans, and S. Z. Lewin, *op. cit.*, 1960, pt. II, pp. 1139–1280. (General discussion.)

8   L. W. Tilton and J. K. Taylor, "Physical Methods in Chemical Analysis," 2d ed., vol. 1, W. G. Berl (ed.), Academic Press Inc., New York, 1960, pp. 411–561. (General discussion.)

9   E. M. Chamot and C. W. Mason, "Handbook of Chemical Microscopy," 2d ed., vol. 1, John Wiley & Sons, Inc., New York, 1938, pp. 358–384. (Microscopical methods.)

10   Siggia, *op. cit.*, pp. 12–16. (Continuous methods.)

11   G. W. Thompson, Physical Methods, in A. Weissberger (ed.), "Technique of Organic Chemistry," 3d ed., vol. I, pt. I, Interscience Publishers (Division of John Wiley & Sons, Inc.), New York, 1959, pp. 402–552.

12   W. Swietoslawski and John R. Anderson, Physical Methods, in A. Weissberger (ed.), "Technique of Organic Chemistry," 3d ed., vol. I, pt. I, Interscience Publishers (Division of John Wiley & Sons, Inc.), New York, 1959, pp. 357–399.

13   M. Dole, "Physical Methods in Chemical Analysis," vol. II, W. G. Berl (ed.), Academic Press Inc., New York, 1951, pp. 306–331.

14   W. D. Harkins and A. E. Alexander, Physical Methods, in A. Weissberger (ed.), "Technique of Organic Chemistry," 3d ed., vol. I, pt. II, Interscience Publishers (Division of John Wiley & Sons, Inc.), New York, 1959, pp. 758–814.

15   Siggia, *op. cit.*, pp. 162–199.

16   *Ibid.*, pp. 245–277.

17   F. Daniels and R. A. Alberty, "Physical Chemistry," John Wiley & Sons, Inc., New York, 1955, pp. 165, 220.

18   P. W. Selwood, Physical Methods, in A. Weissberger (ed.), "Technique of Organic Chemistry," 3d ed., vol. I, pt. IV, Interscience Publishers (Division of John Wiley & Sons, Inc.), New York, 1959, pp. 2873–2913.

19   Sörensen, *Biochem. Z.*, **21**:131, 201 (1909).

Suggested Readings

Density

Bauer, N., and S. Z. Lewin: Physical Methods, in A. Weissberger (ed.), "Technique of Organic Chemistry," 3d ed., vol. I, pt. I, Interscience Publishers (Division of John Wiley & Sons, Inc.), New York, 1959, pp. 131–190. (General reference, mainly for laboratory methods of measurements.)

Kirshenbaum, I.: Density and Specific Gravity, in B. E. Kirk and D. F. Othmer (eds.), "Encyclopedia of Chemical Technology," 2d ed., vol. 6, Interscience Publishers (Division of John Wiley & Sons, Inc.), New York, 1965, pp. 755–777. (Excellent brief survey.)

Siggia, S.: "Continuous Analysis of Chemical Process Systems," John Wiley & Sons, Inc., New York, 1959, pp. 27–52. (Automatic continuous in-process methods of measurement.)

Viscosity

Siggia, S.: *op. cit.*, pp. 53–75. (On-stream, continuous, automatic methods only.)

Stross, F. H., and P. E. Porter: Viscometry, in R. E. Kirk and D. F. Othmer (eds.), "Encyclopedia of Chemical Technology," vol. 14, Interscience Publishers (Division of John Wiley & Sons, Inc.), New York, 1955, pp. 756–776.

Swindells, J. F., R. Ullman, and H. Mark: Physical Methods, in A. Weissberger (ed.), "Technique of Organic Chemistry," 3d ed., vol. I, pt. I, Interscience Publishers (Division of John Wiley & Sons, Inc.), New York, 1959, pp. 689–726. (General discussion, all-inclusive except for in-process, on-stream, automatic methods.)

Refractive Index

Bauer, N., K. Fajans, and S. Z. Lewin: *op. cit.*, 1960, pt. II, pp. 1139–1280. (General discussion.)

Chamot, E. M., and C. W. Mason: "Handbook of Chemical Microscopy,"
2d ed., vol. 1, John Wiley & Sons, Inc., New York, 1938, pp. 358–384.
(Microscopical methods.)
Siggia, S.: *op. cit.*, pp. 12–16. (Continuous methods.)
Tilton, L. W., and J. K. Taylor: "Physical Methods in Chemical Analysis,"
2d ed., vol. 1, W. G. Berl (ed.), Academic Press Inc., New York, 1960,
pp. 411–561. (General discussion.)

Vapor Pressure

Thompson, G. W.: Physical Methods, in A. Weissberger (ed.), "Technique
of Organic Chemistry," 3d ed., vol. I, pt. I, Interscience Publishers (Division
of John Wiley & Sons, Inc.), New York, 1959, pp. 402–552.

Boiling Point

Swietoslawski, W., and John R. Anderson: Physical Methods, in A. Weissberger (ed.), "Technique of Organic Chemistry," 3d ed., vol. I, pt. I,
Interscience Publishers (Division of John Wiley & Sons, Inc.), New York,
1959, pp. 357–399.

Freezing Point

Skau, E. L., J. C. Arthur, Jr., and H. Wakeham: Physical Methods, in A.
Weissberger (ed.), "Technique of Organic Chemistry," 3d ed., vol. I, pt. I,
Interscience Publishers (Division of John Wiley & Sons, Inc.), New York,
1959, pp. 288–354.

Surface Tension

Dole, M.: "Physical Methods in Chemical Analysis," vol. II, W. G. Berl (ed.),
Academic Press Inc., New York, 1951, pp. 306–331.
Harkins, W. D., and A. E. Alexander: Physical Methods, in A. Weissberger
(ed.), "Technique of Organic Chemistry," 3d ed., vol. I, pt. II, Interscience
Publishers (Division of John Wiley & Sons, Inc.), New York, 1959, pp.
758–814.

pH

Bates, R. G.: "Determination of pH," John Wiley & Sons, Inc., New York,
1964. (Good detailed text.)
Willard, H. H., L. L. Merritt, Jr., and J. A. Dean: "Instrumental Methods of
Analysis," 4th ed., D. Van Nostrand Company, Inc., Princeton, N.J.,
1965, pp. 582–613. (Good summary material.)

pK

Brown, H. C., D. H. McDaniel, and O. Häfliger: Dissociation Constants, in
E. A. Braude and F. C. Nachod (eds.), "Determination of Organic Structures by Physical Methods," Academic Press Inc., New York, 1955, pp.
567–655. (Discussion of variation of pK with structure and substituents.)

SEVEN

GROSS AND
SURFACE
EXAMINATION
OF MATERIALS

Though most of us do not realize it, we are analyzing a material when we look at it, smell it, feel it, and taste it. It is not intended that we go into a discussion of the senses as applied to analysis; however, it is in order that we discuss instrumental extension of the senses as they apply to analysis. For example, the microscope has extended our sight and enables us to gain much elucidation of a material under investigation. Also, other techniques exist as shown below to shed light on the nature and thickness of surfaces and on their composition, so that we need not rely on sight and touch alone.

Another area that can be listed under gross analysis is particle-size distribution. This is often a necessary parameter of powdered materials, and a discussion is in order.

MICROSCOPY

The microscope provides us with a simple way to gain much information about a sample: its identity, morphology, surface characteristics, optical properties, homogeneity, physical constants, composition, stability, particle size, fiber or film thickness, degree of penetration of one material into another. The total desired information may not be obtainable by the microscope alone, but a little preliminary microscopic examination can often save much experimental work. For example, a granular chemical product was being compacted to form cakes; the cake made from the material of one manufacturer crumbled, the cake made from the competitor's material was firm. Impurities were thought to be the cause since the materials were chemically identical. However, microscopic examination revealed a "skin" covering the granules of the bad material and none covering the granules of the competitor's material. This skin evidently prevented the granules from merging. The skin was determined chemically to be a proteinaceous protective colloid used to produce the granules in the bad case. Action was instituted to degrade this skin after processing; this resulted in an acceptable product.

In another case, two different sodium carbonate samples behaved differently on handling. One was a free-flowing powder, the other compacted and would not fall free of the transferring machinery. Hygroscopic impurities were suspected, since the non-free-flowing material appeared damp by behavior. However, microscopic examination indicated a different morphology for the two sodium carbonates.

In the studies of fibers and sheets, the microscope is of paramount importance. It is used to identify natural fibers via visible appearance and refractive index. Elucidation of fiber behavior toward stretching, pinking, moisture, as well as characterization of fiber structure, is possible microscopically.

Any chemical or physical property of a material can be used to identify it in the presence of other materials. The optical microscope has extended the ability to measure some of these properties on microgram quantities of materials whose particle size is as low as 10 μ. With no more than this amount, the microscope can determine shape, size, color, fluorescence, crystal habit, crystal angles, refractive index, and optical behavior under polarized light. Indeed, changes in the material under applied conditions such as heat (melting point and decomposition), light, mechanical and chemical reactions can be followed under the microscope. Reactions can be run on a microscope slide, with the formation of crystalline materials which can be identified by their crystal habit, angles, and optical behavior. Portions of a sample can be sublimed or otherwise crystallized under a microscope, making identification possible. All this can be done with microgram quantities. It is well to mention that, in the early days of the atomic bomb studies, plutonium was first chemically isolated and its identity proven, all on a microscopic scale [1].

Microscopy is also a useful adjunct to x-ray diffraction studies. X-ray effects depend on crystallographic properties of materials, and the microscope yields crystallographic parameters. Since amorphous materials yield no x-ray diffraction, it is usually worth looking at a sample microscopically to see if it is crystalline, before subjecting it to x-ray analysis.

The microscope is a good tool for measuring small parameters. With calibrated eyepieces, one can measure the thickness of fiber or films on sheets, the size of particles, the depth of penetration of dyes into fibers, the size of defects in crystals or other materials. The observation of size distribution of particles is a widely used application of the microscope; it is applied in all areas where powdered solids are used.

The range of application of the microscope to analytical problems is extended with the electron microscope. This instrument uses a beam of electrons to form the image, with magnetic fields as "lenses" to focus the beams. The increase in magnification is due to the wavelength of the radiation used. The light microscope uses radiation between 2500 and 6500 Å. With an average instrument, this results in a magnification of 550, a resolution of 1800 Å, and a depth of field of 1000 Å. The average electron microscope, using 50-kv electrons, produces an image-forming radiation of 0.05 to 0.06 Å wavelength and results in a magnification of 20,000, a resolution of 20 to 50 Å, and a depth of field of 18,000 Å. Excellent optical microscopes can attain a magnification of 2,000, while modern electron microscopes can obtain magnifications of 100,000. In each case, photographic enlargement of the images can further magnify them up to tenfold.

PARTICLE-SIZE DISTRIBUTION*

Particle-size distribution is an essential determination for many industrial products, such as paint pigments, color pigments in the plastics industry, products applied from aerosol spray cans, flour and other dry ingredients in the food industry, slip-agent particles in coated cellophane, and many others.

Of a variety of methods for this determination, no single technique can be recommended for all samples, since the size range, particle shape, density, and other factors control the applicability of any given method. First consideration is given here to methods which utilize apparatus commercially available or easily constructed in the laboratory. Then, methods requiring specialized equipment are described.

Visual microscopic observations are preferred at least for preliminary examination of particles larger than about 0.5 μ, because the full range of sizes and shapes is directly viewed. However, a determination of the exact size distribution by this method is tedious, since at least several hundred particles must be individually classified as to size. The electron microscope is applicable in a similar way to particles from about 0.01 to 5 μ. Automation of microscopic size analysis has been achieved with electronic scanning devices for counting and classifying particles in

* Written by G. L. Beyer, Research Laboratory, Eastman Kodak Co., Rochester, N.Y.

micrographs, or even by direct viewing of images on screens; the expense and complication of these devices may be justified in some applications.

Sieve analysis, that is, sifting of particles through a stack of metal screens of calibrated wire spacing, is a rapid method usually applicable to particles larger than about 70 μ, though nonwoven screens with apertures as small as 5 μ are now available. The weight remaining on each screen, after adequate shaking of the nest of screens, is easily converted into a size-distribution histogram adequate for many needs.

Gravitational sedimentation of particles suspended in a liquid is favored by many workers for samples whose particle size ranges between about 2 and 50 μ. Various types of apparatus can be constructed easily or purchased from many laboratory suppliers. The range of sedimentation methods can be extended to sizes as small as about 0.1 μ by the use of laboratory centrifuges. Sampling for the total weight sedimented after various times of sedimentation, or at constant time with variable suspension heights (for centrifugation), provides integral curves which often are sufficiently exact despite mixing and other errors.

Turning now to apparatus manufactured especially for determination of particle-size distribution, the Mine Safety Appliances Co. supplies equipment and procedures applicable for samples with particles as small as 0.1 μ. Their system utilizes centrifugal sedimentation of a liquid suspension and visual observation of the amount of sediment after various times and speeds of centrifugation.

The rate of sedimentation of dry powder samples is utilized in the Micromerograph, manufactured by the Sharples Co. In order to slow the settling rate, the particles fall through a column of upward-flowing air, and are collected successively on the pan of a recording balance. The integral size-distribution curve can be derived from the time-weight record so produced.

The Roller Particle Size Analyzer, manufactured by the American Instrument Co., is a single-stage elutriator which disperses dry particles in an air stream and floats out into a receiver one fraction containing the smallest particles present. In a series of steps at increasing flow rates, fractions may be removed and weighed to obtain a histogram representing the size distribution. This process may require days for some samples, and therefore a new cascade design permitting up to nine simultaneous separations from a single sample appears very attractive; it is claimed that separations may be completed in hours.

Direct counts of individual particles, coupled with simultaneous size estimation, are accomplished rapidly by the Coulter Counter, manufactured by the Coulter Electronics Co. Particles suspended in water are passed through a small orifice separating two compartments containing electrodes. As each particle obstructs the orifice, it causes a momentary change in electrical resistance in proportion to its projected area. The electrical pulses of different magnitude are analyzed electronically, and the number of pulses for various ranges of equivalent particle diameters can be read out easily. Rapid measurements of the complete size distribution are thus possible in the range from about 2 to 70 μ, or from 0.5 to 5 μ for the finest orifice.

The intensity of light scattered at small angles by a suspension of particles has been shown to provide a measure of the distribution of sizes. Instruments manufactured by Leeds and Northrup and by the Phoenix Precision Instrument Co. are designed to record the required angular scattering pattern at small angles from the emerging light beam. Applications of this method have been made in the size range from 0.2 to 10 μ, and further extensions and use of this technique should be forthcoming.

It is sometimes possible to obtain a satisfactory approximation of the particle-size distribution by use of background knowledge plus a rapid determination of average particle size by one of the numerous methods used for this purpose. This is practical when a variety of samples of one type has been characterized as to particle-size distribution by one of the methods above, and the results have been shown to fit some type of mathematical distribution function. For example, in many cases, plotting of distributions on log-probability graph paper will produce straight lines indicating conformity to the log-normal probability function. In this case, additional samples of the same type can probably be characterized by locating an experimentally determined average diameter on the graph paper and drawing a line parallel to those for well-characterized samples. Thus, the entire distribution is approximated with sufficient accuracy for many purposes.

EXAMINATION OF SURFACES

In the practice of chemistry, it is often required that we gain insight into the nature of surfaces. Some surfaces are to be coated, so the nature of the base surface is required; other surfaces are coated, and the nature of the coated surface is needed. In some cases, a film forms on a surface by corrosion or exposure to foreign materials, and the nature of this film must be elucidated. The examination of surfaces includes the physical nature of the surface, the composition of a surface coating, and the thickness of a surface film or coating.

Physical Nature of Surfaces

Whether a surface is smooth, pitted, striated, etched, etc., is best determined by microscopy. Light microscopy, employed up to magnifi-

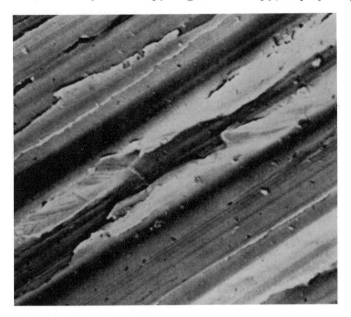

Fig. 7-1 Electron micrograph of a positive carbon replica of a finely ground steel surface. (1,212 microinches C.L.A.) 5,000 ×. (*Reprinted with permission from G. L. Clark, "The Encyclopedia of Microscopy," Reinhold Publishing Corporation, New York, 1961, p. 311.*)

cation limits discussed on page 213, can be used directly on the sample or on surfaces on which metals have been evaporated. These coated surfaces produce more contrast, and more detail can be brought out. Another approach is to replicate a surface, for example by coating it with a solution of a plastic, allowing the solvent to evaporate, and peeling off the plastic film. This film contains the imprint of the surface and can be examined as is with the electron microscope, or the film can be "shadow-coated" with an evaporated metal film to obtain the necessary contrast. Figures 7-1 through 7-3 show photomicrographs of surfaces.

Composition of a Surface Coating

The qualitative composition of a surface coating can be determined in several ways. The *optical absorption techniques* involving *infrared, ultraviolet,* and *visible* light are useful here. Of course, the absorption

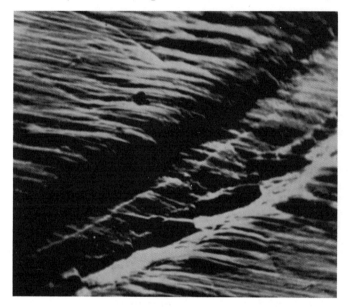

Fig. 7-2   Direct reflection electron micrograph showing a scratch on a mechanically polished surface finished with finest abrasive paper. 2,500 ×. (*Reprinted with permission of G. L. Clark, "The Encyclopedia of Microscopy," Reinhold Publishing Corporation, New York, 1961, p. 311.*)

spectrum of the surface coating is obtained by reflection and not by transmission of the light. Transmission techniques can be used if the surface can be removed to be examined. The spectra are the same when obtained by reflection or transmission, except that more resolution can be obtained with transmission spectra if the coating is in solution. As indicated in more detail (pages 98–99), infrared spectra are the most definitive of the optical absorption methods for qualitative identification of materials. Ultraviolet and visible spectra are not too readily applicable for identification purposes, though they can be used in isolated cases. These optical methods are ideal for organic coatings which absorb well, especially in the infrared region of the spectrum. Inorganic coatings do not generally absorb well, though some do. Figure 7-4, for example, shows the infrared spectrum of an alumina coating on aluminum obtained by reflectance.

Electron diffraction is another approach for quantitatively identifying crystalline coatings, especially on metals. Electron diffraction is com-

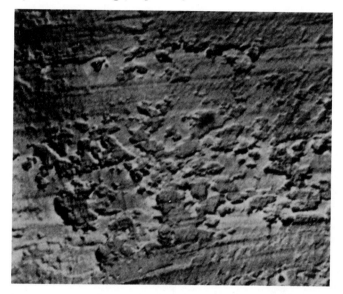

Fig. 7-3   Reversed print of an electron micrograph of a shadowed "Formvar" replica of a worn steel surface lubricated with a mineral oil containing an E.P. additive. 13,500 X. (*Reprinted with permission of G. L. Clark, "The Encyclopedia of Microscopy," Reinhold Publishing Corporation, New York, 1961, p. 312.*)

pletely analogous to x-ray diffraction (pages 116–121), except that a beam of electrons is used instead of x-rays. The theory is identical, and even the measured parameters in the x-ray diffraction literature can be used with electron diffraction, since both relate to the same crystal parameters. Electron diffraction has one advantage over x-ray diffraction in that electrons do not penetrate as deeply as x-rays, and hence can obtain a pattern for the material on the surface without an interfering pattern from the matrix of the base material. With this technique,

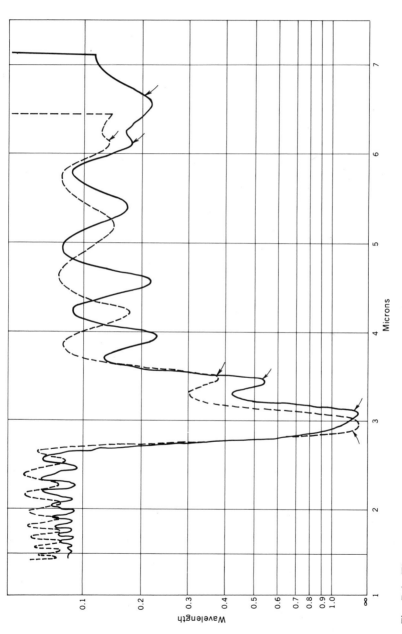

Fig. 7-4 The arrows show absorption bands. The other peaks are interference fringes. The dashes and continuous lines represent different coatings.

corrosion or other inorganic layers on metals can be determined; occasionally a pigment in a paint coating can be identified; the surface treatment of metals can be identified through the identification of the residual coating produced. Coatings on metals are particularly amenable since the metal base stops the electrons effectively. However, crystalline coatings on paper, wood, and plastics are not amenable to this approach, since the base material is too easily penetrated. Figure 7-5 shows an electron-diffraction pattern of α-Fe_2O_3 on iron.

Fig. 7-5   Ring powder pattern. Reflection from iron showing a layer of α-Fe_2O_3 on iron. [*Reprinted with permission from W. G. Berl (ed.), "Physical Methods of Chemical Analysis," Academic Press Inc., New York, 1950, p. 173.*]

Spot chemical tests, as described by Sawicki in Chap. 8 for trace quantities, can be used to identify materials on the surface of a sample. In fact, some of the gross chemical tests for elements (pages 33–34) or functional groups (pages 77–78) can often be used if the coating is thick enough and/or if the base material does not interfere, should the reagent penetrate that far.

Thickness of Surface Films or Coatings

Microscopy, as mentioned above, is a good method for determining surface-coating thickness. The most common technique is to cross-section the sample so that the cross section of the coating is visible and can be measured with the microscope, using a calibrated eyepiece. Thicknesses down to 0.5 μ can be measured with optical microscopes and down to 4 to 5 Å with modern electron microscopes. *Ellipsometry* can also be used to measure coating thickness. In this approach, plane-polarized light is passed through a coating and is reflected back out from the base material. The emergent light is elliptically polarized by the coating. By determining the ellipticity of the emergent light, the thickness of the film can be computed. The ellipsometer can generally measure coating thickness from 1 to 100 Å with no calibration. It can measure thicknesses from 100 to several thousand Å, but calibration with films of known thickness is necessary.

X-ray absorption can be used to measure thin coatings that are difficult to measure by other methods, for example, evaporated metal films on piezoelectric crystals. For this application, the x-rays are passed through the coating and reflected off the base crystalline material at the proper Bragg angle to a detector. The intensity of the x-rays is reduced by the absorption due to the two passes through the coating. The relationship between the x-ray absorption and the coating thickness is as follows:

$$\frac{I_t}{I_0} = \exp\left[-2\mu \frac{t}{\sin\theta}\right]$$

where I_t = x-ray intensity after two passes through coating
I_0 = x-ray intensity reflected off uncoated material
μ = absorption coefficient for coating material
t = coating thickness
θ = angle of incidence of x-ray with crystal plane on base material

Another x-ray technique, namely fluorescence, can also be used to measure coating thickness. This method depends on x-rays penetrating the coating and exciting the base material, causing it to emit characteristic fluorescent x-radiation (pages 23–25). This radiation is partially absorbed by passing through the coating. The amount of absorption is related to the thickness. The measurement is made by comparing the fluorescence of the coated sample with that of an uncoated sample. This technique is used to determine the thickness of electrically plated coatings on metals or of other metal coatings on metals. For example, tin and zinc plates on iron and steel are monitored in this way.

Interferometry has also been used to measure coating thickness. This is accomplished by measuring the interference lines obtained by reflectance. Normally a reflectance-type spectrophotometric measurement is made as discussed on page 217 to identify a coating. However, superimposed on the absorption spectrum will be a series of waves which represent the interference pattern obtained when the light passing through the coating reflected off the base material interferes with the light reflected off the surface of coating. Figure 7-4 shows the interference bands superimposed on the infrared spectrum of an alumina film on aluminum. The distance between interference bands will be seen to vary with the wavelength as theory dictates.

By counting the number of interference fringes n between any two wavelengths λ_1 and λ_2, and knowing the refractive index u of the coating film, the thickness in microns l of the surface coating can be calculated by the equation below, which is a modified form of the Bragg equation

$$l = \frac{n\lambda_1\lambda_2}{2(\lambda_1 - \lambda_2)u}$$

The limiting thickness measurable is of the order of 1 to 10 wavelengths of the light used.

Interference microscopes also exist for measuring the thickness of surface coatings. This is accomplished by the measurement of observed interference fringes. The calculations are analogous to those shown above for reflectance techniques. This technique will measure thicknesses as low as one-tenth of the wavelength of the light used.

THICKNESS GAUGING

Thickness can be measured by observing cross sections of the material and measuring the thickness *microscopically* with calibrated eyepieces. Of course, *calipers* can also be used if the material and the thickness range are amenable to such measurements. *X-ray absorption* can be used if the material is dense enough to absorb the x-rays significantly (e.g., metals). Though calipers can be used in these cases, x-rays are more amenable to continuous monitoring of sheet material in process. X-rays are too penetrating for thickness gauging of materials such as cellophane or other plastics, paper, etc. In these cases, *β-ray absorption* is used.

Literature Cited

1 M. Cefola, *Microchem. J.*, **2**:205–217 (1958).

Suggested Readings

Microscopy

Light

Chamot, E. M., and C. W. Mason: "Handbook of Chemical Microscopy," 2d ed., vol. 2, 3d ed., vol. 1, John Wiley & Sons, Inc., New York, 1940, 1958. (Both volumes are useful texts.)

Clark, G. L.: "The Encyclopedia of Microscopy," Reinhold Publishing Corporation, New York, 1961.

Jelley, E. E.: Physical Methods, in A. Weissberger (ed.), "Technique of Organic Chemistry," 3d ed., vol. 1, pt. II, Interscience Publishers (Division of John Wiley & Sons, Inc.), New York, 1959, pp. 1349–1472. (Comprehensive survey chapter.)

Electron

Clark, G. L.: "The Encyclopedia of Microscopy," Reinhold Publishing Corporation, New York, 1961.

Hamm, F. A.: Physical Methods, in A. Weissberger (ed.), "Technique of Organic Chemistry," 3d ed., vol. 1, pt. II, Interscience Publishers (Division of John Wiley & Sons, Inc.), New York, 1960, pp. 1561–1638. (Comprehensive survey chapter.)

Heidenreich, R. D., and C. V. Calbrick: "Physical Methods in Chemical Analysis," 2d ed., vol. 1, W. G. Berl (ed.), Academic Press Inc., New York, 1960, pp. 547–613. (Comprehensive survey chapter.)

Particle Size

Beyer, G. L.: Physical Methods, in A. Weissberger (ed.), "Technique of Organic Chemistry," 3d ed., vol. 1, pt. I, Interscience Publishers (Division of John Wiley & Sons, Inc.), New York, 1959, pp. 191–259. (Comprehensive survey chapter.)

Cadle, R. D.: "Particle Size: Theory & Industrial Application," Reinhold Publishing Corporation, New York, 1965. (Text.)

Kay, B. H.: "Standard Methods for Chemical Analysis," 6th ed., vol. 3, pt. A, F. Welcher (ed.), D. Van Nostrand Company, Inc., Princeton, N.J., 1966, pp. 794–834. (Excellent brief survey.)

Reflectance Spectroscopy

Bigelow, W. C.: "Physical Methods in Chemical Analysis," 2d ed., vol. 1, W. G. Berl (ed.), Academic Press Inc., New York, 1960, pp. 619–660. (Comprehensive survey chapter.)

Wendlandt, W. W., and H. G. Hecht: "Reflectance Spectroscopy," Interscience Publishers (Division of John Wiley & Sons, Inc.), 1966. (Text.)

Ellipsometry

Ellipsometry in the Measurement of Surfaces and Thin Films, *Symposium Proceeding, Washington, D.C., 1963, Nat. Bur. Std., Misc. Publ. No. 256.*

X-ray (Absorption and Fluorescence)

Clark, G. L.: "Physical Methods in Chemical Analysis," 2d ed., vol. 1, W. G. Berl (ed.), Academic Press Inc., New York, 1960, pp. 4–6. (Comprehensive survey chapter.)

Interferometry

Tolansky, S.: "An Introduction to Interferometry," John Wiley & Sons, Inc., New York, 1955. (Text.)
Williams, W. E.: "Applications of Interferometry," John Wiley & Sons, Inc., New York, 1930. (Text.)

EIGHT

ANALYSIS FOR
TRACE QUANTITIES*

This section will confine itself to a discussion of the detection, characterization, and determination of trace amounts (1 picogram to 100 μg) of elements and compounds in mixtures weighing anywhere from a fraction of a microgram to several grams. Trace detection and determination of the elements have already been discussed to some degree in Chap. 2.

The mixtures which are analyzed today vary tremendously. They can be classified as: natural nonliving material such as ocean water and silt, forest soil, urban air, metals, rocks and minerals, and meteorites; natural living material such as plant and animal tissue as well as its products and by-products; man-made materials such as industrial chemicals, medicines, cosmetics, and pollutants of air, water, and food.

Some of the types of complex mixtures which have been investigated are shown in Table 8-1.

Some of the difficulties in analyzing for trace amounts of material are due to decomposition, adsorption, background material, interferences, and contamination. When a minute amount of a chemical is in contact with relatively huge amounts of other chemical material or light, a percentage of the material greater than normal can be decomposed in a shorter time. Trace amounts of a chemical are also more readily overshadowed by interferences with somewhat similar properties or may be covered up by the mass of background unknowns. A particularly annoying difficulty is presented by adsorption. A small constant amount of a chemical may be adsorbed on glassware or other surfaces, but when this chemical is present in very small amounts, a substantial amount of it, if not all, may disappear in this fashion. Another frustrating difficulty is the presence of interfering impurities in adsorbents, reagents, or solvents used in the analytical work. Contamination is another difficulty. This can come from chemicals adsorbed onto glassware such as pipettes or beakers, it can come from the laboratory dust

* Written by Eugene Sawicki, Division of Air Pollution, Robert A. Taft Sanitary Engineering Center, Cincinnati, Ohio.

Table 8-1   Analysis of complex mixtures

Mixture	Analyzed compounds (no.)	Procedure*	(Ref.)
Urban atmosphere (50 cities)	n-Alkanes $(C_{18}-C_{32})$ (15)	CC → GC	[1]
Urban atmosphere (Los Angeles)	Aliphatic and aromatic hydrocarbons (C_2-C_8) (15)	GC	[2]
Gasoline engine exhaust	Aliphatic hydro- carbons (C_2-C_5) (18)	GC	[3]
Tobacco and tobacco smoke	Aliphatic hydrocarbons (C_8-C_{34})	CC → GC	[4]
Gasoline engine exhaust	Polynuclear aromatic hydrocarbons (24)	CC → PC → SP	[5]
Cigarette smoke	Polynuclear aromatic hydrocarbons (18)	CC → $(PC)_n$ → SP	[6]
Urban atmosphere (14 cities)	Polynuclear aromatic hydrocarbons (8)	CC → SP	[7]
Incinerator effluents	Polynuclear aza heterocyclic hydro- carbons (25)	CC → TLC → SPF	[8]
Coal-tar-pitch– polluted air	Polynuclear imino heterocyclic hydro- carbons (3)	$(TLC)_2$ → SPF	[9]
River water	Aliphatic acids (5)	CC	[10]
Cows' milk fat	Acids (65)	CC → GC → SP,IR	[11, 12]
Cigarette smoke	Phenolic acids (12)	PC	[13]
Plants	Phenolic acids (21)	2 dimens. PC	[14]
Human skin waxes	Wax esters	GC	[15]
Sea water	Amino acids	TLC	[16]
Dairy products	Chlorinated pesticides	CC → GC†	[17]
Urine‡	Simple sugars	PC	[18]
Pregnancy urine	Estrogens (3)	GC	[19]
Urine	17-Oxosteroids (11)	CC	[20]
Human blood	Adrenocortical steroids (4)	CC	[21]

* CC = column chromatography; GC = gas chromatography; PC = paper chromatography; $(PC)_n$ = variable number of runs dependent on compound; SP = ultraviolet–visible absorption spectrophotometry; TLC = thin-layer chromatography; SPF = spectrophotofluorometry; IR = infrared spectrophotometry.
† Electron capture detector.
‡ In patients with lactosuria, galactosuria, glucosuria, fructosuria, and xylulosuria.

which may contain some of the chemicals for which analyses are being made, or it can come from the conditioned air which constantly flows through the room.

To minimize these difficulties, trace analysis procedures should be carried out quickly and efficiently. Adsorbents should be washed free of interferences while standards, reagents, and solvents must be purified by crystallization, distillation, and/or chromatography. All glassware and equipment must be scrupulously clean. Blanks should be run with every analytical procedure; standards should be analyzed by the procedure also at regular intervals. If possible, syntheses should not be allowed in an analytical laboratory. The laboratory should be kept clean by regular dusting. If necessary, the air coming into the laboratory can be filtered. In the same way, any work with light-sensitive chemicals can be done in a room, or a section of the room, from which the ultraviolet light has been filtered.

In many fields of trace analysis, the aim has been to get more information in shorter time on smaller amounts of mixture. This is true of air and blood analysis. The aim in all fields has been toward greater simplicity, selectivity, and an improved sensitivity—all this with meaningful accuracy and precision.

We are in an age where a large number of analytical techniques are available for most types of compounds. Many of these methods are competitive in some cases. Because of the rapid changes in equipment and methodology it is difficult to tell which method will soon become obsolete. This is because modification, replacement, and combination are proceeding at the same time in all techniques.

Trace analysis usually involves separation of the element or compound in question from its matrix in order to make analysis possible. However, since separation techniques are discussed in Chap. 11, this section will concern itself only with techniques for detection and determination of trace quantities of elements or compounds. These techniques will be divided into two groups, noninstrumental and instrumental.

NONINSTRUMENTAL METHODS

Most of the methods in this group are of the spot-test type. Although some titrimetric procedures would be included in this section, these cannot normally be applied in the trace range. The spot test methods can be subdivided into color, fluorescence, low-temperature fluorescence, phosphorescence, and light-emission tests.

Color Spot Test

A most valuable approach for the detection of a compound or a functional group in a mixture is through the formation of an intensely colored compound. These tests are often very sensitive, extending into the parts-per-billion region, and very selective, depending on very specific chemical reactions for the compound or group involved.

Fluorescence Spot Test

Because of the very high sensitivity and selectivity of these tests they are excellent for the detection of trace quantities. However, they suffer from many interferences which affect fluorescence. The fluorescence mentioned here is the visually observed type used for detection purposes. Fluorimetry is discussed in more detail on pages 229–230.

Low-temperature Luminescence Spot Test

The use of low-temperature fluorescence and phosphorescence colors in spot testing has been reviewed and investigated [22]. The liquid-nitrogen temperature fluorescence and phosphorescence colors and detection limits of over 80 compounds were reported under neutral, acid and alkaline conditions. The technique involves examination of the spot on glass-fiber paper immersed in liquid nitrogen under an ultraviolet light. It has been found that many compounds give different fluorescence colors at room or liquid-nitrogen temperatures, depending on whether the chemical on the adsorbent was in solution or in the dry state. The phosphorescence colors of the neutral chemicals showed this phenomenon also, but in this case most compounds were nonphosphorescent in the dry state. Many polar compounds that are not fluorescent at room temperature become fluorescent at a low temperature. Many nonfluorescent azo dyes become fluorescent in acid solution at low temperatures. Many nonfluorescent nitroarenes and 4-nitrophenylhydrazones become fluorescent at low temperatures. It must be emphasized that the terms low-temperature fluorescence and phosphorescence are used only in a qualitatively visual manner. However, a spectrophotophosphorimeter can distinguish between the two. These various color changes prove analytically useful, especially when they are applied as low-temperature fluorimetric and phosphorimetric procedures directly on chromatograms. The high order of sensitivity—detection limits ranging from about 0.5 ng to 2 μg—for a large number of the compounds makes this adaptation feasible.

INSTRUMENTAL METHODS

Ultraviolet–Visible Absorption Spectrometry

Colorimetric methods have been extremely popular because of their speed, simplicity, and accuracy and will probably be of value for many years to come. The methods have been used extensively in clinical chemistry [23, 24]. Colorimetric methods are also used in the air pollution field [25] and will probably see more extensive use in the future.

In the development of many of the methods for colorimetric analysis, the aim is to change the test substance(s) into an intensely colored chromogen(s) which will absorb with greater intensity further into the visible, so that the mass of ultraviolet-absorbing background material will not interfere in the analysis. In addition, it is preferred that the method be highly selective for either one compound or a group of compounds which have a reacting functional group in common. A large number of such methods have been described in a review on organic spectrophotometric analysis [26]. Many of these methods have only recently been originated and thus have not seen much application yet. A very large number of colorimetric methods have been compiled by the Snells [27]. An excellent series of books, especially for the analyst working in chromatography, is the Organic Electronic Spectral Data volumes [28]. Absorption-wavelength maxima of a tremendous number of compounds are listed. However, in the characterization of an unknown compound, the final step should be a spectral comparison of the unknown and the pure standard in the same solvent. For this comparison, the complete absorption spectral curves of standard and unknown should be obtained. Further discussion of these techniques is contained on pages 98–99.

With modern spectral equipment much information can be obtained from a spot test. For example, direct spectra from an adsorbent or a microtube can be obtained in all the spot-test methods. To be specific, excitation and emission spectra can be obtained from a fluorescence spot test on an adsorbent or in a microcell, but, in addition, estimation will be more readily accomplished this way than can be visually.

The high order of sensitivity of the spot test when it is examined spectrally has been shown in the comparison of about 13 tests for formaldehyde [29] and 8 tests for malonaldehyde [30]. The detection limit with the chromotropic acid or 3-methyl-2-benzothiazolinone hydrazone visible-color spot tests for formaldehyde is about 100 ng; with the J-acid spectrophotofluorimetric spot test, the detection limit is 0.5 ng. Even more dramatic is the comparison of the thiobarbituric acid spot test for malonaldehyde with a detection limit of 40 ng and the 4,4'-sulfonyldianiline spectrophotofluormetric spot test with a detection limit of 50 ng. It should be possible to modify these sensitive and selective spot tests slightly and to develop them into quick, simple microestimation methods in which the spot would be examined spectrophotofluorimetrically.

Low-temperature Fluorimetry

In general, more fine structure should be expected in the fluorescence spectra of compounds at lower temperatures. In addition the maxima are intensified and sharpened because of a reduction of the background.

Quenchofluorimetry

A serious interference in fluorescence analysis is fluorescence quenching. Quenching agents can be selective and can quench interfering fluorescence, permitting measurement of the fluorescence of a desired material. Also, known fluorescent materials can be used as reagents; their decrease in fluorescence on addition to samples containing known quenching agents can be used to measure the concentration of the quenching agent. This field of trace analysis has been named quenchofluorimetric analysis. By varying the solvent system, and thus its particular type of quenching effect, fluorescence methods of analysis are made more highly selective. For example, polynuclear aromatic hydrocarbons containing the fluoranthenic ring system can be determined in the presence of all other types of hydrocarbons when the analysis takes place in nitromethane solution [31]. Thus, fluoranthene can be determined in the presence of pyrene, benz[a]anthracene, chrysene, phenanthrene, perylene, and anthracene. Although all of these compounds fluoresce strongly in most organic solutions, all but fluoranthene are quenched in nitromethane solution. The wide range of analyses possible in quenchofluorimetry has been demonstrated with the analyses of aza heterocyclic hydrocarbons in the presence of other types of polynuclear compounds and vice versa, aza heterocyclic hydrocarbons in the presence of aromatic amines and vice versa, aza heterocyclic hydrocarbons in the presence of imino heterocyclic hydrocarbons and vice versa, and perylene in the presence of other polynuclear aromatic hydrocarbons [32].

Block and Morgan were able to determine iron in the parts-per-billion range by the quenching of the fluorescence of the aluminum complex of Pontamine Blue Black R [33]. The quenching phenomenon was linear over a range from 0.02 to 0.2 μg iron per milliliter of solution.

Phosphorimetry

The field of spectrophotophosphorimetric analysis is relatively unexplored. The difficulty in this field has been mainly due to the necessity for a solvent system that would dissolve the test compound and yet be a clear glass at low temperatures. The situation has improved somewhat with the availability of a wider range of solvents [34, 35]. The phosphorimetric properties of organic compounds were investigated by Kasha in 1944 [36]. It was not until 1957 that the method was evaluated quantitatively by analyzing synthetic binary mixtures of compounds [37]. It was found that these mixtures could be resolved by choice of excitation wavelength, by choice of emission wavelength, by choice of observation time after cutoff of excitation radiation, or by a combination of any of the above.

In phosphorimetry, as well as in fluorimetry, the choice of excitation and emission conditions allows an increased selectivity over most other methods. Since many of the larger molecules absorbing at wavelengths greater than 370 mμ phosphoresce weakly, if at all, phosphorimetric analysis is of value in the analysis of the smaller molecules in the presence of the more colored and more fluorescent larger molecules.

The literature on the applications of this method of analysis is sparse.

Quenchophosphorimetry

Although there are few methods in the literature using this principle, it is mentioned for the sake of completeness. Quenching reagents used in quenchofluorimetry should be useful here. In this fashion, phosphorimetry can be made even more highly selective [35].

Comparison of Spectral Methods

Intensity readings obtained with an absorption spectrophotometer are reproducible over lengthy periods of time. With fluorimeters and phosphorimeters, intensity readings decrease over a period of months as the strength of the phototube decreases with use. Consequently, it is necessary to use standards automatically in every analytical procedure.

The natural selectivity of analytical methods for organic compounds in mixtures (i.e., without changing their structure) is in the order: quenchophosphorimetry, quenchofluorimetry, phosphorimetry, fluorimetry, visible absorption spectrometry, ultraviolet absorption spectrometry, infrared absorption spectrometry. Colorimetric analysis is based on the increase of selectivity of an absorption-spectrometric method by the formation of a derivative which absorbs at longer wavelengths. In this fashion, the spectrum is moved away from similarly absorbing compounds and away from the mass of unknown compounds from which the background absorption is derived. This type of technique has only rarely been used in fluorimetric analysis. This organic synthetic approach has not yet been used in the various quenching and phosphorimetric procedures. With the selectivities and sensitivities that can be obtained in these fields, this approach will be well worth investigating.

Many more compounds have absorption spectra than have fluorescence spectra. However, when a compound or its derivative is fluorescent, the fluorimetric procedure is usually much more sensitive than the comparable absorptimetric procedure. For example, in Fig. 8-1 the absorption and fluorescence emission spectra of benzo[a]pyrene are shown at the detection limits. On the basis of these two spectra, the limits are 0.25 and 2500 ng of benzo[a]pyrene in the fluorimetric and absorptimetric spectra, respectively. Since the phosphorescence of benzo[a]-pyrene is relatively negligible, phosphorimetry cannot be used in the direct analysis of benzo[a]pyrene. For the same reason, it cannot be used in the analysis of many of the more highly conjugated compounds that absorb near, or in, the visible.

For compounds like triphenylene, absorptimetric analysis in a fairly complicated mixture is difficult because this compound absorbs at short wavelengths, so that its bands are hidden in the background absorption derived from the other aromatic compounds in the mixture. Triphenylene is also one of the most weakly fluorescent polycylic hydrocarbons. In addition, its fluorescence excitation- and emission-wavelength maxima are at fairly short wavelengths, so that interference from background material is fairly serious. However, the detection limit in phosphorimetry is 2 ng. So this would be the method of choice.

For many of the smaller polar compounds which are usually non-fluorescent and have relatively weak broad bands in their absorption spectra, phosphorimetry could be the ideal method of analysis. p-Nitroaniline is an example of this type of molecule. Its fluorescence is negligible. The detection limit at its long-wavelength absorption band is

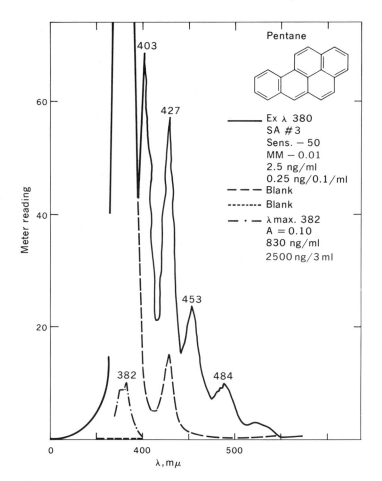

Fig. 8-1 The absorption and fluorescence emission spectra of benzo[a]pyrene.

about 3,500 ng/ml, while the detection limit phosphorimetrically is 1 ng/0.1 ml.

The absorption spectra of organic molecules are not usually affected drastically by solvent changes. An example of an unusually drastic change is shown by solutions of 4'-(4-nitrophenylazo)phenol which has a molar absorptivity of 60,000 at wavelength maximum 605 mμ in alkaline dimethylformamide, and 24,000 at wavelength maximum 450 mμ in alkaline 2,2,2-trifluoroethanol [38].

In fluorimetry, the intensity of every fluorescent molecule can be

changed drastically by a change in the solvent system or a change in
the excitation or emission wavelength at which readings are taken. The
relative intensities of fluorescent molecules can be varied just as drastically by similar changes in solvent, etc. The high order of selectivity
in fluorimetric analysis is based to a large extent on these factors.
With quenchers, the fluorescence can be destroyed completely; with
enhancers, the fluorescence can be considerably increased. Very little
research has been done on quenchers and practically none on enhancers.
The wide range of intensity is reflected by the detection limits of
organic compounds in various solvents (Table 8-2). Spectrophospho-

Table 8-2   Solvent effects on fluorescence detection limits (ng/0.1 ml) [32]

Solvent*	Benz[c]-acridine	Fluor-anthene	Perylene	Benzo[a]-pyrene
Pentane	10	5	0.1	0.25
Acetophenone + 1% TFA	4	560	17	60
Carbon disulfide + 1% TFA	70	330	2	∞ †
o-Cresol + 1% TFA	∞	30	1	3
5% m-Dinitrobenzene + 1% TFA in CHCl₃	4	High	2,500	∞
Nitromethane + 10% AlCl₃	330	∞	∞	∞
Pyrrole	∞	∞	6	100

* TFA = trifluoroacetic acid.
† Fluorescence quenched.

rimetry should show the same type of phenomena.

In the fluorimetric and phosphorimetric methods, the entire spectra
can be obtained frequently from limited mixtures. This, of course,
cannot be done with absorption spectra. The quenching methods
would make it even more possible to obtain the entire spectrum of a
compound from a mixture. However, absorptimetric methods have the
advantage that, in a limited mixture of aromatic or heterocyclic hydrocarbons, the sharp narrow bands of some of the compounds stick out of
the background absorption, with the wavelength position of each individual hydrocarbon unaffected by the other members of the mixture.

Infrared Absorption Spectrometry

Collections of infrared spectral curves can be obtained from the
National Research Council, the National Bureau of Standards, Samuel

P. Sadtler and Sons, Philadelphia, Pennsylvania, and Butterworth Scientific Publications, London, England.

Methods based on this technique are the least sensitive and have the poorest selectivity of all the spectral methods, especially when they are applied to mixtures. However, when these techniques are applied after separation, excellent, highly selective spectra can result, especially if enough material is obtained.

Gas Chromatography*

By its ability to use and detect small quantities of materials, gas chromatography is a natural approach to detection and determination of trace quantities of chemical materials. Normal gas chromatography uses from 1 to 50 μl of sample, and Table 8-3 indicates the approximate

Table 8-3

Detector	Limit of detection (estimate),[a] μg
Thermistor	1
Hot wire	2–5[b]
Flame ionization	1×10^{-5}
Argon	1×10^{-4}[†]
Electron capture	1×10^{-7}[†] (depends greatly on electronegativity of fraction being detected)
Cross section	20[†]
Gas density	1–10
Ultrasonic	Not obtainable

[a] These are estimates of orders of magnitude to show general relative sensitivities. Specific material may give markedly different sensitivities, as will different operating parameters and instrument design. These values are pooled from private conversations with Perkin-Elmer, Varian (Wilkins), F & M, Gow-Mac, and Microtek representatives.

[b] Figures are obtained from H. M. McNair and E. J. Bonnelli, "Basic Gas Chromatography," Varian Aerograph, 2700 Mitchell Dr., Walnut Creek, Calif., April, 1966, V-1 through V-15.

quantity of each fraction it can detect with the various types of detectors. It should be kept in mind that the values stated below vary some-

* Written by S. Siggia.

what with the particular instrument used and with the specific material being detected.

The thermistor and hot-wire detectors are generally nonspecific detectors depending on the thermal conductivity of the eluting fraction for detection. Since all materials have a relatively low thermal conductivity relative to helium, these detectors will detect essentially all materials. The thermistor bead is essentially the more sensitive at temperatures below 150°C, and hot wire is the more sensitive at temperatures above 150°C. Flame ionization is a very good general detector for trace quantities, since it will detect any material that will ionize in a flame. This covers essentially all organic materials, but would not include materials such as water or nitrogen. The functioning of a flame detector can be outlined as follows [39]:

$$H_2 + O_2 + \text{organic} \rightarrow CO_2 + H_2O + e^- + (\text{ions})^+ + (\text{ions})^-$$
$$e^- + (\text{ions})^- \rightarrow \text{current}$$

The Pye-argon detector is based on ionization of any of the rare gases, producing excited atoms of rather long life. Argon was the first gas used, hence the name, but other rare gases can be used. The activated species are nonconducting because they are not ionized. When the activated atoms strike an organic molecule, they ionize it to yield an ion plus an electron. This results in a flow of current.

$$Ar^* + M \rightarrow Ar + M^+ + e^-$$

The electron-capture detector is finding much use in trace analysis, especially in the areas of the determination of pesticide residues on foods or in water. It is also used for determining traces of polynuclear aromatic hydrocarbons in air. This detector depends on the ability of the eluting fraction to capture electrons. The detector uses a tritium source as the source of beta emission. This emission ionizes the nitrogen carrier gas, emitting slow electrons which then fall on an electrometer. If an electron-capturing fraction passes between the electron source and the electron detector, it will decrease the number of electrons reaching the detector, and this decrease will then be registered as a drop in current.

The operation of the electron-capture detector can be outlined as follows [39]:

$$\beta + N_2 \rightarrow N_2^+ + e^-_{\text{slow}}$$
$$e^-_{\text{slow}} + \text{compound} \rightarrow \text{compound}$$
$$\text{loss of } e^- \rightarrow \text{reduced current}$$

This detector has selectivity since only electronegative materials will capture electrons. Halogenated, nitro group-bearing, and polynuclear aromatic compounds are good electron-capturing materials and hence are sensitively detected. Since most pesticides are halogenated, the electron-capture detector fits this type of work very well. Figure 8-2 shows a chromatogram for 0.1 ppm DDT in broccoli. The selectivity of this detector decreases chances for interference, and thus less cleanup of sample and lower chromatographic resolution are required. Figure 8-3 is a gas chromatogram of several pesticides showing the low limit of detection.

The micro-cross-section detector is much like the electron-capture detector. In this case, the tritium source emitting β particles ionizes the compound going through the detector. The carrier gas (H_2 or He $+ 3\%$ CH_4) also ionizes to some degree, causing background. The operation of this detector can be outlined as follows [39]:

$$\beta + \text{carrier gas} \rightarrow (\text{carrier gas})^+ + e^- \text{ (background)}$$
$$\beta + \text{compound} \rightarrow (\text{compound})^+ + e_x^-$$
$$e_x^- \rightarrow \text{current}$$

The gas-density detector is merely a gas-density balance that detects the change in gas density as fractions come out of the column. An advantage of this type of detector is that it reads directly in grams, knowing the molecular weight of the gas involved. It does not need response factors as do the other detectors (see page 179).

The ultrasonic detector depends on the variation of the velocity of sound waves traveling through different gaseous media. The time required for a sound wave to travel through a sample cell is compared with the time required for the sound wave to travel through the same distance of carrier gas. The comparison is made by measuring the phase difference between the reference and sample signals. The phase difference is related to sample composition.

Of course, preparative or large-scale gas chromatography is also used for analysis of trace quantities. This permits the use of a large sample ($50 \, \mu l$ to 2 to 5 ml) to obtain enough of the desired fraction to be detectable. The trace component can either be detected directly, or the preparative-scale procedure can be used to concentrate the desired material in an impure fraction which can be isolated and then inserted into a normal-scale chromatograph for further resolution. Very large batches of material, up to several liters, can also be chromatographed in increments of a few milliliters per individual run. Fraction collectors pool

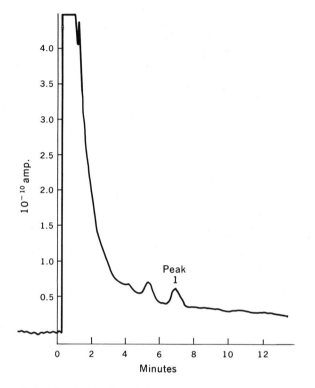

Fig. 8-2 Analysis of broccoli extract. Column: 6 ft × 0.085 in. 1.0, stainless steel. Column packing: SE-30 methyl silicone gum rubber on HMDS-treated Chromosorb W, 80/100 mesh (1.5/98.5 w/w). Carrier gas: 5% CH₄ in A. Carrier gas flow rate: analytical column—100 ml/min; scavenge—66 ml/min. Temperature of injector, column, and detector: 275, 185, and 220°C, respectively. Model 800 gas chromatograph with electron capture detector. Applied potential: pulse. Leeds & Northrup Speedomax 6.5 mv recorder with attenuation × 200. Peak 1 approximately 0.1 ppm p, p¹ — DDT. (*Reprinted with permission from Perkin-Elmer Corp., E. W. Cieplinski, Application Bulletin No. GC-AP-005 1964.*)

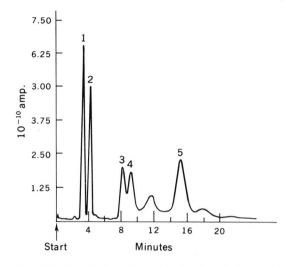

Fig. 8-3 Analysis of a standard solution of pesticides. Column: 6 ft × 0.085 in. I.D., stainless steel. Column packing: SE-30 silicone gum rubber on HMDS-treated Chromosorb W, 80/100 mesh (1.5/98.5, w/w). Carrier gas: 5% CH_4 in argon. Carrier gas flow rate: analytical column—30 ml/min; scavenge—45 ml/min. Temperature of injection block, column, and detector: 250, 175, and 210°C, respectively. Model 800 gas chromatograph with electron capture detector. Applied potential: Pulse. Leeds & Northrup Speedomax 65-mv recorder with attenuation × 500. Peaks: 1 Heptachlor (2×10^{-9} g); 2 Aldrin (1×10^{-9} g); 3 Dieldrin (3×10^{-9} g); 4 Endrin (2×10^{-9} g); 5 DDT (6×10^{-9} g). (*Reprinted with permission from Perkin-Elmer Corp., E. W. Cieplinski, Application Bulletin No. GC-AP-005, 1964.*)

amounts eluting at specific retention times. This practice permits further concentration of small quantities.

Polarography

Polarography was discussed on pages 35–37 for the detection and determination of small quantities of elements and on pages 79–87 for the detection and determination of small quantities of compounds via their functional groups.

Table 8-4 Trace analysis—summary comparison of methods

Approach	General qualitative applicability	General quantitative applicability		Cost†	Destructive or nondestructive analysis	Problems with interferences	General time of analysis‡	Usage
		Sensitivity*	Selectivity					
Color spot test	High	...	...	Low	D	Depend on specific case	Generally short	Widespread
Fluorescence spot test	Low	...	...	Low	D or ND	Variable	Generally short	Limited
Low-temperature luminescence	Low	...	...	Low	ND	Variable	Short to moderate	Limited
Ultraviolet and visible absorption	Fair	0.1–100 ppm	Good	Low to moderate	D and ND§	Circumventable	Short to moderate	Widespread
Fluorimetry	Fair	1 ppb–10 ppm	Good	Low to moderate	D and ND	Common but circumventable	Short to moderate	Limited
Quenchofluorimetry	Low	1 ppb–10 ppm	Excellent	Low to moderate	D and ND	Common but circumventable	Short to moderate	Limited
Phosphorimetry	Low	1 ppb–10 ppm	Good	Low to moderate	D and ND	Common but circumventable	Short to moderate	Very limited
Gas chromatography	Fair	1 ppb–100 ppm	Excellent	Low to moderate	ND	Slight	Short	Very widespread
Polarography	Fair	1–100 ppm	Good	Low	D	Variable	Short to moderate	Fairly widespread

Table 8-4 Trace analysis—summary comparison of methods (continued)

Approach	General qualitative applicability	General quantitative applicability		Cost†	Destructive or nondestructive analysis	Problems with interferences	General time of analysis‡	Usage
		Sensitivity*	Selectivity					
Mass spectrometry	Excellent	10 ppb–10 ppm	Excellent	High	D	Variable	Short to moderate	Limited now but growing rapidly
Atomic absorption Arc-spark spectroscopy Neutron activation Flame photometry } See Chap. 2.								

* Sensitivity is given in relative quantities. The range stated is the general lower limit of sensitivity. In a few cases tests may be more sensitive than the low end of the stated range, and in a few cases tests may not be as sensitive as the high end of the stated range.

† Low denotes <$5,000; moderate denotes $5,000 to $25,000; high denotes >$25,000.

‡ Short denotes <1 hr; moderate denotes 1 to 4 hr; long denotes >4 hr.

§ If reactions are used before the spectrophotometric measurement, the analysis is destructive.

Mass Spectrometry

Double-focusing mass spectrometry, as discussed on pages 31–33 and 46 for the elements, on page 87 for functional groups, and on pages 100–102 for compounds, has made possible the detection and determination of trace quantities. It is being used to a progressively greater degree, especially in the analysis of highly pure metals.

Literature Cited

1   F. T. Fox, E. Sawicki, and S. McPherson, Pittsburgh Conference on Analytical Chemistry and Applied Spectroscopy, March 1962. Also in discussion by F. T. Fox, Symposium on Analysis of Carcinogenic Air Pollutants, in E. Sawicki and K. Cassel, Jr. (eds.), *Natl. Cancer Inst. Monograph*, (9):220 (1962).

2   A. P. Altshuller and T. A. Bellar, *J. Air Pollution Control Assoc.*, **13**:81 (1963).

3   F. T. Eggertsen and F. M. Nelsen, *Anal. Chem.*, **30**:1040 (1958).

4   N. Carugno, Analysis of Carcinogenic Air Pollutants, in E. Sawicki and K. Cassel, Jr. (eds.), *Natl. Cancer Inst. Monograph*, (9):171 (1962).

5   D. Hoffman and E. C. Wynder, *Cancer*, **15**:93 (1962).

6   B. L. Van Duuren, *J. Natl. Cancer Inst.*, **21**(1):623 (1958).

7   E. Sawicki, T. R. Hauser, W. C. Elbert, F. T. Fox, and J. E. Meeker, *Am. Ind. Hyg. Assoc. J.*, **23**:137 (1962).

8   E. Sawicki, J. Meeker, and M. Morgan, *Intern. J. Air Water Pollution*, **9**:291(1965).

9   D. Bender, E. Sawicki, and R. Wilson, Jr., *Intern. J. Air Water Pollution*, 1964.

10 H. F. Mueller, T. E. Larson, and W. J. Lennarz, *Anal. Chem.*, **30**:41 (1958).

11 P. Magidman, S. F. Herb, R. A. Barbord, and R. W. Riemenschneider, *J. Am. Oil Chemists' Soc.*, **39**:137 (1962).

12 S. F. Herb, P. Magidman, F. E. Luddy, and R. W. Riemenschneider, *J. Am. Oil Chemists' Soc.*, **39**:142 (1962).

13 C. Yang and S. H. Wender, *J. Chromatog.*, **8**:82 (1962).

14 R. K. Ibrahim and G. H. N. Towers, *Arch. Biochem. Biophys.*, **87**:125 (1960).

15 E. O. A. Haahti and E. C. Horning, *Acta Chem. Scand.*, **15**:930 (1961).

16 K. H. Palmork, *Acta Chem. Scand.*, **17**:1456 (1963).

17 B. E. Langlois, A. R. Stemp, and B. J. Liska, *J. Agr. Food Chem.*, **12**:243 (1964).

18 J. Montreuil, *Pathol. Biol. Semaine Hop.*, **10**:719 (1962).

19 H. H. Wotiz and H. F. Martin, *Anal. Biochem.*, **3**:97 (1962).

20 E. Dingemanse, L. G. H. Veld, and S. L. Hartogh-Katz, *J. Clin. Endocrinol. Metab.*, **12**:66 (1952).

21 C. J. O. R. Morris and D. C. Williams, *Ciba Found. Colloq. Endocrinol.*, **8**:157 (1955), Churchill, London.

22 E. Sawicki and H. Johnson, *Microchem. J.*, **8**:85 (1964).

23 H. Varley, "Practical Clinical Biochemistry," 3d ed., Interscience Publishers (Division of John Wiley & Sons, Inc.), New York, 1963.

24 R. J. Henry, "Clinical Chemistry: Principles and Technics," Harper & Row, Publishers, Incorporated, New York, 1964.

25 M. B. Jacobs, "The Chemical Analysis of Air Pollutants," John Wiley & Sons, Inc., New York, 1960.

26 E. Sawicki, *Record Chem. Progr.*, **22**:249 (1961).

27 F. D. Snell, C. T. Snell, and C. A. Snell, "Colorimetric Methods of Analysis," vol. III A, D. Van Nostrand Company, Inc., Princeton, N.J., 1959. (And other volumes in the series.)

28 "Organic Electronic Spectral Data," vols. I, II, III, IV, etc., Interscience Publishers (Division of John Wiley & Sons, Inc.), New York. (Literature covered from 1946 to 1959, etc.)

29 E. Sawicki, T. W. Stanley, and J. Pfaff, *Chemist-Analyst*, **51**:9 (1962).

30 E. Sawicki, T. W. Stanley, and H. Johnson, *Chemist-Analyst*, **52**:4 (1963).

31 E. Sawicki, T. W. Stanley, and W. C. Elbert, *Talanta*, **11**: 1431–1439 (1964).

32 E. Sawicki, T. W. Stanley, and H. Johnson, *Mikrochim. Acta.*, 118 (1965).

33 J. Black and E. Morgan, *Anal. Chem.*, **34**:1647 (1962).

34 J. D. Winefordner and P. A. St. John, *Anal. Chem.*, **35**:2211 (1963).

35 E. Sawicki and J. D. Pfaff, *Mikrochim. Acta.*, 322 (1966).

36 G. N. Lewis and M. Kasha, *J. Am. Chem. Soc.*, **66**:2100 (1944).

37 R. J. Kiers, R. D. Britt, Jr., and W. E. Wentworth, *Anal. Chem.*, **29**:202 (1957).

38 E. Sawicki, T. R. Hauser, and T. W. Stanley, *Anal. Chem.*, **31**:2063 (1959).

39 H. M. McNair and E. J. Bonnelli, "Basic Gas Chromatography," pp. v-1 to v-15, Varian Aerograph, 2700 Mitchell Dr., Walnut Creek, Calif., April, 1966.

Suggested Readings
General

Yoe, J. H., and H. J. Koch: "Trace Analysis," John Wiley & Sons, Inc., New York, 1957. (General methods for elements and compounds.)

Color Spot Tests

Felgl, F.: "Spot Tests," vols. 1 and 2, Elsevier Publishing Company, Amsterdam, 1954.

Fluorescence and Phosphorescence

Hercules, D. M.: "Fluorescence & Phosphorescence Analysis: Principles & Applications," John Wiley & Sons, Inc., New York, 1966.

Udenfriend, S.: "Fluorescence Assay in Biology & Medicine," Academic Press Inc., New York, 1962.

White, C. E., and A. Weissler: Fluorometric Analysis, in "Standard Methods of Chemical Analysis," 6th ed., vol. 3, pt. A, F. Welcher (ed.), D. Van Nostrand Company, Inc., Princeton, N.J., 1966, pp. 78–104. (Brief survey on fluorimetry.)

Colorimetry and Nephelometry

Snell, F. D.: "Colorimetry," 3d ed., D. Van Nostrand Company, Inc., Princeton, N.J., 1948–1959. (Comprehensive four volumes covering elements and compounds.)

Gas Chromatography

Dal Nogare, S., and R. S. Juvet: "Gas-Liquid Chromatography," Interscience Publishers (Division of John Wiley & Sons, Inc.), New York, 1962. (Comprehensive text covering theory and practice.)

McNair, H. M., and E. J. Bonelli: "Basic Gas Chromatography," Varian Aerograph, 2700 Mitchell Dr., Walnut Creek, Calif., April, 1966. (Excellent compilation, especially for beginners in gas chromatography.)

NINE

ASSAY IN THE
RANGE OF
HIGH PURITY

In our modern technology it is frequently essential that we obtain high-purity materials. This is true not only in the area of pharmaceuticals and semiconductors, but high-purity metals are now being manufactured and new ones sought. For example, aluminum of purity greater than 99.99% is required for certain bright-finishing operations. This material is also used for foil in electrical capacitors and in battery applications. Copper of better than 99.9% purity is used where high conductivity is required, and tantalum of greater than 99.9% purity is used in capacitors. Also, high-purity chemicals are no longer a rarity; for example, 99% or higher purity hydrofluoric acid is used in the preparation of nuclear fuel materials, 99.999% purity ammonia is required in certain metal-finishing operations. Monomers are generally of higher purity than 99%, since small amounts of impurities can affect the rate of polymerization and hence the quality of the final polymer.

High purity, of course, is a relative term. Ninety-five percent purity is high for certain organic materials. The common quantitative analytical techniques generally permit assays to a precision or accuracy of no better than ±0.5 to 1% relative. For materials of 95% purity or less, the assay methods discussed elsewhere in this text will apply. However, as the purity approaches 100%, the existing assay methods cannot apply. For example, such methods could not adequately assay a 99% material, since the range of the methods is the range of purity. In this chapter, when we speak of a high purity, we are discussing materials better than 98% pure. There are cases in our technology where purities better than 99.999% are demanded.

One common method of determining the purity of a high-purity material is to determine all the impurities and subtract their amount from 100% to obtain the content of the major component. This overcomes the previously mentioned problem of the lack of sufficient precision and accuracy of the common direct assay methods. Let us say we have 1.0% of total impurities; we can readily obtain this figure to ±0.1% absolute or better, but we can only get a direct assay of the major component to ±1% absolute. Hence, by the difference technique our value of 99.0% for the major component can only be off by ±0.1%. This technique is good only *if all the impurities in the system are known;* any unknown component gets included with the major component in the sample. It must be added that since we rarely know all the impurities in a sample, this technique is subject to error.

The preferred technique for assay is one which measures the major component.

FREEZING-POINT COOLING-CURVE TECHNIQUE

It is known that impurities in a material will lower its freezing point. Within limits, the freezing-point lowering is proportional to the molal content of the impurity.

$$\Delta T = m_i k$$

where T = freezing-point lowering

m_i = moles of impurity in 1,000 g of sample

k = a constant

If a plot is made of temperature versus time on cooling a pure liquid, a curve such as I in Fig. 9-1 is obtained. The rapid drop in temperature shown by A is the initial cooling of the sample caused by the refrigerant. The dip B is due to supercooling of the material before crystallization takes place. As soon as crystallization starts, the temperature rises to the solid-liquid equilibrium temperature (freezing or melting point) and remains at that level C, due to the heat of fusion of the material, until all the liquid has frozen. Then, after the sample is completely frozen, the temperature will resume its decline as shown in D. The freezing point X is determined by extrapolating the C portion of the curve back to A.

If the liquid is impure, however, a curve such as II, Fig. 9-1, is obtained. In this case, the freezing point X_1 is lower, due to the impurity; also, the liquid-solid equilibrium portion of the curve is no longer linear but slopes downward. This is due to the fact that on freezing only the major component or a eutectic thereof solidifies, leaving the remaining liquid less pure than before. This liquid then freezes at a lower and lower temperature as more major component freezes out of solution.

The purity of the sample can be calculated by measuring the tem-

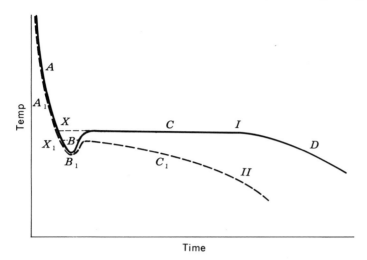

Fig. 9-1 Freezing curves of pure and impure liquids.
[*Reprinted with permission from S. Siggia and H. J. Stolten,
"An Introduction to Modern Organic Analysis," Interscience
Publishers (Division of John Wiley & Sons, Inc.), 1954, p. 134.*]

perature lowering $(X - X_1)$ or ΔT. It is known from theory that one
mole of impurity per 1,000 g of material will lower the freezing point of
that material by a constant amount. This constant k is known as the
molal freezing-point (depression) constant or cryoscopic constant. The
value of k is determined with pure material by adding known amounts
of impurity, measuring the resultant lowering, and then calculating on
the basis of one mole of impurity per 1,000 g of material, using the
equation below. Thus, knowing k for the material in question, if W_s
grams of sample containing m_i moles of impurity were taken and frozen,
then the observed temperature lowering follows the expression

$$\Delta T = m_i k \frac{1,000}{W_s}$$

Since W_s is the weighed sample, k is predetermined with pure material, and ΔT is the observed freezing point subtracted from the freezing
point of the pure material, one can then calculate m_i, moles of impurity
in an unknown sample. Knowing the molecular weight of the impurity,
the weight can be computed and with this a weight-percent purity.

For the best work, one should have a pure sample of the material of
interest, so that an accurate value for the freezing point of this material
can be obtained. Also, a good value for k can be obtained. Thus the

values for ΔT and k will be experimentally as sound as possible. However, it is not always possible to obtain an absolutely pure sample; the shape of the cooling curve reveals the presence of impurity, as discussed above. There is a technique for estimating the freezing point of the pure form of a material using an impure sample of that material. With this value, one can then determine the approximate purity of the impure material. This is accomplished by cooling a sample at a constant rate. The cooling curve is plotted as in Fig. 9-2. The solid-liquid portion

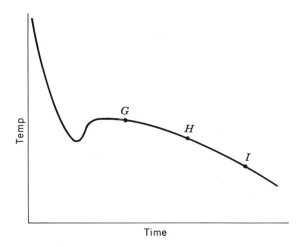

Fig. 9-2 Obtaining the freezing point of a pure material from an impure sample. [*Reprinted with permission from S. Siggia and H. J. Stolten, "An Introduction to Modern Organic Analysis," Interscience Publishers (Division of John Wiley & Sons, Inc.), 1954, p. 135.*]

of this curve should represent ¼ to ½ of the total sample (to ensure good equilibrium, a good slush should be maintained. If the sample gets too solid, the temperature readings can be in error). Points G, H, and I are selected on this curve so that H is the midpoint between G and I. The freezing point of the pure material, t_p, can be calculated using the equation*

$$t_p = t_G + \frac{(t_G - t_I)}{(u - 1)}$$

* The derivation of this equation and further details concerning this technique can be found in Ref. 1.

where $u = (t_H - t_I)/(t_G - t_H)$

t_G, t_H, t_I = freezing temperatures of the impure sample at points G, H, and I

It was discussed above that the freezing temperature of an impure sample decreases as freezing occurs, because of the continual concentration of the impurity in the unfrozen portion; the equation above is based on the fact that, keeping the cooling rate constant, the rate of change of the freezing temperature is a function of the amount of impurity present.

Knowing the approximate value for t_p and determining the freezing point of the actual sample by extrapolation (see page 247), one then has Δt and can calculate the approximate purity of the sample at hand. The value for k can be determined by known additions as described above. These t_p and purity values are described as only *approximate*, because of experimental limitations. In theory, these values should be true values. However, it is difficult to maintain a constant rate of cooling in many cases. Also, supercooling often results in too much crystallization early in the freezing step and one has too small an equilibrium portion of the curve for good data. Hence, though the t_p and purity values are generally good and quite usable, they are rarely as good as the values obtained when measurements are made with a pure sample.

There are several points to keep in mind in assaying materials by the freezing-point–cooling-curve technique. Cooling must not be too fast. Since an equilibrium between liquid and solid states is being observed, time must be allowed for true equilibrium conditions to be established. Too fast freezing results in trapping liquid phase in the solid, thus deviating from true equilibrium. Also, too fast cooling can result in too much supercooling of the liquid, resulting in massive crystallization when this is initated. This then results not only in much trapped liquid phase in the solid phase, but also in too little liquid phase for good temperature measurements.

Some materials tend to supercool and good freezing curves cannot be obtained. In these cases, a melting curve is obtained. This curve is just the reverse of the freezing curve, and supercooling (or rather superheating, since we are talking in reverse) cannot occur. One might ask why not determine the freezing point from the melting curve all the time. The problem is one of mechanics. In melting, one starts with a solid; this is difficult to agitate to get good heat transfer, and thus one cannot get good solid-liquid equilibrium.

It is well to remind the reader that a freezing-point assay yields molal purity owing to the nature of the process and the calculations.

To obtain weight-percent purity, one needs the molecular weight of the impurity. Since the impurities are not always known, weight-percent assays are sometimes not possible.

Another point of which the reader should be aware is that the impurities are not always present in the sample in molecular form. These impurities often interact with each other, or with themselves (dimerize or otherwise polymerize). Hence, their effect on the temperature lowering is less than what is expected. The determined molal purity, of course, will be a true value; however, a weight-percent purity cannot be computed, because the true molecular weight of the impurities in solution cannot be determined. In other cases, the impurities will dissociate into multiple ions, yielding a larger temperature-lowering than expected.

It is well also for the reader to keep in mind that "purity" in the freezing sense can mean something different from what might be expected. For example, a eutectic mixture is a "pure" material when examined by the freezing-point–cooling-curve technique. This is a mixture that crystallized out in constant composition, and hence will appear as a single material. Also, if a mixture contains a number of materials, some of which form a eutectic, the eutectic will appear as an additional impurity, different from any of the others, even though it is composed of them; hence, there will appear to be $x + 1$ materials in this case. Hydrates and solvates in general act as eutectics. A crystallized material may come down as an apparently pure material; the cooling curve verifies purity, yet molar equivalents of solvent may be incorporated in that solid which are undesirable to the chemist. Thus, he would miss them with a freezing-point–cooling-curve assay.

The sensitivity of the freezing-assay method depends on:

1. *The nature of the material* (crystallization properties, such as tendency to supercool, tendency to form a glass rather than to crystallize).

2. *The magnitude of the molal depression constant k* for the material in question (the bigger the constant, the bigger the temperature effect per amount of impurity). Table 9-1 shows k values for some common materials.

3. *The sensitivity of the temperature-measuring device.* (We are assuming adequate agitation which is critical.)

Items 1 and 2 cannot be controlled, because they are inherent in the sample. Item 3 can be controlled, however. Thermometers reading to 0.1°C are common. Beckmann thermometers reading to 0.005°C are also common. Platinum-resistance thermometers measuring to 0.0005°C are obtainable. Also, thermistors are usable to 0.0001°C. In the case of thermistors, however, though temperature differences (Δt

Table 9-1   Cryoscopic constants for various materials

Solvent	k
Water	1.86
Acetic acid	3.9
Benzene	5.1
Naphthalene	6.9
Bromoform	14.4
Cyclohexane	20.0
Camphor	37.7

SOURCE: Reprinted with permission from S. Siggia and H. J. Stolten, "An Introduction to Modern Organic Analysis," Interscience Publishers, New York, 1954, p. 132.

above) can be accurately and sensitively measured, the determination of the actual temperature of the system is difficult. The same can be said of the Beckmann thermometer. Thermocouples with sensitivities better than $\pm0.1°C$ are not common. However, thermopiles (series of multiple thermocouples) can be constructed which magnify the sensitivity according to the number of junctions used. However, operating troubles are also magnified with the number of junctions.

The freezing-assay method is widely used. The degree of sensitivity of the assay by freezing can be roughly gauged as follows. If we assume a material that gives no crystallization problems and which has a k of $10°$ per mole of impurity per 1,000 g of material, a temperature measurement limit of $0.1°C$ would be equivalent to 0.01 mole of impurity. If we assume a molecular weight of 100, this then means 1 g of impurity per 1,000 g of sample or 0.1%. Every factor of 10 in the temperature sensitivity affects the limit of sensitivity accordingly. Thus, if one can measure to $0.001°C$ in the above case, one should be able to assay the material to 0.001% impurity. Though this discussion of sensitivity has been idealized, it gives some idea of the sensitivity of this approach, and indicates that direct assays of 98% or purer material are quite possible.

Some common applications of the freezing-assay method in the chemical industry are the assay of benzene, phenol, and mercury. Also, monomers such as styrene and vinylpyrrolidone are often assayed by this technique, because high and reproducible purity of monomers is required for polymers with the correct and reproducible properties.

BOILING-POINT METHOD

The approach is analogous to the freezing-point approach and the mathematics is identical, except that Δt in this case is a temperature rise instead of the lowering seen in the freezing-point method. The effect of an impurity in a material can be pictured as follows: the molecules of impurity get in the way of the molecules of the pure material. On cooling, these molecules of impurity impede the alignment of the molecules of pure material into crystals; hence more cooling is required with impure materials to achieve crystallization than with pure ones. Similarly, on boiling, the molecules of impurity impede the molecules of pure material from going from the liquid state to the gaseous state. This means that more heat has to be put in to overcome this impedance, and hence the boiling point is raised.

The boiling-point method, however, has some distinct disadvantages over the freezing-point method. In the freezing method, supercooling occurs, but once crystallization begins, a good, stable equilibrium between solid and liquid phases is obtained, and hence, good temperature readings are obtained. However, in the boiling method, super-heating occurs continually and erratically, causing difficulty in obtaining good temperature readings. The higher the sensitivity required of the measurement, the more important this temperature behavior becomes. Superheating is minimized with boiling chips, sealed glass capillaries, glass wool, and the like, but it is difficult to eradicate. For the boiling method to work, the temperature measurement must be made in the boiling liquid. If one measures the temperature of the condensing liquid in the vapor space of the vessel, one gets the condensation temperature of the vapor which is the boiling point of the pure solvent, if the impurity is nonvolatile and hence still in the boiling liquid. The condensate may contain an impurity from the system that boils lower than the major component, and the condensation temperature is then quite far from the actual boiling temperature. In impure materials, the condensation temperature is always lower than the actual boiling temperature.

The freezing-point–cooling-curve method has its problems with eutectic or constant-freezing compositions; the boiling method involves azeotropic or constant-boiling compositions, and a mixture of A and B can exist as an azeotrope AB which will appear as a pure material. The discussions of eutectics on page 250 can be applied exactly to azeotropes.

All in all, the boiling approach is used little for determining purity. The freezing approach is used much more widely.

PHASE-SOLUBILITY ANALYSIS*

Phase-solubility analysis is nothing more than the determination of the equilibrium solubility of a material in a given solvent under specific conditions. A pure material will have a specific solubility. However, an impure material will appear to yield a greater solubility, because of the presence of the impurities in the solution. Each component in an impure sample will dissolve independently to its own solubility, so that the net dissolved material is the sum of the solubilities of each component (this is analogous to the relationship of partial pressures of a gas mixture to total pressure). This statement holds if there are no solute-solute interactions; if such interactions occur, solubility can be augmented beyond the simple sum or it can be inhibited, depending on the specific effect of the interaction.

The phase-solubility analysis is carried out by adding varying amounts of solute to constant volumes of solvent and allowing equilibrium to establish itself by agitation at constant conditions. The solution portions are then analyzed for dissolved material. A phase diagram is constructed, plotting the weight of solute found per unit volume of solution against the weight of sample added per unit volume of solvent used. The phase-solubility curve obtained for a pure material is shown in Fig. 9-3. The segment AB represents the portion of the curve where all the sample dissolved and, as a result, has a slope of unity. Segment BC represents the equilibrium solubility where a fixed amount dissolved, regardless of how much sample was added. Extrapolation of BC to the axis at S indicates the solubility of the sample.

Figure 9-4 is the phase-solubility diagram for a three-component system. Segment AB again represents the total solution of sample and has a slope of unity. At point B the solution is saturated with respect to one component, and line BC represents continued solubility of the other two components. At point C the solution is saturated with respect to two components, and segment CD represents the continued solubility of the third component. At point D the solution is saturated with respect to all components. The order in which components reach saturation depends on their solubilities and their concentrations in the sample. The extrapolation of BC of the curve yields the solubility of the first component to reach saturation. The extrapolation of CD yields the sum of the solubilities of the first two materials to reach saturation; and the extrapolation of DE represents the total solubility of the sample. Since line BC represents the solubility of the two components not at

* This discussion is an abbreviated version of Ref. 2.

saturation, the slope of BC is equal to the fraction of these two components. Similarly, the slope of CD is equal to the fraction of the third component. Evaluation of the slopes therefore can yield the fractional composition of the mixture.

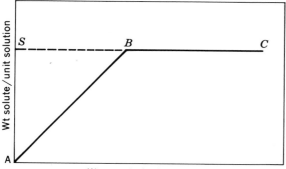

Fig. 9-3 Phase-solubility diagram of a pure compound. [*Reprinted with permission from T. Higuchi and K. A. Connors, "Advances in Analytical Chemistry and Instrumentation," C. N. Reilley (ed.), vol. 4, Interscience Publishers (Division of John Wiley & Sons, Inc.), New York, 1965.*]

The limitations of the phase solubility method are as follows [2, p. 131]:

1. The solubility of each component must not be affected by the presence of the other component.

2. The components must not form a solid solution.

3. The components must not be present in the sample in the ratio of their solubilities.

Item 1 is considered the most commonly occurring drawback.

The solvent chosen for phase-solubility analysis is such that only about 0.1 to 1% of the major component dissolves, and the solvent must permit easy analysis of the solution phase.

There are variations in procedure. The above technique is an approach where solubility is measured under fixed conditions. However, Reeve and Adams [3] kept sample and solvent constant and varied the temperature, determining a "temperature of solution." Stenger, Crummett, and Kramer [4] carried out a Soxhlet extraction, removing the impurity with a solvent in which the main component is only spar-

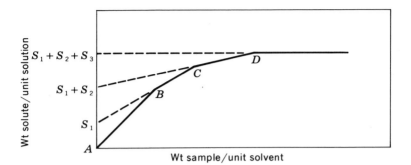

Fig. 9-4   Phase-solubility diagram of a three-component mixture. [*Reprinted with permission from T. Higuchi and K. A. Connors, "Advances in Analytical Chemistry and Instrumentation," C. N. Reilley (ed.), vol. 4, Interscience Publishers (Division of John Wiley & Sons, Inc.), New York, 1965.*]

ingly soluble. This permits analysis of high-purity materials with less than 0.5% of impurity. The conventional phase-solubility approach cannot generally distinguish impurity levels below this value.

ELECTRICAL TECHNIQUES*

There are four electrical techniques of measurement which can be applied to the assay of high-purity materials. These four techniques are *conductivity, Hall effect, residual resistivity,* and *thermally stimulated currents.* The first two are applied to semiconductors, the third is applied to metals, and the fourth to insulators. All techniques are non-specific with regard to impurities and measure solely the net effect of all impurities, yielding the general impurity level of an ultrahigh-purity material. These methods are used mainly with inorganic solids, though they can be applied to inorganic liquids also.

The four electrical techniques discussed below have the following advantages: (1) they are of very high sensitivity, extending to 1 ppb in some cases; (2) the measurements take only from 10 to 100 min to accomplish; (3) the measurements have a fairly high relative precision of about 10%; (4) the analyses are nondestructive; (5) the equipment generally costs less than $5,000.

* This section is an abbreviated form of Ref. 5.

Table 9-2 below shows each approach. The materials on which it is applied, the resistivities p of these materials, and the effect of the impurities used as a basis of the measurement are summarized.

Table 9-2

Method	Effect of impurity	Material
Conductivity and Hall effect	Adds current carriers (electrons, holes, ions)	Semiconductors ($10^{-4} > p > 10^4$)
Residual resistivity	Scatters current carriers (lowers mobility)	Metals ($p > 10^{-4}$)
Thermally stimulated currents	Traps current carriers	Insulators ($p > 10^4$)

Conductivity

The sample to be measured can be solid or liquid, and monocrsytalline or polycrystalline. The resistance (reciprocal of conductivity) is measured by measuring the current flowing through a sample when a

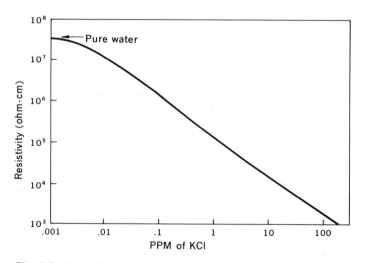

Fig. 9-5   Variation of resistivity with impurity concentration in water at room temperature. [*Reprinted with permission from L. R. Weisberg, Anal. Chem.,* **38**:34A (1966).]

known voltage is applied. The resistivity p (or conductivity σ) is measured using the equation

(1) $p = \dfrac{RA}{L} = \dfrac{1}{\sigma}$

where R = measured resistance
A = cross-sectional area
L = distance between contacts

The impurity concentration level n per cubic centimeter is given by the equation

(2) $n = \dfrac{1}{peu}$

where e = electronic charge
u = Hall mobility

But since u is not absolutely known, Eq. (2) is not usable unless the Hall effect is applied to determine u (see page 258).

Conductivity measurements are usually used in semiconductor-type materials where there are so few electrons present that the electrons contributed by the impurities have a significant effect. Figure 9-5 shows the variation of resistivity of water with traces of salt present and Fig. 9-6 shows the same type of plot for impurities in germanium.

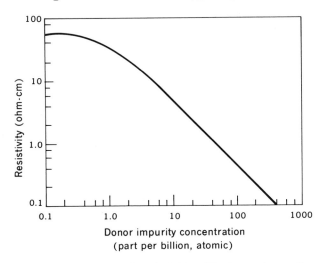

Fig. 9-6 Variation of resistivity with donor impurity concentration in germanium at room temperature. [*Reprinted with permission from L. R. Weisberg, Anal. Chem.*, **38**:35A (1966).]

Hall Effect

In this measurement, the sample with thickness t is placed in a magnetic field and a current I is passed through the sample. The magnetic field causes a transverse voltage, the Hall voltage V_H, to be

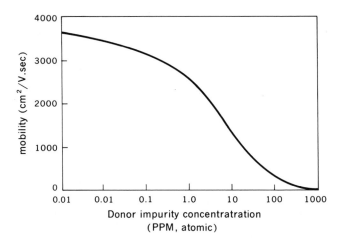

Fig. 9-7   Variation of electron Hall mobility with donor impurity concentration in germanium at room temperature. [*Reprinted with permission from L. R. Weisberg, Anal. Chem.,* **38**:35A (1966).]

set up across the sample. This voltage is measured. The impurity concentration n is then:

$$(3) \quad n = \frac{-IH10^{-8}}{V_H}$$

where H = magnetic field

The Hall effect is independent of the mobility u; so the value of u can be calculated by getting the impurity level n from Eq. (3) and substituting it into Eq. (2), providing the resistivity is known.

The Hall effect is also used on semiconductor materials, and for the same reasons as discussed above for conductivity, electrons added by impurities to an electron-deficient material have a pronounced effect on current. Figure 9-7 shows the variation of Hall mobility with impurity concentration in the case of germanium at room temperature.

Residual Resistivity Measurement

This is a resistivity measurement, as discussed above under conductivity; however, instead of measuring the resistivity directly, a ratio of the resistivity at room temperature or other conditions to the resistivity at 4.2°K (liquid He temperature) is used. Employing the ratio minimizes extraneous factors such as sample geometry, anisotropy, or electrode spacings.

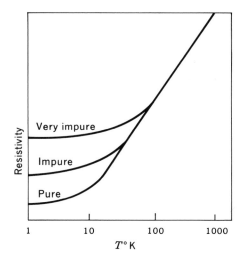

Fig. 9-8 Variation of resistivity with temperature in a metal. [*Reprinted with permission from L. R. Weisberg, Anal. Chem.*, **38**:33A (1966).]

Residual resistivity is used to determine the impurities in metals where there are so many electrons present that they overwhelm the effect of the electrons from impurities. This situation makes impossible the use of direct resistivity as discussed above.

In this case, the scattering of the electrons by the impurities is the basis of the measurement. The scattering varies with temperature and causes the variation in resistivity. Figure 9-8 shows the variation of resistivity with temperature. This is the basis of this measurement.

This technique has been used to measure the purity of copper, aluminum, gallium, and indium, among others.

Thermally Stimulated Current

In insulating materials, the trace impurities far outnumber the electrons, so one uses the trapping effect of the impurities on the electrons to detect their presence. The escape of the electrons from a trap is a temperature-dependent process. If a trap is filled at low temperatures (below 78°K), the charge carriers cannot escape except after very long

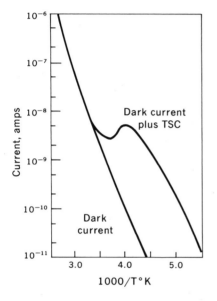

Fig. 9-9 Variation of current with temperature with 100 volts applied to GaAs crystal: Dark current, and dark current plus thermally stimulated current (TSC). [*Reprinted with permission from L. R. Weisberg, Anal. Chem.,* **38**:39A (1966).]

periods of time, hours or days. However, on heating, a temperature is reached at which the electrons escape rapidly. When the electrons escape, a current can flow in the sample if a voltage is applied. This is called the thermally stimulated current (TSC) and causes a peak in the plot of current versus temperature (see Fig. 9-9). By integrating the area under the peak, the total number of electrons N_{tsc} that have flowed can be counted. However, this figure does not include the electrons that escaped from the traps on their own. The ratio of electrons

Table 9-3 High purity analysis—summary table of methods

Approach	Main limitations	General limit of measurement	General cost of equipment*	General time of analysis†	Remarks
Freezing point–cooling curve	1. Material must crystallize 2. Material must be stable at melting point 3. Excessive supercooling must be avoided 4. Eutectic mixtures and solvates must be watched for	$\pm 0.001 - \pm 1\%$	Low	Moderate	Widely used
Boiling point	1. Superheating yields erratic temperature behavior 2. Material must be stable at the boiling point 3. Azeotropes are a problem	$\pm 0.001 - \pm 1\%$	Low	Moderate	Seldom used because problems under Main limitations are quite severe in this case, especially item 1
Phase solubility	1. Finding appropriate solvent system 2. Rather low sensitivity (see next column)	$\pm 0.5\%$	Low	High	Used widely for materials that decompose on melting and/or boiling
Electrical methods	1. Materials on which measurements can be made	Widely variable, depending on material	Low to moderate	Moderate	Used solely on conducting materials (metals) and insulators. Of little value with organic materials

* Low denotes <$5,000; moderate denotes $5,000 to $15,000; high denotes >$15,000.
† Low denotes <0.5 hr; moderate denotes 0.5 to 2 hr; high denotes >2 hr.

that escaped to those actually counted is measured by generating in the sample a known concentration of electrons per unit volume per second, N_{pc}, shining a calibrated light source on it and measuring the photo-current ΔI. The impurity concentration n is given by the equation:

$$n = \frac{N_{tsc}N_{pc}}{\Delta I}$$

Literature Cited

1   A. R. Glasgow, Jr., A. J. Streiff, and F. D. Rossini, *J. Res. Nat. Bur. Std.*, **35**:355 (1945).
2   T. Higuchi and K. A. Connors, "Advances in Analytical Chemistry and Instrumentation," vol. 4, C. N. Reilley (ed.), Interscience Publishers (Division of John Wiley & Sons, Inc.), New York, 1965, pp. 117–210. (Good summary.)
3   W. Reeve and R. Adams, *Anal. Chem.*, **22**:755 (1950).
4   V. A. Stenger, W. B. Crummett, and W. R. Kramer, *ibid.*, **25**:974 (1953).
5   L. R. Weisberg, *Anal. Chem.*, **38**:31A–40A (1966). (A relatively short discussion of the subject.)

Suggested Readings

Freezing-point Cooling-curve Technique

Hickman, J. B.: *J. Chem. Ed.*, **25**:163–167 (1948).
Kirk, R. E., and D. F. Othmer (eds.): "Encyclopedia of Chemical Technology," vol. 8, pp. 839–857, Interscience Publishers (Division of John Wiley & Sons, Inc.), New York, 1952.
Mair, B. J., A. R. Glasgow, Jr., and F. D. Rossini: *J. Res. Natl. Bur. Std.*, **26**:591 (1941).
Skau, E. L., and H. R. Wakeman: Melting and Freezing Temperatures, in A. Weissberger (ed.), "Physical Methods of Organic Chemistry," 2d ed., vol. 1, pt. 1, pp. 49–105, Interscience Publishers (Division of John Wiley & Sons, Inc.), New York, 1949.
Streif, A. J., and F. D. Rossini: *J. Res. Natl. Bur. Std.*, **32**:185 (1944).
Taylor, W. J., and F. D. Rossini: *ibid.*, **32**:197 (1944).

Boiling-point Technique

Swietoslawski, W., and J. R. Anderson: Physical Methods, in A. Weissberger (ed.), "Technique of Organic Chemistry," 3d ed., vol. I, pt. I, Interscience Publishers (Division of John Wiley & Sons, Inc.), New York, pp. 384–390.

Phase-solubility Analysis

Higuchi, T., and K. A. Connors: "Advances in Analytical Chemistry and Instrumentation," C. N. Reilley (ed.), vol. 4, Interscience Publishers (Division of John Wiley & Sons, Inc.), New York, 1965, pp. 117–210.

Mader, W. J.: "Organic Analysis," vol. 2, Interscience Publishers (Division of John Wiley & Sons, Inc.), New York, 1954, p. 253.

Electrical Techniques

Weisberg, L. R.: Non-specific Methods for Analysis of Solids, George H. Morrison (ed.), "Trace Analysis," John Wiley & Sons, Inc., New York, 1965. (This a more detailed version of Ref. 5 and includes references to further details.)

TEN
TRACERS

NONRADIOACTIVE TRACERS

On mention of the word "tracers" one normally thinks of radioactive tracers; however, in practice many nonradioactive materials are used as tracers. A tracer, as the name implies, is a material used to determine the fate or source of a particular element or compound. In the case of elements, tracers are also used to help determine the structure of compounds and reaction mechanisms. Any element or compound that can be detected in very minute quantities and which is not common to the systems being studied makes a good tracer. For example, the author of this text has used lithium to trace water leakage into his laboratory. Lithium nitrate spread on the building roof leaked into the laboratory (though the laboratory was three stories below the roof). Lithium is not commonly found in concrete, and is easily and sensitively detected by flame photometry. The author has also used lithium to determine if the source of water in a product was from a mechanical leak in the cooling jacket, allowing cooling water to get into the reactors. Lithium nitrate was added to the cooling water. Manufacturers often "tag" their product with a specific element or compound which is sensitively and specifically detected. In this way they can quickly check with certainty that a given sample was manufactured by them.

Colored materials make excellent tracers. Seepage of sewage into water systems, for example, is often monitored by adding highly colored dyes to the sewage and watching the approaches to the water systems. Fluorescent materials are used to trace items and people unobtrusively, with ultraviolet light used to observe the tracer.

The advent of very sensitive gas-chromatographic techniques, such as that employing electron-capture detectors (pages 235–237), makes possible the use of volatile, easily detectable compounds as tracers. For example, carbon tetrachloride was added to a plant effluent to gauge the extent of river pollution. Carbon tetrachloride is readily detectable by electron-capture gas chromatography and is soluble enough for the purpose intended.

Odorous materials such as hydrogen sulfide, mercaptans, and other sulfur compounds are used in gases (or liquids) to trace leaks.

Nonradioactive isotopes such as deuterium, oxygen,[18] and nitrogen[15] are often used to elucidate reaction mechanisms. The isotope is placed in a given molecular position; then the reaction under study is carried out and the fate of the isotope is determined, usually by mass spectrometry. For example, the mechanism of the esterification reaction was traced by using methyl alcohol containing O^{18} isotope. The reaction

$$RCOOH + HO^{18}CH_3 \rightarrow RCOO^{18}CH_3 + H_2O$$

was run and the O^{18} was detected not in the water but in the ester. This indicates that the oxygen in the water originates in the acid [1].

Structure studies are also made simpler by the insertion of nonradioactive isotopes. Using starting materials containing isotopic atoms results in a compound with tags in certain areas. Mass spectrometry fragments the molecule, the fragments containing the tag are quickly spotted, and one can better interpret the fragmentation. In the area of structure determination, nuclear magnetic resonance spectrometry makes good use of nonradioactive atoms as tags. For example, hydrogen (proton) contains a magnetic nucleus which exhibits magnetic resonance. Deuterium does not have such a nucleus and hence is not detected by NMR. Hence, protons in suspected structures can be substituted by deuterium; if the resonances in question disappear, the point is made. Similar studies can be made with C^{13} which exhibits NMR properties while C^{12} does not; Sn^{119} exhibits NMR interaction, the other isotopes do not.

RADIOACTIVE TRACERS

Radioactive atoms make excellent tracers since very minute quantities of radioactivity can be detected. This type of tracing cannot be used as broadly as nonradioactive tracing because of the precautions and regulations in dealing with radioactivity. These tracers cannot be used where human exposure is involved. In most of the applications cited above in the discussion of nonradioactive tracers, it would be illegal to use radioactive tracers. Also, radioactive tracers have an additional disadvantage in that the molecule containing the tracer may be destroyed, but the radioactivity remains in one or more of the degradation products to yield misleading results. For example, in tracing pesticides, the pesticide may be metabolized by the plant or animal so that no active pesticide remains, yet the radioactivity remains in the breakdown products lodged in the plant or animal parts, making it appear that the pesticide is in these parts.

However, radioactive tracers have the advantage of being very easily detected in minute quantities; generally lower levels can be detected than by any other method. They can be detected photographically or electrically.

Photographic Detection

The fact that radioactive materials will affect a photographic emulsion is used in this approach. The blackening of the film or plate depends on the amount of radiation received. In general, the sample is prepared so that a flat plane can be put directly on the film or plate. Occasionally a sheet of cellophane, paper, or mica is put between the sample and the film. The exposure time varies with the activity of the tracer and the content of tracer in the material. The sample can be exposed as long as is needed to obtain the desired photographic image. The half-life of the isotope must be taken into account in the selected exposure time, since time intervals of longer than two half-lives produce little further blackening of the film. Fine-grained x-ray films, metallographic plates, or special alpha-ray plates are used. This is due to the fact that photographic enlargement is usually required, and grain size should be minimized in the resultant photographs.

The enlarged autoradiographs are similar to photomicrographs; only the distribution of the radioactive material is visible. For example, the effectiveness of cigarette filters was studied by incorporating a C^{14} tag in the tobacco during its growth. The resultant cigarette butts, all smoked to different lengths and containing the different filters, were sliced lengthwise and the flat portions of the hemicylinders were placed on photographic plates. The exposure to radioactivity made visible the distribution of combustion products through the butt and filter. Another example is the monitoring of the penetration of an antifungal agent through human skin. The agent was tagged with a radioactive tracer and was applied to a skin sample. The skin then was cross-sectioned. The cross section was applied to a photographic plate and an autoradiograph was obtained, showing insignificant penetration. Figure 10-1 shows the concentration of radiophosphorus in different parts of a plant.

Fig. 10-1 Autoradiogram of selectively absorbed radiophosphorus. (*Reprinted with permission from J. M. Cork, "Radioactivity and Nuclear Physics," 3d ed., D. Van Nostrand Company, Inc., Princeton, N.J., 1957, p. 351.*)

Electrical Detection

Radioactive tracers can be monitored by placing the material on one plate of a parallel-plate condenser with vacuum between the plates. The other plate is connected to a ground through a very sensitive galvanometer. The radioactivity will cause a small current to be detected.

Another method of detection is through ionization. When the radiation from the tracer strikes a material (a gas in this case), energy is transferred and ionization of the material takes place, forming equal numbers of positively charged ions and electrons. If allowed time, these ions and electrons would recombine. However, if these charged particles were exposed to an electric field, the positive ions would flow toward one electrode and the electrons would flow toward the other, causing a current to flow.

Counters utilize the ionization principle; the ionization chamber has a low capacitance and the detecting device can detect low voltages. Thus, on exposure to radiation of one particle at a time, individual pulses can be discriminated. There are many forms of counters, depending on the particles being monitored, the sensitivity desired, the sample being handled, and the information desired.

Literature Cited

1 J. B. Conant, "The Chemistry of Organic Compounds," The Macmillan Company, New York, 1939, p. 98.

Suggested Readings

Langer, Alois: "Physical Methods in Chemical Analysis," W. G. Berl (ed.), Academic Press Inc., New York, 1951, pp. 439–498. (Summary review for radiotracers only.)

Overman, R. T., and H. M. Clark: "Radioisotope Techniques," McGraw-Hill Book Company, New York, 1960.

Tollbert, B. M., and W. E. Siri: Physical Methods, in A. Weissberger (ed.), "Technique of Organic Chemistry," 3d ed., vol. 1, pt. IV, Interscience Publishers (Division of John Wiley & Sons, Inc.), New York, 1960, pp. 3335–3447. (Detailed review of radioactive measurements only.)

ELEVEN

ANALYTICAL
SEPARATIONS*

The purpose of this chapter is to examine the factors that influence the selection of a particular separative method for analyzing a specific sample. In the past, convention tied too many chemists to precipitation and distillation; currently, the broad applicability and success of gas chromatography have lulled many into thinking less than they should about optimizing the selection and performance of a separation. For that reason, an attempt has been made here to state explicitly some generalizations about different types of methods. For the most part, detailed descriptions of individual processes and lists of applications have not been given. These may be found in one or more of the references.

GOALS OF SEPARATION

Laboratory separations are carried out either for preparative or analytical purposes. In both cases, the chief goal is to isolate a pure compound from impurities which may include the solvent (or "carrier" component). The yield is generally of little concern in separations carried out only to identify the components of a sample. Even in preparative work, yield is usually of secondary interest to purity. However, in analytical separations that precede quantitative determinations, the more stringent the quantitative demands, the greater the emphasis on details that affect the reproducibility and completeness of the separation.

THE SEPARATION PROBLEM

From the standpoint of the physical-chemical principles involved and the number of possible variables, separations are easily understood.

* Written by L. B. Rogers, Chemistry Department, Purdue University, Lafayette, Ind.

After all, there are only three states of matter and a limited number of physical properties of chemical species on which separations can be based, such as size and shape, valence of an ion, polarity, polarizability, hydrogen-bonding ability of a molecule, and chemical reactivity. In practice, the situation is quite different. Except for valence, which changes in a step-function, a virtual continuum extends from one extreme to the other in *each* property, whether it be molecular weight or London interactions. In addition, the number of chemical compounds that can be called upon to sharpen separations by superimposing competitive chemical reactions or physical interactions is extremely large. Furthermore, any particular combination of species can have its interactions further modified by changes in temperature or pressure. Fortunately, the one or two approaches most likely to succeed for a particular sample can usually be selected on the assumption that one or two factors will dominate the rest.

The selection of the optimum procedure would indeed be relatively simple if only physical-chemical principles were involved, but there are other considerations which often prove to be overriding. First, the nature of the sample can be a powerful constraint. If the sample is very small, thermally and/or chemically unstable, very insoluble, or likely to contain a number of unknown substances, a number of otherwise obvious choices may be ruled out. A second constraint is the time available (or permitted) for the analysis. Time may be a deciding factor when a large number of samples are to be analyzed or a rapid reaction has to be followed. A third constraint is the level of accuracy and/or precision required. Unnecessarily high requirements for quantitation usually lead to excessively time-consuming procedures. The final limitation arises from a combination of availability of equipment and familiarity of the chemist with a wide variety of separation methods. Too often, a chemist falls into the habit of thinking in terms of only one or two separation techniques rather than considering the basic aspects of each separation problem.

BASIC TERMINOLOGY

Distribution

Separation implies that two or more species are moved away from one another in response to a force. Movement through a single medium such as an aqueous solution or a permeable membrane may occur in response to a difference in temperature, pressure, electrical potential, magnetic field, or gravitational or centrifugal field. In a heterogeneous system, movement from one immiscible phase to another takes place to a greater or lesser extent as a result of physical or chemical interaction. In every case, the rate of movement (or extent of transfer) of a species is a function of a partition coefficient. For theoretical purposes, the *thermodynamic partition coefficient* is a constant for a single species in a defined system. The concentration terms are expressed as activities or fugacities.

For practical purposes, it is not necessary to know the thermodynamic partition coefficient. Instead, one works with the more readily measured *formal concentration ratio*. The ease of determining formal concentrations rather than activities can be illustrated by the well-known extraction of iron(III) from aqueous hydrochloric acid by diethyl ether. An aqueous solution of iron(III) chloride usually contains a mixture of $FeOH^{++}$, $FeCl^{++}$, and other iron(III) species. One usually refers to the iron(III) in the system as though it were a single species having the formal ("analytical") concentration determined by a method for total iron(III). The price one pays for using a concentration ratio is its frequent lack of constancy over a wide range of concentrations because of shifts in the competing equilibria within each phase. Nevertheless, over limited ranges of operating variables, the concentration ratio often changes so little that separation behavior can be used as a basis for identification. Furthermore, the sensitivity of the concentration ratio to changes in operating conditions can often be turned to advantage in improving a particular separation.

If the volumes of two phases involved in a heterogeneous equilibrium are known, calculation of the amounts of a solute in each phase is a simple matter when the concentration ratio is known. The distribution may then be expressed as a *capacity ratio*, the product of the concentration ratio and the ratio of the phase volumes. For a fixed-volume ratio, the capacity ratio can be treated as a constant in the same fashion as the concentration ratio. The capacity ratio is widely used, especially in chromatographic processes, where the peak positions (in time or volume units) and the amount of work required for separation of a given pair of components are sensitive functions of its absolute value.

Operations and Goals

Another set of terms is concerned with the type of phase contact in a heterogeneous system. When, for example, a small portion ("batch") of an aqueous sample is equilibrated with a portion of an immiscible liquid, the single *equilibrium contact* will result in removal of an impurity (plus some of the product) from the sample. If product rather than impurity is the major component removed and if the volume of the extract is smaller than that of the original sample, removal and *concentration* of the product are attained simultaneously. If the original sample is contacted successively by one or more additional portions of the immiscible liquid, a *crosscurrent multistage* equilibrium process is performed. (Crystallizing a product, evaporating down the solution, and cooling it to take out another batch of crystals is another example.) Under the most favorable conditions, in which one substance has a very high value for its concentration ratio and a second substance has a very low value, two substances can be separated more or less completely. Ordinarily, however, one must choose between *yield* and *purity* in a crosscurrent operation. One can demonstrate this easily by assuming two different capacity ratios and noting the changes in relative amounts of each substance removed on successive extractions or washings.

Likewise, three substances cannot be separated from one another in a simple crosscurrent operation. In order to *fractionate* three or more substances (i.e., simultaneously obtain each of two or more substances in both high yield and high purity) under a constant set of conditions, a new mode of operation is required. A *pseudo-countercurrent* process is one in which one phase moves past (or through) another phase. All forms of chromatography fall into this category, as does the Craig machine, a device for performing multiple liquid-liquid extractions. This machine is an automated equivalent of a series of extraction flasks, each of which contains the same volume of one phase that remains in the flasks. After an immiscible sample has been added to, and equilibrated with, the liquid in the first flask, the added sample phase is moved to the second flask and, in its place, a second portion of the same phase, *minus* the dissolved components of the sample, is added. After the phases in both flasks have been equilibrated, the portions of sample phase are moved along: that in flask 2 to 3, that in flask 1 to 2, and the pure-sample phase to flask 1. Craig machines frequently have from 10 to 1,000 tubes.

Three points should be noted. First, one can show by means of simple calculations that a very small fraction of every component in the original sample will be found in every flask. However, the amounts in many flasks may be so small that one or all of the components may be undetectable. Hence, "complete" separation is a matter of arbitrary definition that involves the significance of the amounts of the unwanted substance(s) present. "Complete" recovery is, likewise, a matter of definition. Second, the average rate of travel of a substance through a separation system is expressed in terms of the movement of its peak concentration. This rate is a function of the rate of travel of the moving phase and of the fraction of that substance in that phase in any equilibrium contact. For example, if, at equilibrium, 60% of a material is in the moving phase and 40% in the stationary phase that remains behind in the flasks, the peak for that substance will travel through the separation system at 60% of the rate of the moving phase. The similarity to a nonequilibrium situation based solely upon different rates of travel within one medium, such as electromigration of Li^+ and Cs^+ in an aqueous solution, is obvious. Third, the larger the separation system (number of flasks), the farther apart the peaks will be. At the same time, the maximum concentration of a substance in the separation system will decrease, because the same amount of substance will be distributed in a larger number of flasks. As a result, a tiny sample may be "lost" (be undetectable) in an excessively large separation system.

The nonequilibrium counterpart of the Craig machine is a chromatographic column or a thin layer (or sheet) of an adsorbent. Although equilibrium may be approached very closely, it can never be attained, because the continuous movement of one phase forces the concentration of solute in that phase to change continuously. Such a nonequilibrium process has an optimum flow rate above and below which the separation deteriorates.

Most analytical separations, especially pseudo-countercurrent operations, are carried out under conditions such that the components behave independently of one another. However, in columnar adsorption chromatography, a competitive *displacement-analysis* technique may also be used. In that technique, after a small portion of sample has been placed on the column, an eluent is selected on the basis of its ability to displace quantitatively all of the solutes in the sample. It may be either a different solvent or a solute in the original solvent. As a multicomponent sample is gradually displaced through the column, the components of the sample compete for adsorption sites, the least adsorbed component being concentrated at the leading edge followed by adjacent bands of progressively more strongly adsorbed components and, finally, by the displacing agent. This situation, in which successive (overlapping) bands of components are removed from a system, is quite similar to that found in a multicomponent fractional distillation that is operated so as to collect product at a constant rate. One can obtain relatively pure product by discarding the portions of major overlap. The displacement approach, like fractional distillation, is not widely used for quantitative purposes. Like distillation, it offers an attractive preparative approach, but its potential is still unappreciated and unrealized.

A third approach to chromatography that permits a rapid qualitative and, sometimes, semiquantitative estimate of the components in a sample is *frontal analysis*. Unlike elution and displacement, a sample is poured continuously into the column, and the breakthrough of one component after another is noted until the sample comes out unchanged. The chief use of frontal analysis is to provide a means for estimating the probable suitability of a column packing for separation of the components by conventional elution. Short columns are employed so as to minimize both the amount of sample and the time required to saturate the column with the components in the sample.

Tiselius is credited with the invention of both displacement and frontal analysis techniques.

GENERAL CONSIDERATIONS

Quantitative Separations

The earlier discussion alluded to the fact that when successive batches of product from a crosscurrent operation were combined, the overall yield increased but purity decreased. Another "either-or" choice in separations is that between the resolution of a given separation system and the sample size (or capacity) it can handle. First, resolution of two peaks in a chromatographic system is defined as the distance (time or volume) between them in standard-deviation units (t units for the normal curve of error). The peak width at the base, neglecting the tails, is considered to be four units. Because peak widths (and heights) increase with sample size but peak positions do not change, resolution decreases with increase in sample size. Thus, the peaks for two substances may have a portion of flat base line between them when both substances are present in small amounts, but the peaks for larger amounts may overlap badly. Problems with overlap are maximized in trace analysis, where a major component will often completely hide a nearby trace component because of the tremendous disparity in amounts.

Criteria for Selection of a Technique

The generalizations stated below are intended to serve as a checklist of obvious points to consider before making a detailed examination of factors involved in a particular separation procedure. Like other generalizations, they are subject to exceptions.

First, it may be advantageous to consider the ease of converting neutral species into ions or vice versa. For example, amines can be extracted from organic solvents by aqueous solutions containing acid or silver(I) ions. By proper control of pH, fractionation can be optimized. Likewise, ions can advantageously be converted to neutral species. Formation by metal ions of chelates and ion pairs greatly extends the fractionation possibilities. Obviously, ion-exchange processes are very sensitive to ion-molecule equilibria.

Second, effects of changes in temperature and pressure on equilibria are especially large when a gas phase is involved (gas-liquid chromatography, distillation, sublimation). Furthermore, rates of diffusion in the gas phase are high, so establishment of an equilibrium is generally limited by the rate of diffusion into the other phase. Most equilibria involving solids concern only the surface (though pores and similar "internal" surfaces may be included), because diffusion through the lattice of a solid is usually so slow.

Third, adsorption, whether on a solid or liquid surface, may result in denaturation of large molecules, such as proteins, or even chemical reaction. Because surfaces of solids have sites with a wide range of energies, capacity ratios change rather rapidly with the fraction of the surface covered by adsorbed species. One must, therefore, be especially cautious in using adsorption chromatography for identification purposes over wide ranges of sample concentration or size. On the other hand, the comparatively rigid structure of a solid permits some separations to be made on the basis of shape and size (molecular sieving, dialysis, and gel permeation). As a result, adsorption on solids, through a combination of adsorption and sieving, appears to offer a potentially high selectivity.

Fourth, nucleation and agglomeration of phases can be very time-consuming. Formation of pure, filterable precipitates in high yield is a classical problem in quantitative analysis. Breaking stable emulsions, which are frequently encountered in liquid-liquid extractions of species of biochemical interest, is a similar problem. When the number of suitable partitioning solvents is limited, emulsion formation can be particularly trying.

Fifth, the fractionation processes of least utility for general analytical purposes are true countercurrent processes and diffusion processes based upon gradients of temperature or pressure. However, these processes are of major importance in preparative work, especially on an industrial scale. Electromigration is the only diffusion process that has been exploited to a significant extent on a quantitative analytical basis.

Finally, there are general considerations shared with quantitative measurements. The major group involves the nature of the sample: thermal stability, amount of sample available, relative concentrations of the components, whether the components are known or unknown, whether the sample can be destroyed (i.e., changed into other chemical species that may undergo easier separation), and whether the sample is one-of-a-kind or the first of many. Another group is related to the type of information desired: if qualitative, the identification of a species or merely the establishment of its presence or absence; if quantitative, the desired degree of precision and accuracy. The time factor often proves to be the factor that ultimately forces one to adopt more reasonable qualitative and quantitative goals than those with which one is usually inclined to start.

INDIVIDUAL PROCESSES

Heterogeneous Equilibria

In the sections that follow, terms for processes have been divided into those involving bulk equilibria and those involving surface equilibria. The bulk processes have, in turn, been subdivided into processes potentially capable of reaching equilibrium and columnar processes, which only approach, but never attain, true equilibrium. The latter can be thought of as "pseudo-equilibrium" processes.

On many occasions, even in single-stage equilibrium processes, equilibrium may be reached slowly, and, hence, rate is a very important consideration. For example, if an extractable species such as a chelate is formed slowly, a quantitative liquid-liquid extraction may require a period of hours, rather than minutes, to reach equilibrium. Similarly, poor mixing of phases may extend the equilibration time. Thus, a liquid-liquid extraction that can be equilibrated with less than three minutes of vigorous wrist action may take nearly one hour on a mechanical shaker. For purposes of the present discussion, these phenomena have not been classed as rate processes but, instead, only those based upon diffusion within a single phase or through a membrane have been so classed.

Gas-Liquid Contact

Virtually all of the processes in Table 11-1 involve a combination of volatilization and condensation. The outstanding exception is absorp-

Table 11-1   Gas-liquid contact processes

Bulk equilibrium
 Single stage—Absorption (CO_2 + $NaOH_{aq.}$)
       Condensation
       Degassification (deaeration)
       Distillation (no reflux)
        Simple
        Carrier gas (steam; nitrogen)
 Fractionation—Virtually never employed
Bulk pseudo-equilibrium
 Single contact—High-vacuum ("molecular") distillation
 Fractionation—Condensation
       Chromothermography (carrier gas)
       "Regular"
      Distillation (with reflux)
       Azeotropic
       Extractive
       "Regular"
Surface
 Single contact—never employed
 Pseudo-equilibrium—foam fractionation

---

tion (or evolution) of a gas which, in its single-stage form, is usually assisted chemically so as to force the partition quantitatively toward one phase or the other. The corresponding columnar process is isothermal gas-liquid chromatography.

Foam separation also falls into this category. Its use for quantitative separations appears to be limited to crosscurrent removal. Like a fractionation carried out by distillation, there is generally an overlap of adjacent components in the separation system.

An important feature of most forms of distillation is the effect of lowering the pressure. An obvious advantage is the greater ease of isolating larger, less volatile, and thermally unstable molecules. However, as a result of the lower pressure, the average path-length in the gas phase is greater and, hence, the height of a theoretical plate is greater. As the extreme case, high-vacuum molecular distillations are irreversible one-step processes based upon relative rates of volatilization (or condensation).

Gas-Solid Contact

Like gas-liquid systems, gas-solid systems are very susceptible to changes in temperature and pressure. The smaller size of Table 11-2

Table 11-2   Gas-solid contact processes

Bulk equilibrium *Bulk pseudo-equilibrium* } Virtually nonexistent	

Surface: Single stage—Sorption

   Drying (of solids) (includes drying of gases by physical and chemical action [SiO_2, molecular sieves, $CaCl_2$, P_2O_5])

   Sublimation and Condensation

  Pseudo-equilibrium—Gas-solid chromatography

reflects the fact that an equilibrium with bulk-solid phase is attained very slowly or, for most practical purposes, never. (The case of hydrogen diffusion through palladium metal is an outstanding exception.) Diffusion of gases (or liquids) in capillaries within gross particles of a solid is, of course, another matter.

It is important to note that "good" adsorbents such as alumina, charcoal, and silica have specific surface areas of the order of several hundred square meters per gram. In contrast, finely divided crystalline solids have areas of about one square meter per gram. As a result, extremely small samples must be used if crystalline compounds are used as adsorbents, in order to obtain fractionations involving comparable fractions of surface coverage.

Sublimation is a technique that appears to deserve wider use. When combined with a decreasing temperature along a condenser surface, fractionation of complex solid samples is possible.

Liquid-Liquid Contact

By far the most important variable is the possibility of employing a variety of competing chemical equilibria to supplement the physical interactions. Proper selection of complexing, chelating, or ion-pairing agent(s), in combination with appropriate adjustments of reagent concentration and pH, make liquid-liquid contact an extremely versatile approach. Because most separations are carried out at room temperature, the method is often used for thermally unstable solutes.

In contrast to gas-liquid and gas-solid systems, liquid-liquid equilibria are relatively insensitive to modest changes in temperature and pressure. However, the mutual solubilities of the liquids are often of crucial importance. Significant increases in mutual solubility, which usually lead to appreciably lower selectivity, may result from changes in temperature or from changes in concentrations of the solutes.

Other than the problem of finding two mutually insoluble liquids in which the sample components are soluble, the most difficult problem is emulsion formation. In such cases, instead of shaking the phases together, it appears preferable to obtain intimate contact through the use of a partition column. Such a column employs a porous inert solid to hold one liquid phase while the second flows past in the usual way. Depending upon the capacity ratios and also the availabilities and relative costs of the solvents, one phase or the other might be selected as the stationary phase.

With respect to specific techniques, several points are noteworthy. First, although immiscible phases are generally thought of in terms of water and an immiscible organic liquid, water need not be one of the components. More surprising are the systems in which water is a major component of *both* phases. For example, such a system, termed *phase separation* in Table 11-3, results when polyethylene glycol, polyvinyl-

Table 11-3   Liquid-liquid contact processes

Bulk equilibrium
 Single stage—Electrodeposition (species soluble in the
   liquid electrode)
    Liquid ion exchange
    Phase separation
    "Regular" extraction
 Fractionation—Individual stages, i.e., Craig machine
Bulk pseudo-equilibrium
 Columnar electrodeposition (liquid-electrode)
 Partition chromatography ("regular" and "reverse-
 phase")
Surface
 Single stage—Adsorption of macromolecules (and
   solids)
 Pseudo-equilibrium—Emulsion chromatography

---

pyrrolidine, and an aqueous electrolyte are shaken together. Two phases are formed. Although the electrolyte and low-molecular-weight polymers are distributed almost uniformly between the phases, one phase will be richer in the higher polymers. In fact, the latter are often concentrated at the interface, just as solids often are in binary systems of immiscible liquids.

A second point to note is that, although separations by electrodeposition are usually carried out by performing successive electrolyses at progressively more cathodic (or anodic) potentials, columnar fractionations using a liquid electrode (mercury) at a single potential are feasible for elements having very similar redox potentials. The method is best suited for isolation of carrier-free tracers so that both the magnitude and the changes in potential can be minimized.

A third point concerns liquid ion exchangers, compounds which are often long-chain amines or carboxylic acids. Their separating ability relies, in principle, upon ion pairing. An early example was the use of amines in a nonaqueous solvent to separate aqueous mixtures of nitric and sulfuric acids. More recently, many cations and anions have been separated. For separations that require few contact steps, liquid ion exchangers are more convenient to use than ion-exchange resins.

Finally, one should note that emulsion chromatography exists, but that it has found little analytical or preparative use.

Liquid-Solid Contact

In a few classical studies of coprecipitation, homogeneous distribution of an impurity within the crystals of a solid has been demonstrated. In most cases, however, equilibrium involves only the surface layer. Even in ion-exchange resins, diffusion of ions within the resin particle is almost entirely in the liquid portion of the gel.

It may be helpful to note implied differences between three related terms in Table 11-4. Crystallization, for example, is a general term applied to formation of crystals from a melt or solution as the result of a change in temperature. In clathration, a "host" substance (e.g., urea) is added and, after the product has been isolated, the host must, in turn, be separated. The term precipitation is also often associated with the addition of a substance such that a chemical reaction rather than an imposed temperature change leads to formation of the solid phase.

Zone refining is a column process that combines melting and crystallization. It is most widely used as a crosscurrent type of operation in which an impurity, originally distributed uniformly throughout the

Table 11-4   Liquid-solid contact processes

Single contact—Crystallization (including clathration)
      Electrodeposition (solids)
      Leaching (extraction)
      Precipitation
      Sorption—Ion exchange using resins (gels) or zeolites
           Molecules on charcoal, SiO_2, molecular sieves
Fractionation—Individual stages (items above)
      Pseudo-equilibrium—Crystallization (and precipitation)
           Gel permeation
           Melting (in conjunction with crystalliza-
           tion)
           Sorption
            Ion exchange
            Ion exclusion (salting-in and -out)
            Ion retardation
            "Regular"
           Thin-layer (including paper) chroma-
           tography
           Zone refining

---

system, is finally concentrated at one end. Recently, a proposal has been made to use the zone-refining operation for fractionation by adding a sample to one end of the system. Because of the inconvenience in handling and analyzing the solid-fractionation system and the general lack of knowledge about selection of the solid phase, this approach will probably be low on most priority lists.

As stated earlier, sorption by solids appears to be sensitive to size and shape of a molecule or ion. Molecular sieves prepared from natural or synthetic zeolites are the best known examples. Straight-chain alkanes, as opposed to the branched isomers, are strongly sorbed, presumably because they can enter the pores created by prior dehydration of the zeolites. Recently, columns of dextran gels have been employed to fractionate water-soluble macromolecules having molecular weights up to about 100,000. However, sorption appears to play a minor role in those separations, compared to exclusion or sieving.

Similar phenomena are encountered in using ion-exchange resins. Large ions that cannot enter the gel phase will be sorbed only slightly on the exterior surface, while smaller ions will penetrate the gel. For ions of about the same size, those of higher valence will be held more strongly.

Two other chromatographic terms are *ion exclusion* and *ion retardation*. The former applies to retardation of a nonelectrolyte, because of its solubility in an ion-exchange resin, compared to an electrolyte that is not retarded because its cation or anion is the same as the exchangeable ion on the resin. Fractionation of nonelectrolytes can be facilitated by systematic changes in the concentration of electrolyte (salting-in or salting-out). Ion retardation is a similar operation that uses a mixture of cationic and anionic resin sites to hold back a salt, thereby serving to concentrate it or to separate it from a nonelectrolyte that is not retarded by the resin. In principle, it could be used in a restricted way for fractionating mixtures of electrolytes that share a common cation or anion.

Separate mention has been made of paper chromatography as a form of thin-layer chromatography. Substitution of a thin sheet for a column is convenient for microgram samples and is sometimes very rapid. Furthermore, resolution seems to be greater than in a column of the same adsorbent. All materials suitable for columnar adsorption can be used as thin-sheet adsorbents. In addition, because some separations depend mainly on differences in rates of diffusion through a maze of fibers, sheets of inert materials such as nylon and polyethylene have also been used successfully.

Rates

Table 11-5 contains both a list of gradients and a list of methods of separation based upon rates of travel through a single medium or a membrane. Omitted from the list are separations based upon rates of establishing equilibria between two immiscible phases, even though a slow chemical step, such as formation or dissociation of a chelate, may greatly facilitate a separation.

As one might expect, the methods in Table 11-5 are heavily dependent upon differences in charge and size (molecular weight). In some cases, shape is also a governing factor. On the other hand, chemical equilibria generally play a much smaller role, except in electromigration methods.

Electromigration has taken many forms and is referred to by many different names. The Hittorf approach, which uses solutions in U tubes, is rarely employed without "stabilizers." An inert gel, for example, minimizes convective transport and sharpens the boundaries. One of the most versatile forms of electromigration uses a paper sheet as the stabilizing medium. However, "papers" have ranged in composition

Table 11-5 Gradients and processes based upon rates

Gradients
   Centrifugal and gravitational
   Concentration
   Density
   Electrical and magnetic
   Pressure
Processes
   Single medium (with or without phase stabilizer)
      Density gradient
      Electromigration
      Flotation
      Thermal diffusion (gases or liquids)
      Ultracentrifugation
   Barrier (orifice or membrane)
      Dialysis
      Electromigration (electrodialysis, electrochromatography)
      Gaseous diffusion ($Pd-H_2$, isotopic uranium(VI) fluorides)
      Ultrafiltration

---

from cellulose to ion-exchange resin. Like conventional paper chromatography, this method is ideal for microgram samples; by using thicker sheets, it can be extended to small-scale preparative work.

In another modification, the sample is added slowly to the top of a vertical sheet across which an electrical gradient is applied to give continuous fractionation. If only the separation were faster, continuous analysis for control purposes would be feasible. The only form of crossed gradients suited to continuous separation and quantitative analysis is that used in the mass spectrometer, in which ions that have been accelerated by an electrical gradient are later separated by a magnetic gradient.

Methods based upon diffusion through orifices or barrier membranes are generally not used for analytical fractionations. The same is true for flotation and "simple" diffusion due to a concentration gradient. Instead, these methods are used as one-stage operations for concentration or removal of one or more components. One exception to the rule is paper chromatography where, as the solvent flows under capillary forces, some fractionation may result from the difference in rates with which large ions or molecules thread their ways through the barrier of fibers. Less clear-cut exceptions are the columns of zeolitic "molecular sieves" and their counterparts in gels (e.g., cross-linked dextran), which have been applied to separations of rare gases, nitrogen, and oxygen, and to separations of proteins, respectively. A final exception is the time-of-flight mass spectrometer in which the permeability of the electrically charged barriers to ions depends upon the rates of ion migration. Although these methods are a small fraction of the list in Table 11-5, they are disproportionately important in the overall framework of separations.

The last two processes to be discussed, *density gradient* and *ultracentrifugation*, bear certain points of resemblance. Density gradient is a method in which two liquids are carefully poured together into an upright transparent cylinder in such a way that the composition changes continuously from most dense at the bottom to least dense at the top. When a mixture of macroscopic particles of different densities is carefully dropped into the liquid, the particles settle under the force of gravity until each reaches the level at which its density is the same as that of the liquid. When ultracentrifugation is called upon to assist the force of gravity, the range of particle sizes is extended to colloidal dimensions. Measurements can be based either on steady-state or on rate behavior of the colloidal components.

Miscellaneous

The discussion so far has made no mention of "mechanical" or of biological separations which are used primarily for concentration or removal. The first group includes Pasteur's separation of the *d*- and *l*-isomers of tartaric acid by their distinctive crystalline forms, the use of a magnet to concentrate magnetic ore from gangue, and simple filtration. The second group, biological separations, includes methods that involve biological destruction of one substance in the presence of a second one from which separation is extremely difficult by other means. For example, enzymatic reactions are often employed to destroy one of a pair of isomers. The biological agent is merely a highly specific chemical reagent that converts one substance into another that is more readily separable from the desired product.

RELATED FACTORS

Minimization of Time

When a particular type of sample is to be analyzed more than once, and especially if it is to be done routinely many times, it is definitely worthwhile to attempt optimization of conditions so as to meet the minimum requirement for resolution and/or yield at minimum expense. Because the cost either of direct operator time or of total elapsed time between receiving a sample and finding the result usually far outweighs all other costs, the mere discovery that a separation is possible is often the least demanding step of the overall problem. Fortunately, many of the later steps that one should take toward optimizing a particular separation are general ones.

Gradients

The deliberate use of either step-function or continuous changes in a variable, such as temperature or concentration of a reagent, may greatly shorten the time for a chromatogram—at the cost of some resolution. One example is the linear programming of column temperature in gas-liquid chromatography. Because a linear increase in temperature results in logarithmic increase in the vapor pressure of a liquid (and, hence, the concentration ratio), an increase of about 10 C°/min in column temperature forces less volatile compounds to elute in about half the time required under isothermal conditions. Linear temperature programming has the further advantage that qualitative identification of organic homologs is possible by inspection. This is related to the fact that the logarithm of the capacity ratio (or concentration ratio) is linear with respect to the boiling point of the homologs. For complex mixtures, complicated temperature programs can be selected which combine periods of linear change with periods of isothermal operation, so as to gain speed in parts of the elution where resolution is no problem while retaining resolution in other parts.

Temperature programming of a chromatographic separation which employs a liquid moving phase is more difficult, because of the higher heat capacity of the liquid. Furthermore, the temperature coefficients of the capacity ratios are generally much smaller. As a result, the programmed variable is usually the concentration of a reagent or the percentage(s) of additional solvent(s). Thus, in ion exchange, it is the concentration of the eluting agent (sometimes the hydrogen ion); in molecular adsorption, it is the concentration of polar solvent. Various types of devices have been designed which allow one to alter the composition linearly, logarithmically, or in any other desired fashion.

An ingenious double gradient has been reported which permits fractional crystallization (or precipitation) to be carried out in a chromatographic column. Polymers have been fractionated by continuously increasing the percentage of a solubilizing component in the eluting solvent while decreasing the temperature of the column from inlet to outlet. In principle, the smaller, more soluble fractions are leached out near the start by relatively poor solvent. Upon reaching cooler portions of the column, fractional precipitation occurs. As progressively better solvent enters the column, some of the precipitate redissolves and later reprecipitates. Meanwhile, heavier fractions from the original sample dissolve and start the same cycle. Repetition of these steps occurs again and again as the components proceed to the end of the column. Adaptation of this process to less difficult fractional crystallizations appears to deserve more consideration than it has received, especially in preparative work.

Adjustment of the Volume Ratio

When the capacity ratio cannot conveniently be altered by changing the concentration ratio as just described, it may sometimes be feasible to change the volume ratio of the phases. Unfortunately, there is no convenient way to do this in a columnar process, except in gas-liquid chromatography, so it is largely restricted to single- or multi-plate processes carried out under equilibrium conditions. In general, if the volume ratio is such that the substances most difficult to separate have capacity ratios which are the reciprocal of one another, conditions for the separation will be close to optimum. In gas-liquid chromatography, the capacity ratio for the more strongly retained compound of the pair should be in the range of 2 to 3.

Use of Second System

Another way to minimize time is to make a second separation under different conditions. One of the most convenient ways in which that has been done is illustrated by two-way paper (thin-layer) chromatography. Using a square sheet and placing the sample on one corner, development is first carried out in the normal way with one solvent. After drying the paper and turning it ninety degrees, a second solvent is used for development. A two-dimensional array of spots is revealed by development. Much the same can now be accomplished easily in gas chromatography by using a two-column instrument, each column having a different partitioning phase in it. If desired, incompletely resolved mixtures can be collected from the effluent of one column and used as samples in the second.

Table 11-6   Separation methods—summary evaluation

Approach	Qualitative applicability[a]	Quantitative applicability[b]	Applicability for isolating and/or concentrating desired material	Preparative applicability[c]	Main limitations	General cost of equipment[d]	General time for separation[e]	Remarks
Distillation	Poor	Poor	Good	Good (1) Fair (2)	General lack of complete separation of desired material Decomposition of material at the boiling point	Low to moderate	High	Excellent for preparing large quantities of rather pure material but not as good as gas chromatography for preparing high-purity material
Extraction *a*) Solids	Poor	Poor	Fair	Good (1) Fair (2)	Finding suitable solvents General lack of complete separation of solids	Low to high	Low to high	Widely used for preparing rather large quantities of rather pure materials; also for isolating and concentrating component to be measured
b) Liquids	Fair	Fair to good	Good	Good (1) Fair (2)	Finding suitable solvents	Low to high	Low to high	Widely used for preparing rather large quantities of rather pure materials; also for isolating and concentrating component to be measured

Table 11-6 Separation methods—summary evaluation (continued)

Approach	Qualitative applicability[a]	Quantitative applicability[b]	Applicability for isolating and/or concentrating desired material	Preparative applicability[c]	Main limitations	General cost of equipment[d]	General time for separation[e]	Remarks
Liquid-solid chromatography	Fair	Fair to good	Good	Poor (1) Good (2)	Finding suitable solid adsorbent and solvent system	Low	Low to high	Widely used for isolating and concentrating component to be measured; also widely used for preparing high-purity material
Gas chromatography	Fair	Good	Good	Fair (1)[f] Good (2)	Sample must be volatile	Low to moderate	Low	Probably the most widely applied of all analytical separative approaches
Crystallization	Poor	Poor	Fair to good	Good (1) Fair to good (2)	Sample must crystallize	Low	Low to moderate	Used mainly for preparative work
Dialysis	Poor	Poor	Fair to good	Fair (1) Fair (2)	Finding proper membrane and solvent system. General lack of complete separation. Molecular sizes of components to be separated must be quite different	Low	High	Lacks general utility

Table 11-6 Separation methods—summary evaluation (continued)

Approach	Qualitative applicability[a]	Quantitative applicability[b]	Applicability for isolating and/or concentrating desired material	Preparative applicability[c]	Main limitations	General cost of equipment[d]	General time for separation[e]	Remarks
Electrophoresis	Poor to fair	Poor	Good	Fair (1) Good (2)	Components must be charged Proper solvent system and electrolyte must be found	Low to moderate	Low to high	Lacks general utility
Diffusion	Poor	Poor	Good	Fair (1) Fair (2)	Used solely for gases	Low to high	Low to high	Lacks general utility
Precipitation	Poor to good	Good	Good	Good (1) Good (2)	Finding suitable solvent and precipitant	Low	Low to moderate	Widely used

[a] Qualitative applicability means that the separation technique yields parameters applicable to identifying materials (i.e., retention time).

[b] Quantitative applicability means that the separation technique yields a direct measure of the material being sought, as happens with gas chromatography. Needless to say, all separation methods have wide application in both qualitative and quantitative analyses. This factor is accounted for in column 3. Columns 1 and 2 reflect the utility of the separation methods themselves as qualitative and quantitative methods.

[c] (1) indicates applicability for preparing a rather large quantity of material, and (2) indicates applicability for preparing high-purity material.

[d] Low denotes <$5,000; moderate denotes $5,000–$15,000; high denotes >$15,000.

[e] Low denotes <0.5 hr; moderate denotes 0.5 to 2 hr; high denotes >2 hr.

[f] Good for small quantities, slow for large quantities. Practicality of large-scale preparative GC is growing rapidly.

Detection

Although the detection step is not a part of the separation process, it often plays a key role. Would gas-liquid chromatography be as widely used if one had to collect hundreds of individual gas samples and analyze them by a microadaptation of the Orsat apparatus? Sometimes, in using a Craig machine for separations of large molecules of biological interest, gravimetry, though tedious, is the most suitable approach (this requires the use of volatile solvents and buffers!). In brief, the detection system may play a significant role in the overall decision.

As in any determination, the choice depends upon one's need either for a nonselective detector or for a highly selective detector. For example, in gas chromatography, a thermal conductivity recorder is a nearly universal detector, whereas a photometer for measuring spectral absorption in the ultraviolet region would permit aromatics to be detected and determined even when completely overlapped by saturated aliphatic hydrocarbons. Obviously, it is desirable to have both a nonselective detector and a series of highly selective detectors available.

Detectors which permit direct determination without a prior chemical reaction are preferred for quantitative work, because uncertainty about completeness of the reaction is ruled out. Furthermore, reactions destroy the sample as do some detectors themselves, e.g., the flame-ionization detector for gas chromatography. However, the latter possesses very high sensitivity for most organic compounds, so that one can often tolerate the loss.

In general, the most nearly universal detectors for chromatography are probably temperature-sensing devices, either thermocouples or thermistors, and refractometers or interferometers. These detectors would probably be much more widely applied to follow separations, if it were not for widespread use of gradients which often introduce much larger changes in the physical properties than those due to the chromatographic peaks.

Suggested Readings

General

Berg, E. W.: "Physical and Chemical Methods of Separation," McGraw-Hill Book Company, New York, 1963. (Comprehensive text.)

Kolthoff, I. M., and P. J. Elving (eds.): "Treatise on Analytical Chemistry," vols. 2 and 3, pt. I, Interscience Publishers (Division of John Wiley &

Sons, Inc.), New York, 1961. (Comprehensive discussions of analytical separations.)

Weissberger, A. (ed.): "Technique of Organic Chemistry," vol. III, pt. I, "Separation and Purification," Interscience Publishers (Division of John Wiley & Sons, Inc.), New York, 1956. (Comprehensive detailed text on all types and applications of separations.)

Welcher, F. (ed.): "Standard Methods of Chemical Analysis," 6th ed., vol. 2, pt. A, D. Van Nostrand Company, Inc., Princeton, N.J., 1963, pp. 87–235. (Brief summary discussions of mechanical separations, precipitation, electrolysis, extraction, distillation and evaporation, chromatography, and ion exchange.)

Dialysis

Craig, L. C.: Science **144**:1093 (1964). (Review article on analytical aspects of dialysis.)

Leonard, E. F.: "Encyclopedia of Chemical Technology," R. E. Kirk and D. F. Othmer (eds.), 2d ed., vol. 7, Interscience Publishers (Division of John Wiley & Sons, Inc.), New York, 1965, pp. 1–21. (Brief summary.)

Diffusion Separation Methods

Shacter, J., E. Von Halle, and R. L. Hogland: "Encyclopedia of Chemical Technology," *op. cit.*, pp. 91–175. (Extensive summary.)

Distillation

Holland, C. D., and J. D. Lindsay: "Encyclopedia of Chemical Technology," *op. cit.*, pp. 204–248. (Pertains mainly to industrial distillation, but the theoretical discussions of the various types of distillation processes are well discussed.)

Weissberger, A. (ed.): "Technique of Organic Chemistry," 2d ed., vol. IV, Interscience Publishers (Division of John Wiley & Sons, Inc.), New York, 1965. (Detailed text.)

Electrophoresis

Bier, M.: "Electrophoresis, Theory, Methods and Applications," Academic Press Inc., New York, 1959.

Smith, I.: "Chromatography and Electrophoresis," vol. II, John Wiley & Sons, Inc., New York, 1960.

Strickland, R. D.: "Standard Methods of Chemical Analysis," 6th ed., vol. 3, pt. A, F. Welcher (ed.), D. Van Nostrand Company, Inc., Princeton, N.J., 1966, pp. 685–715. (Brief, general survey.)

Extraction

Morrison, G. H., and H. Freiser: "Solvent Extraction in Analytical Chemistry," John Wiley & Sons, Inc., New York, 1957.

Gas Chromatography

Cassidy, H.: "Fundamentals of Chromatography," Interscience Publishers (Division of John Wiley & Sons, Inc.), New York, 1957. (Covers packed column liquid chromatography, gas chromatography, ion exchange, and foam-emulsion fractionation.)

Dal Nogare, S., and R. S. Juvet: "Gas-Liquid Chromatography," Interscience Publishers (Division of John Wiley & Sons, Inc.), New York, 1962. (Comprehensive text covering theory and practice.)

McNair, H. M., and E. J. Bonnelli: "Basic Gas Chromatography," Varian Aerograph, 2700 Mitchell Dr., Walnut Creek, Calif., April, 1966. (Excellent compilation, especially for beginners in gas chromatography.)

Ion Exchange

Helfferich, F.: "Ion Exchange," McGraw-Hill Book Company, New York, 1962. (Comprehensive text.)

Samuelson, O.: "Ion Exchangers in Analytical Chemistry," John Wiley & Sons, Inc., New York, 1963. (Good general coverage of the different analytical applications of ion exchange.)

Thin-layer Chromatography

Bobbitt, J.: "Thin-layer Chromatography," Reinhold Publishing Corporation, New York, 1963. (Comprehensive text.)

Malins, D. C., and H. K. Mangold: "Standard Methods of Chemical Analysis," 6th ed., vol. 3, pt. A, F. Welcher (ed.), D. Van Nostrand Company, Inc., Princeton, N.J., 1966, pp. 735–780. (Brief survey.)

TWELVE

AUTOMATIC
ANALYSIS

Applied analytical chemistry has moved definitely toward automatic analysis. Laboratories have automated many of their routine analyses and, also, many analyses are now performed directly in plant-process equipment without the necessity of taking samples to the laboratory. The reasons for the strong surge toward automation are as follows.

1. *Time*. Automatic analysis significantly cuts down the time between sampling and analysis. This is particularly necessary with the current high-volume continuous processes, where a short time of off-specification production means a large amount of unsalable material.

Also, where hazards (explosion, fire, toxic fumes, etc.) could be involved, the hazardous condition must be detected immediately, or else the analysis is of little value.

2. *Cost*. Saving time as in (1) also saves money. Moreover, automatic analysis usually requires less personnel to obtain the analysis. This also cuts operating cost. However, automatic equipment costs money and raises capital cost. Overall saving has to be proven to justify automatic analysis.

3. *Better Sampling*. Accurate sampling of modern production systems can be difficult. Visualize the monitoring of a hydrogen chloride distillation column. The contents of the column are liquid at column conditions, but are gaseous on removal. If one tries to sample the liquid into a chilled bottle, some vapor is lost, causing disproportionation of the sample. Also, condensation of water from the air occurs in the collection container and in the sample, causing contamination. If one attempts to use a bomb-type collection vessel, the materials of construction become of paramount importance because of the corrosivity of the sample. On-stream analysis is by far the preferred approach here.

Another sampling problem involves getting a sample of the true system rather than just material trapped in dead space of the sampling area. For example, valves and pipes leading to and from valves will often trap material which does not circulate with the rest of the reaction system. On removal of a "grab" sample one can get the contents of this dead space and not necessarily material representative of the system at that time. Continuous analysis of a constantly flowing sample helps to ensure that the sample is a true one for that time interval.

4. *Safety.* Many materials used in chemical processes are toxic, highly corrosive, explosive, or otherwise dangerous, for example, hydrogen chloride, chlorine, phosgene, fuming sulfuric acid, fluorine, hydrogen. These materials present hazards to operating personnel. It is desirable not to remove samples manually from the process but to analyze *in situ.*

Another safety aspect of automatic analysis is the continued monitoring of plant air to detect leaks of noxious, toxic, flammable or explosive gases.

5. *Accuracy of Analysis.* Automatic analyzers minimize human errors. These are erratic, nonsystematic errors. The automatic devices are not foolproof, of course, but errors tend to be easily spotted. Since analyses are fast, data are generally obtained quickly when automatically accomplished, and standard samples can be periodically (and also automatically) admitted to check the accuracy of the device. In critical cases, every other sample can be a standard.

There are also disadvantages to automatic analysis. Usually (though not always), the instrumentation is somewhat expensive. In addition, the devices not only need attention and repair, but samples must be properly presented to the devices. There has been much disillusionment with automatic analysis, mainly due to expecting more from the devices than they give, and, also, due to realizing that some expertise is needed in using them and keeping them operating. A common public conception of the automatic analyzer is that you "plug it in" as you would a household appliance and then run it with inexperienced people. This is rarely the case. Most chemical and petroleum companies have trained groups whose duties are (1) to find the applications for automatic devices, (2) to select the proper manufactured devices when these exist, or to build special devices of their own when none can be purchased, (3) to install the devices with proper sampling and readout systems for each application, (4) to train operating personnel to use the devices properly, (5) to troubleshoot the devices when troubles arise.

Automatic analyzers fall into two classes: continuous and repetitive. Continuous analysis means that the sample is going through the instrument continuously and that a measurement is recorded continuously. Some analytical measurements are very amenable to continuous analysis, as, for example, optical-absorption measurements where the sample flows through the cell, and changes in transmittance are recorded; measurements of viscosity (by the rotating cylinder), density, thermal conductivity, capacitance, and electrical conductance are also truly continuous. Repetitive analysis can be termed "squirt-wise" analysis; a sample is taken, and an analysis is made and recorded. Then another sample is taken and the process is repeated. A repetitive system has to be used when the analytical method cannot be applied on a continuous basis, for example, gas chromatography, by its principle, cannot be made continuous. A sample must be taken, allowed to go through the column, detected, and recorded. The next sample is then taken. Most laboratory automatic analyzers are repetitive in type. In these cases, the laboratory samples are placed on a turntable, belt, or other device feeding into the instrument. The instrument then proceeds from sample to sample, analyzing each in sequence.

It should be stated that it is not uncommon to find continuous analyzers applied to laboratory systems. It is convenient to monitor some laboratory reaction systems by attaching the analyzer to the synthesis apparatus. This is mentioned only to illustrate that, though process analyzers are found mainly in plants, they are also usable in laboratories.

The analytical principles used in automatic analyzers, either of the laboratory or of the on-stream, plant process type, are the same as those for conventional analysis. They measure the chemical, optical, thermal, magnetic, electrical, and other physical properties of the material under test. The only difference is that, in automatic analysis, mechanical, electrical, and/or electronic components are added to carry out each step of the analysis, take the sample, and if necessary, dilute, react, and/or heat it, then measure the analytical parameter, and finally, read out the analysis in a proper form for the analytical chemist or plant operator.

The automatic analyzers themselves will be taken for granted in this discussion, since they are purchased as units and are all generally operable as purchased. However, a key element in the successful use of automatic analysis is the sampling unit. The sample to be analyzed must be in proper condition, not only for optimum analysis, but for optimum life of the instrument or cells thereof. A common problem, for example, is dirt in a sample stream. This dirt can gradually plug the narrow lines or orifices in the analytical devices, or it can coat cells of optical, thermal, and electrical detecting devices and result in shortened life and/or sensitivity. Hence, filtration of sample streams is common. Condensable liquids in gas streams are another common problem.

These condense in cells and achieve the same effects as dirt. Proper condensers in gas streams eliminate this problem. Trapped or dissolved gases in liquid streams disrupt sample measurements which are volumetric. The gases can form bubbles in the sampling device, resulting in erratic volume measurements. Also, some sample streams are hot and, if injected directly into an instrument, can cause precipitates or crystals to form in the device. Properly heated inlets or filtration units to remove or prevent offending precipitates must be included. Highly viscous liquids will not flow into sampling units which are capillary in nature. Means for diluting or heating must be incorporated into the sampling unit to permit sample flow. An automatic analyzer may operate at atmospheric pressure but the sample stream may be under high pressure; therefore, proper pressure reduction must be considered before the device will work. Thus, though the analyzer portion of several automatic installations may be the same, the sampling units can vary widely.

Another variable in similar installations is the readout of the data. Some automatic systems merely have an indicating meter that is periodically read by an operator, while other installations print out data on a tape (either a legible tape or a computer tape) or on a typewriter chart. One of the most common readout methods is the graphical plot. This gives continuous readings of analysis versus time, and often from many locations in the plant. These plots can be on circular charts or strip charts, and can appear as bar graphs (for repetitive analysis) or as continuous plots.

In many cases, the signal used to record the data can be used to actuate controlling units which will alter the process (change temperature, pressure, amounts of reactants) until the analysis is back within desired limits. These signals can also actuate alarm systems if dangerous conditions exist, and can even be used for reasons of safety to shut down a process entirely.

The advantages of automatic analysis are so pronounced that it is easy to see the reasons for not only the current surge in this direction but also for a trend toward much more automation of analysis in the future.

Suggested Reading

Siggia, S.: "Continuous Analysis of Chemical Process Systems," John Wiley & Sons, Inc., New York, 1959.

INDEX

Arc-spark spectroscopy, 10–18, 47
Argon detector for gas chromatography, 235–237
Atomic absorption, 20–23, 47, 50
Automatic analysis, 178–190, 295–298

β-ray absorption, 222
Boiling point, in high purity assay, 252, 261–262
  measurement, 196, 210
  method for molecular weight, 148–151, 172, 174
Boron analysis, in organic compounds, 46

Capacitance, 202
Carbon-hydrogen analysis, 40
Chemical methods, elements, 33–35, 48, 51
  functional groups, 77–79, 89, 92
  identification and structure, 97–98, 135
  surface coatings, 220
  in trace analysis, 228
Chromatography, 271–294
  (*See also* Gas chromatography)
Chromophoric groups, infrared, 58–61
  near infrared, 66–67
  ultraviolet-visible, 68–69
Colthup chart, 58–61
Conductivity, electrical, 202
  in high purity assay, 255–257
Continuous analysis, 178–190, 295–298
Coulter Counter, 215
Cryoscopic method for molecular weight, 144–148, 172

Density, measurement, 177–182
  on gases, 177–179
  on liquids, 177, 179–181
  on solids, 177, 181–182
  references, 209
  (*See also under* Gas density)
Detectors for gas chromatography, 235–237

Detergents, 1, 95–96, 165–166
Dialysis, 293
Dielectric constant, 79, 202
Differential scanning calorimetry, 134
Differential thermal analysis, 134
Diffusion, 293
Distillation, 279, 293
Distribution coefficient, 272–273
Dumas nitrogen analysis, 42

Ebullioscopic (*see* Boiling point)
Electrical properties, 202
  in high purity assay, 255–263
Electron capture detector, 235–237
Electron diffraction, 218–220
Electron probe, 25–27, 47, 51
Electron spin resonance, 114–116, 135
Electrophoresis, 278, 285, 293
Elemental analysis, 9–52
  chemical methods, 33–35, 48, 51
  emission methods, 10–31
    arc-spark, 4, 5, 10–18, 47, 50
    atomic absorption, 20–23, 47, 50
    electron probe, 25–27, 47, 51
    flame, 18–20, 47, 50
    mass spectroscopy, 31–33, 46, 48, 51
    neutron activation, 27–31, 47, 51
    x-ray fluorescence, 23–25, 47, 50–51
  inorganic elements, 10–38
  organic elements, 38–46, 52
  polarography, 35–37, 48, 52
  radioactive elements, 38
Ellipsometry, 221–224
Emission spectroscopy (*see* Elemental analysis)
Extraction, 271–294

Flame photometry, 18–20, 47, 50
Fluorescence, interference in Raman spectroscopy, 74–77
  references, 244
  in trace analysis, 228, 230–234, 240
Fluorine analysis in organic compounds, 44–45

Freezing point, in high purity assay,
246–251, 262
measurement, 194–196, 210
method for molecular weight, 144–
148, 172, 174
Functional group analysis, 53–93
chemical methods, 77–79, 89, 92
electroanalytical methods, 79–87, 89,
92
mass spectrometry, 87, 89, 93
for molecular weight determination
(end-group analysis), 155–157,
172, 174
need for, 53–54
nuclear magnetic resonance, 87, 89,
92–93
optical methods, 54–77, 90
general, 54–55
infrared, 56–64, 88, 90–91
near infrared, 64–65, 88, 91
Raman, 74–77, 89, 91
ultraviolet, 65–71, 88, 91
vacuum ultraviolet, 71–72, 89, 91
visible, 72–74, 88, 91

Gas chromatography, detectors, 235–
237
molecular weight determination,
165–167, 173
pesticides analysis, 237–239
references, 244
use in trace analysis, 235–239
(See also Separations)
Gas density for molecular weight,
154–155, 172
Gas density detector for gas chromatography, 235–237
Gel permeation chromatography, 169–
171, 173

Hall effect, 255, 258
Halogens analysis, by nuclear quadrupole, 123
in organic compounds, 43–44
Heat of fusion and vaporization, 134,
202–203

High purity assay, 245–263
boiling-point method, 252, 261–262
electrical methods, 255–263
conductivity, 255–257
Hall effect, 255, 258
residual resistivity, 255, 259
thermally stimulated current, 255,
260–262
freezing-point cooling curves, 246–
251, 261–262
general, 245–246
phase solubility method, 253–255,
261, 263
Hot wire detectors, 235–237

Identification, 95–139
absorption spectrometric methods,
98–99, 135
chemical methods, 97–98, 135
electron spin resonance, 114–116,
135, 137
general discussion, 95–96
mass spectrometry, 100–102, 135
microscopy, 211–213
microwave spectroscopy, 123–126,
136, 138
morphology, 132–134
Mössbauer spectroscopy, 129–131,
136, 138
nuclear magnetic resonance, 102–114,
135, 139
nuclear quadrupole resonance, 123,
136, 138
optical rotatory dispersion, 126–128,
136, 138
Raman spectroscopy, 121–123, 136
thermal methods, 134, 138
x-ray diffraction, 116–121, 135, 137
Ilkovic equation, 83
Infrared absorption methods, functional
groups, 56–64, 88, 90–91
identification and structure, 98–99,
135
surface coatings (reflectance), 217–
218
in trace analysis, 234–235, 240
Inorganic elements (see Elemental
analysis)

Insecticide determination, 237–239
Interferometry, coating thickness, 219, 221–222, 224
  measurement of refractive index, 188–189
Ion exchange, 4, 294

Kjeldahl nitrogen analysis, 42–43

Light scattering, 163–165, 173, 175
Luminescence, 228

Magnetic susceptibility, 203
Mass spectrometry, elemental analysis, 31–33, 48, 51
  functional group analysis, 87, 89, 93
  identification and structure, 100–102, 135
  molecular weight determination, 157, 172, 174
  in trace analysis, 241–242
Melting point, 194–196
Micro-cross-section detector, 235–237
Micromerograph, 214
Microscopy, determination of refractive index, 189–190
  morphology, 211–213
  particle size distribution, 213–214
  thickness gauging, 220, 222–223
Microwave spectroscopy, 123–126, 140
Molecular weight, 141–175
  general discussion, 141–144
  light scattering methods, 163–165, 173, 175
  mass spectrometry, 157, 172, 174
  molecular weight distribution, 165–171
    fractional precipitation methods, 165–169, 173
    gas chromatography, 165–167, 173
    gel permeation chromatography, 169–171, 173
  number averages for molecular weights, 144–156
    cryoscopic methods (freezing-point lowering), 144–148, 172, 174

Molecular weight, number averages for molecular weights, ebullioscopic methods (boiling-point elevation), 148–151, 172, 174
    functional-group methods (end-group analysis), 155–157, 172
    gas density methods, 154–155, 172, 174
    osmotic pressure methods, 152–154, 172, 174
    vapor-pressure-lowering methods, 151–152, 172, 174
  types of molecular weight, 158–159
  ultracentrifugation methods, 159–163, 173, 175
    dynamic sedimentation approach, 161–163, 173
    equilibrium approach, 159–161, 173
  x-ray diffraction, 157–158, 173, 175
Molecular weight distribution (see Molecular weight)
Morphology, microscopic methods, 211–213
  thermal methods, 134
  x-ray methods, 132, 212
Mössbauer spectroscopy, 129–131, 140

Near infrared absorption, functional groups, 64–65, 88, 91
Neutron activation analysis, 27–31, 47, 51
Nitrogen analysis in organic compounds, 42–43
Nuclear magnetic resonance, in functional group analysis, 87, 89, 92–93
  identification and structure, 102–114, 135
Nuclear quadrupole resonance, 123, 140
Number-average molecular weight methods, 144–156

On-stream analysis, 178–190, 295–298
Optical rotatory dispersion, 126–128, 140
Organic elements (see Elemental analysis)

Osmotic pressure method for molecular weight, 152–154, 172, 174
Oxygen analysis in organic compounds, 41

Particle size distribution, 213–216, 223
Partition coefficient, 272–273
pH and pK, 203–208, 210
Phase solubility analysis, 253–255, 261, 263
Phosphorescence measurement, 228, 231–234, 240, 244
Phosphorous analysis in organic compounds, 45–46
Physical properties, 177–210
  boiling point, 196, 210
  density, 177–182, 209
    gases, 177–179
    liquids, 177, 179–181
    solids, 177, 181–182
  electrical properties, conductivity, resistivity, and capacitance, 202
  freezing (melting) point, 194–196, 210
  magnetic properties, susceptibility, 203
  pH and pK, 203–208, 210
  refractive index, 186–190, 209
    continuous measurement, 190
    critical angle method, 188
    differential method, 188
    general, 186–187
    image displacement method, 189
    immersion method, 187
    interferometric method, 188–189
    microscopic method, 189–190
  surface tension, 196–210
    capillary rise method, 197–198
    general, 196–197
    interfacial tension, 201
    maximum bubble pressure method, 198–199
    pendant drop method, 199
    pull on vertical plate, 200
    references, 210
    ring method (torsion balance), 199–200
    sensile drop, 200

Physical properties, surface tension, spreading of oil films, 201
  surface potential, 200–201
  velocity of propagation, 201
  thermal properties, specific heat, thermal conductivity, heats of fusion and vaporization, 202–203
  vapor pressure, 190–194
    boiling point method, 191–193
    gas saturation method, 193–194
    general, 190–191
    isteniscope method, 191
    references, 210
  viscosity, 182–186, 209
    gases, 186
    liquids, 182–186
Polarography, elemental analysis, 35–37, 48, 52
  functional groups, 79–87, 89, 92
  in trace analysis, 239–240
Problem-solving (general), 1–8
  types of problems, 5–8
    at development stage, 6
    at legal stage, 8
    at manufacturing stage, 6–7
    at research stage, 6
    at sales stage, 7–8

Quenchofluorimetry, 230–234, 240
Quenchophosphorimetry, 231–234, 240

Radioactive elements, 38
Radioactivity, elements, 38
  induced (see Neutron activation analysis)
  tracers, 266–269
Raman methods, functional group analysis, 74–77, 89, 91
  identification and structure, 121–123, 140
Reflectance spectroscopy, 217–218, 223
Refractive index (see Physical properties)
Residual resistivity, 255, 259
Resistivity, electrical, 202
Roller Particle Size Analyzer, 214

Schoniger flask methods, 44
Sedimentation, in molecular weight
    determination, 159–163
  in particle size distribution measure-
    ment, 214–215
  in viscosity measurement, 185
Separations, 271–294
Sieve analysis, 214
Specific heat, 134, 202–203
Structure, 95–139
  absorption spectrometric methods,
    98–99, 135
  chemical methods, 97–98, 135
  electron spin resonance, 114–116,
    135, 137
  general discussion, 95–96
  mass spectrometry, 100–102, 135
  microwave spectroscopy, 123–126,
    136, 138
  morphology, 132–134
  Mössbauer spectroscopy, 129–131,
    136, 138
  nuclear magnetic resonance, 102–
    114, 135, 139
  nuclear quadrupole resonance, 123,
    136, 138
  optical rotatory dispersion, 126–128,
    136, 138
  Raman spectroscopy, 121–123
  thermal methods, 134, 138
  x-ray diffraction, 116–121, 135, 137
Sulfur analysis in organic compounds,
    45
Surface active agents (see Detergents)
Surface examination, 215–222
  composition of surface coatings,
    217–220
  microscopic, 215–218
  thickness of surface coatings, 220–
    222
Surface tension (see Physical properties)

Thermal conductivity, 202–203
Thermal properties, 134, 202–203
Thermally stimulated currents, 255,
    260–262
Thermistor detectors, 35–37
Thermogravimetric analysis, 134

Thickness gauging, 220–222
Thin layer chromatography, 284, 294
Trace analysis, 225–244
  elements, 9–52, 241
  general, 225–227
  instrumental methods, 229–242
    fluorimetry, 230–234, 240, 244
    gas chromatography, 235–240,
      244
    infrared, 234–235, 240
    mass spectrometry, 241–242
    phosphorimetry, 231–234, 240,
      244
    polarography, 239, 240
    quenchofluorimetry, 230–234, 240
    quenchophosphorimetry, 231–234,
      240
    ultraviolet-visible, 229–230, 240,
      244
  noninstrumental methods, chemical,
    fluorometric, and phosphori-
    metric, 227–228, 240, 243
Tracers, 265–269
  nonradioactive, 265–266
  radioactive, 266–269

Ultracentrifugation (see Molecular
    weight)
Ultraviolet absorption, functional
    groups, 65–71, 88, 91
  identification and structure, 98–99,
    135
  surface coatings (reflectance), 217–
    218
  in trace analysis, 229–230, 240
  vacuum, 71–72, 89

Vacuum ultraviolet absorption, 71–72,
    89, 91
Vapor pressure, measurement, 190–194
  boiling-point method, 191–193
  gas-saturation method, 193–194
  isoteniscope method, 191
  method for molecular weight, 151–
    152, 172, 174
  references, 210

Viscosity, measurement, 182–186
  molecular weight determination, 159
    on gases, 186
    on liquids, 182–186
  references, 209
Visible absorption, functional groups,
    72–74, 88, 91
  identification and structure, 98–99, 135
  surface coatings (reflectance),
    217–218

Weight-average molecular weight, 158

X-ray absorption, 221–222, 224
X-ray diffraction, correlation with
    microscopy, 212
  identification and structure, 4, 5,
    116–121, 135
  molecular weight determination,
    157–158, 173, 175, 177
X-ray fluorescence, 23–25, 47, 50, 221,
    224

Z-average molecular weight, 159
Zone refining, 282